The Soils of Europe

The Soils of Europe

ILLUSTRATED DIAGNOSIS AND SISTEMATICS

With keys and descriptions for easy identification
of the most important soil formations of Europe
with consideration of the most frequent synonyms.

by

PROF. DR. WALTER L. KUBIËNA ⌐ч

246

CONSEJO SUPERIOR DE INVESTIGACIONES CIENTIFICAS
MADRID - 1953

THOMAS MURBY AND COMPANY
LONDON

FFE

Nuevas Gráficas, S. A.-Andrés Mellado, 18.-Teléf. 24 01 20.-MADRID

Preface

Of the many books remaining to be written in the realm of soil science the following, in my opinion, is the most urgently required. This has been borne out by the insistent demands for the completion of the book. How is this to be accounted for? It is explained by the lack of a firm basis for the correlation of the most diverse observations, results and experiences with particular soils. The number of soil scientists working in the field of systematics who have a sufficient knowledge of soil forms is unfortunately still small. Owing to a lack of expert guidance the essential characterization and naming of soils is not done at all, or only in such a way as to be of little use to anyone. This book is an attempt to make it possible to identify and to give suitable names to soils for all those who need it. It is the first guide book of its kind. It tries to make clear that identifying soils is not difficult and that soil science is not an occult art. On the contrary, with suitable guidance, it is comparatively easy to obtain a comprehensive picture of the diversity of forms and to recognize and name particular forms as accurately as present knowledge permits. The book, therefore, is intended not only as a guide for the soil scientist and soil surveyor, but also for all those to whom it would be of direct or indirect interest, namely the agriculturist, forester, horticulturist, agricultural engineer, plant sociologist, plant ecologist, bioclimatologist, geologist and geographer. It may also stimulate the nature lover to look at the soils of forest and field, of mountain and valley with a new awareness, and this may open the door of a kingdom in which everything appears quite strange although intimately related to all he has known before. He will recognize that an occupation dealing with the study of soils has its reward and fascination as much as any other branch of natural science. Practically no other subject reveals the close interrelation of the living and dead in nature so clearly As landscapes, animals, plants, men and civilizations change, so the soil changes too; these can only be fully understood by considering their continual mutual interaction.

A guide book of this kind will be of great value in teaching soil science at universities. Successful practical work in soil science, in so far as this aims at teaching the individual to identify soils, will not be possible until such a book exists. Just as it has been usual to learn to identify plants, but not animals, owing to the lack of suitable keys, so one may expect that once there are suitable guide books, the identification of soils will be practised, at least in specialized courses. There is no doubt that the systematic identification of natural objects, requiring accurate viewing, testing, constant comparison and concentration on the most outstanding characteristics, will give a better knowledge of forms than the most industrious study of books.

In naming soils, I have tried to avoid creating a new, private nomenclature, but have attempted from the earlier work of my predecessors and from the natural historical development of naming soils to derive universally applicable, objective rules, and thus to build up an ordered soil science nomenclature. The section «On Nomenclature», where this is worked out in detail, shows that soil science, apart from individual short sidetracks, has followed essentially a similar path to Botany and Zoology and it seems to be most advantageous to continue in this direction. For this purpose, it was essential to undertake a more detailed investigation of soil synonymology than had been done in the literature before. The testing of synonyms and subsequent quotation of all those available to me will enable the reader to acquire a knowledge of the most frequently occurring synonyms and to translate soil names unfamiliar to him into those customary in his own country. Every reader can identify soils, therefore, either by the nomenclature of his own country or by that which he personally favours. The book contains a relatively large number of new forms *), partly because research in systematics has been somewhat neglected in recent years and partly because a more exhaustive differentiation of the types and sub-types can be attained by consideration of micromorphological, microdynamic, biological and phenological characteristics. No group of soils has been omitted, not even the usually neglected sub-aqueous soils, so very important for a complete understanding of soil formation. By natural or artificial drying out every sub-aqueous soil can come into use as a cultivated soil and may be considered from this point of view. Respecting peat soils, for simplicity's sake, only the main forms have been

---

*) They are designated by n. f. (nova forma).

included. As there is so much variation of form among them their exact diagnosis would make the preparation of a separate book almost essential. Sub-tropical and tropical soils are considered only in so far as they are important in temperate regions, where they occur as residual or fossilized soils of earlier geological formations and, as such, can be very prominent in many landscapes.

The present work is restricted to the most important European soil formations, but it will apply very nearly to many countries outside Europe. Excluding tropical soils, the number of soils in the world not found in some form in Europe is extremely small. I have had the opportunity to see *in situ* and study almost all the soils discussed in the book. My journeys in Europe have covered large parts of Central and Northern Europe, the Finnish Arctic Sea coast and the nearby Arctic islands, Russia, the Balkans, including Greece and Crete, Italy, Spain, France, Holland, England and Ireland. The opportunity to study the alpine soils of my native country has been of great value to me and, for this, I must thank in particular Univ. Prof. Dr. A. ZELLER, Director of the Federal Research Station for Alpine Agriculture in Admont. Many thanks are due to Professor Dr. JOSÉ MARÍA ALBAREDA, General Secretary of the Consejo Superior de Investigaciones Científicas in Madrid, for his great encouragement in this work, and for the publication in its present form. I must also thank him for the opportunity of becoming acquainted in detail with Spain, which is of such interest for the soil scientist. At the same time I am most grateful to all my colleagues in the various provinces of Spain whose help and friendliness have made my travels possible. Lastly, I must thank my wife, as my first coworker and constant companion on my travels. Her untiring help and sympathy are reflected in every detail of this book: indeed it is hers as well as mine.

The work contains a series of dichotomous keys of varying degrees of difficulty, constructed so as to give as accurate an identification as possible in a short and simple manner. Illustrations are used frequently as they save much discussion and increase the accuracy and rapidity of the work. Drawings have been preferred to photographs, as essential details can be emphasized. The illustration of the book was entrusted to our cousin, the Austrian painter GERTRUD KALLAB-PURTSCHER, of Lienz, who accompanied us to Spain. It is due to her craftsmanship and understanding that the coloured profiles are not only scientifically exact, but also bring out the natural tints without which even the most accurate work remains unreal and incomplete. The original paintings, primarily of material from the soil collections of Madrid and Admont were water colours, 40×33 cm. in size. Great care has been taken in painting the vegetation, as it characterizes so vividly the biological individuality of the soil, its climate, its water and nutrient relations and its relation to particular plant covers. The profiles of plates XI, XXII and XXIII2 were executed in a similar fashion by the painter ANTON PRAZAK of Admont. The micromorphological figures were prepared with great patience, accuracy and skill by the painter FRUTOS ARAGONESES of Madrid. In the preparation of the English edition, the close collaboration of Mr. W. W. EMERSON, seconded from Rothamsted for this purpose, was very much appreciated. My grateful thanks to everyone.

The soil concepts used in this book are much wider than those used in modern agricultural soil surveying, the so-called s o i l u n i t s (local types, Lokalarten). In the latter both the general and local factors of soil formation have been extensively taken into account. One can by means of this book, identify soil categories which, to use a botanical simile, correspond to the species «wheat» or sub-species «Emmer wheat» (*Triticum dicoccum*), but not to the local variety «Manitoba wheat». The latter can be taken as the equivalent of the local type. By limiting himself to more general soil concepts, the author intends to provide a general guide book, similar to those for the identification of plants and animals, and thus to appeal to a wider range of readers. Keys, which take into account local forms also, must *a priori* be limited to smaller areas. Besides, the l o c a l f o r m s (soil series) and l o c a l t y p e s can only acquire their full value as a means of exactly characterizing and naming soils if, at the same time, their relations to particular global types, sub-types or varieties are determined *). Only in this way is it possible to order and classify them correctly and to recognize their true character easily. It must not be forgotten that unrelated specialization is, methodically, almost as bad as generalization with insufficient detail inquiry. It is almost the same as if in animal breeding local race concepts such as Yorkshire, Shorthorn, Berkshire or Karakul were created, but it were still difficult to distinguish clearly whether cattle, sheep, goats or pigs were referred to. Only if the local soil concepts are ordered within a general

---

*) Their ordering according to parent rock, degree of water-logging, location or other individual characteristics is incomplete and does not correspond to the principles of sound systematics.

system of soils do they become understandable to the experts of other countries. Thus, all the experience and information acquired on these soils can be easily related to soils in other parts of the world. This has already been recognized by several authorities; the emphasizing of the global type (great soil group) by CHARLES E. KELLOGG and others seems to be closely related to it.

The author presents his book to the public in the hope that as far as possible it will fulfil its desired aim and bring assistance to his friends. And the only thing which remains to be said, now that the bock which I have prepared with much love and care is ended, may be expressed in the words of DIODORUS SICULUS, written nearly two thousand years ago: «May what is rightly said remain free from spiteful censure and the faults of ignorance be removed by the more expert.» I would ask my colleagues' assistance in informing me of any error or of any important soil formation which I may have omitted, and also in completing the synonymology and in tracing the authors to whom the various soil names are due.

W. L. KUBIËNA

Madrid, May 1950.

Short Guide for Using the Book

The book should be equally useful for those requiring a bare, rough classification of the soils and who are content with a definition of the global type (great soil group) and also those requiring the most exact possible characterization of their soil. The beginner can start with the easy keys for the identification of the most frequent cultivated, grassland and forest soils without preparatory reading of the other sections of the book. If the particular soil lies in Central or Northern Europe, then he starts with the key group No. 2, if in Southern Europe, then with key group No. 3. The easiest key in both cases is that using the soil colour as starting point. A simple test on the chalk content and reaction of the soil will enable him to use, at times, the subsequent keys. A slight knowledge of rocks will help in special cases to make the recognition of particular soil forms very easy by the key based on the kind of parent rock. In a few places in all these keys, when the knowledge of detail described in other parts of the book is essential, it is indicated by the numbers of the soils or pages which are easily looked up. The various keys are complementary to each other, so that a check on information derived is obtained by using more than one key. Furthermore, various soils contained in the key for Southern Europe occur in Central and Northern Europe and vice versa, so that a soil which could not be identified by one group of keys, may perhaps still be found in other groups of keys. Once the desired soil type is found, the location of the detailed description of the soil is possible by using the soil number reference given at the side and this gives a further check on the correctness of the diagnosis. For those soils that have a picture of their profiles a corresponding reference is provided in the same way.

If the soils in question cannot be found with the simple keys Nos. 2 and 3, it is essential to try afresh with the help of the comprehensive, g e n e r a l k e y N o. 5 . To use this key it is necessary to read through first section C of the Introduction and to determine the humus form of the soil in question by key No. 1. Any technical expression which has not been explained in these two sections is to be found in the indices of technical terms at the end of the book.

The identification of Alpine Soils should be easily possible by key No. 4. It also contains the necessary references to the detailed descriptions of the soils, and to diagrams, if any.

The main key, No. 5, is so built up with a scaffolding of categories, that an identification of any required exactitude is possible. Those who require nothing more than the determination of the global type (great soil group) may use its identification only and not proceed beyond it. Those who desire the most exhaustive diagnosis possible and the most exact characterization may continue with the identification up to the ultimate branches as far as our present knowledge enables us. In the main key, the soils are ordered according to the natural system, progressing from the simplest to the most complex. This is done not only to order the various possibilities of the soil formation in a clearly visible way but to show up also the mutual interlocking of the individual types and their correlation, i.e. to present the natural construction of the whole realm of soil formation. In this, certain parallels arise with the natural systems of plants and animals, for the development of the soil depends very much on their phase of development. The soil scientist who is not only interested in the diagnosis of particular soil formations but in systematic problems in general, may therefore also read the last part of the book as an independent publication and consider it as a kind of prodromus to a future much more exhaustive soil systematics.

Certain repetitions in keys and descriptions were allowed to stand purposely so that each part of the book may be used and read separately. In the selection of the kind of characteristics in the different keys, it was natural that preference should be given to those easily determined, if possible, directly in the field. Only where such characteristics were missing or were unsafe for an unequivocal identification have properties

more difficult to determine been chosen in the main key, to
increase the certainty of the diagnosis. However, this was only
necessary in a few cases. Yet I would like to mention that
particulary with the help of soil microscopy in the hand of the
expert, a still much sharper and more exact identification is
possible, particularly in the finer end branches of systematics.
This could only partially be shown in the book.

With the aid of its keys the book enables the identification
of 173 different formations of soils. At the same time it gives
the explanation of 440 different soil names (see «List of soil
names») and of 233 pedological terms (see «Explanations of
some pedological terms» and «List of the terms explained in
the text»). It contains furthermore 47 coloured pictures of profiles, 8 coloured and 16 black and white figures for the micromorphological characterisation of different soil and humus formations (see «List of soils represented by illustrations»).

Designation of the Soil Categories.

Divisions	capital letters	A
Classes	double capital letters	AA
Sub-classes	small letters	a
Types	roman numerals	I
Sub-types	arabic numerals	1
Varieties	idem, with round brackets	(1)
Sub-varieties	idem, with angular brackets	[1]

Each category is numbered continuously and independently so that every
soil form has its individual number and can be easily found by it (see also
«List of the soil formations ordered according to the natural system»). The
final designation indicates the total number of forms within the category
concerned.

Names printed in italics are international designations which correspond
to the rules of nomenclature (example: *Xerorendsina*), designations in normal letters are common names (example: brown earth). In the simple keys
Nos. 2, 3 and 4, intended for the use of the beginner, the most customary
designations (in the first place common names) have primarily been used.

Index of Keys.

Introduction

A. On the Importance of an Exact Soil Identification for the Progress of Research in Soil Science and for Practical Agriculture and Forestry

When a plant physiologist or plant chemist makes an experiment in his own specialised field, he can state exactly with which genus and species or sub-species he has worked. He knows very accurately that only by this means would his work become profitable and thus contribute to the ordered extension of the framework of Botany as a whole. Unfortunately this is the case only to a small extent in the many special branches of pure and applied soil science. Existing soil science has mastered analysis in a brilliant fashion, but in synthesis it is still in the beginning. Therefore today it still is more a soil sample science than a soil science. In spite of all the refinement of analytical technique, true knowledge of soil formations, seen as entities, is progressing only slowly. All those working in some way with soil are not really working together towards a common goal, but rather divergently, and the distances between the individual splinter groups are becoming larger rather than smaller. Systematics is regarded in soil science only to a small degree as the indispensable link, which in other well developed natural sciences combines all the specialized branches and their research results, and which alone makes possible research work in the service of a common goal. It is rather regarded as some other special branch, which is developing almost in the same isolated way as the other doctrines. Therefore the results of soil systematics remain completely foreign and practically unapproachable by the specialist. But it must also be his wish to be able to define and designate the object of his research clearly and unequivocally. The only way to rationalize research in a natural science is on the basis of broad exhaustive systematics. If a book like this could really succeed in making available to everyone the exact determination and unequivocal naming of soil formations one of the most important problems in the organization of the whole research in soil science would be solved with it.

Guidebooks like the following are most essential in all the different bran-

ches of soil utilization, particularly in agriculture and forestry. Here the lack of
knowledge of the soil is not only a theoretical shortcoming but appears at
the same time as a very significant material defect. How is a real advance
conceivable if one is not capable of saying under what conditions, i. e. on which
specific soils this or that method of working or this or that breed of plant
proved particularly successful, and in which areas a similar result can be expected? Must it always remain merely groping and seeking? How could one
evaluate a stock experiment if the experimenter were unable to say with which
animal or which particular breed he is working? How could anything useful
be derived from a variety trial, if the author were unable to define exactly
the plant with which he was working? Is it different in the case of the field
experiment? Each experimenter knows how very much soil differences, even
in a small area, affect the result of an experiment. How large will be the
difference in the result, if one considers the great variety of soils of a district
or a county which differ so much even in their external appearance? The
result of each experiment is true only for a particular soil and can be utilized only from this point of view, in the same way as it is true for a particular plant species or breed. In the absence of sufficient information on the
soil, the whole experiment therefore remains completely in the air, as it would
do, if information on the experimental crop, the manuring or on the method
of cultivation were missing. How many of such imperfect experimental reports are already published! What a large gap becomes evident today between experimental result and application! How much bigger and more perceptible does it become from decade to decade, while experimental technique
advances! But the crisis affects not only the whole field of experimental research, it deeply affects agricultural advisory work, agricultural engineering,
agricultural planning and finally even the whole science of agriculture, all
the more obvious to those who have greater insight. Wherever experience and
knowledge have been acquired on particular soil formations, this remains utiliz-
able only to a very uncertain degree, as long as it is not possible to relate it to
the original soil. We can bring real help to practical agriculture only if the
soils are as exactly and unambiguously characterized and named as the breeds
of cereals, market garden crops, domestic animals and all the rest of the elements of farming, for which a well developed, highly specialized terminology
has become completely familiar.

May the time soon be finally past, when for the characterization of the
soil, it was sufficient to say: «The soil was a clay loam» or a «humic sandy
marl». The soil is characterized so little by such characteristics as the texture,
humus or chalk content, that the layman can scarcely form a conception of
the ambiguity of this kind of data. When ALBRECHT THAER set up his system of soils, he distinguished solely sand, loam, clay, humus and chalk soils.
This book contains 173 different soil formations. This numerical juxtaposi-

tion (in which the possibility of additional distinction of local forms has still not been considered) shows most distinctly to what degree the possibilities of soil characterization have changed.

B. On Nomenclature

For a conscious creation of rules of nomenclature systematics of soils have as yet made no provision. The result of it was a certain wildness and nonconformity in the manner of naming soils. This shows itself in that separate authors created systems of nomenclature of their own, in which already existing soil names were exchanged for new ones, concepts arbitrarily widened or contracted, out-worn names again used for new concepts etc. As the field of soil systematics is being much more worked in than formerly and considering the great importance of such work for the progress of theoretical and practical soil science, a further important increase can be expected. Therefore to continue with this complete freedom is very dangerous. The edifice of soil science can so easily become a «Tower of Babel», that at the end one bricklayer scarcely understands the other, because each speaks as it were his own language. Indeed soil scientists have repeatedly suggested an international fixing of soil names «by agreement» and were very optimistic about this. But subjective attachment to particular soil names and systems of nomenclature is so great, due to personal disposition, influence of teaching or over-riding patriotism, that a solution in this difficult and complicated way can never be expected. It would refer also only to existing knowledge and by no means influence the future method of naming soils. All these considerations make the task of the soil systematist a very responsible one. By the creation of a new system of nomenclature built up on uniform principles with a complete break with the past, he will do nothing more than add one more to the radical attempts made in the last decades. Simply to select any one name at random from existing synonyms, is no less arbitrary a solution and in addition has the disadvantage that it fulfils less the demand for uniformity and clarity of the nomenclature than a newly created system. I now see a way out of this in seeking the solution in the results of soil systematics itself and in deducing rules of nomenclature from the existing customs in naming soils (excluding those systems and manners of naming not rooted in tradition). This should result in a narrower selection of soil names and the principle of priority can then easily decide among the synonyms selected.

A good system of nomenclature should be clear, convenient to handle and easily applicable in all languages. Correlation and relationship should be indicated by the name and all this be done with the shortest designation possible. The binary Linnean system conforms exactly to all these requirements and therefore must be considered as the most perfect solution.

It can serve for us as pattern and test. The principle of the Linnean system consists in creating main concepts (genuses) denoted by substantival names and further in characterizing specific modifications of these (species) by the addition of adjectives. Ternary and quaternary modes of description evolved from the binary system in Botany and Zoology make a still finer differentiation by the use of further adjectival additions (sub-species, variations, local forms). In this way the association of each form with its main form always remains recognizable, and the relationship of the different forms to each other is immediately apparent. What is to be regarded as the main concept in soil science? The answer to this is not difficult. The main concept, the fundamental unit of all systematics is the global type, that unit, in which the variation of the soils in nature is revealed in its most striking and typical way. The essence of the global type is so striking that to us the next lower unit, the sub-type, seems only a modification of the global type and the further special unit, the variety, represents only a variation of the sub-type. It is of great interest, that systematics of soil in the method of designation of these categories have followed a similar method to the Linnean nomenclature. The global type (great soil group) is designated by a noun (chernosem, solontschak, braunerde, rotlehm), the sub-type by an attached adjective (degraded chernosem, wet solontschak, podsolized braunerde, bleached rotlehm). In soil science a new kind of designation for the sub-type appears, using either a prefix (cryptopodsol, phaneropodsol) or a compound noun (humuspodsol, ironpodsol, dygyttja). From the history of pedological nomenclature, the advantages and disadvantages of this or that particular step can be easily recognized. In this way, drawing on experience from other natural sciences, one arrives to guiding principles, which arise so to speak automatically. Simply to take over any rules of nomenclature in Botany and Zoology would be of little advantage, for the rules must be derived from soil systematics themselves and besides must not stand in too great opposition to what has already been created. Soil science has not taken the same course as Linneus in using Latin for international communication from the outset. This makes the solution of the task more dificult, but in no way impossible. It requires only a somewhat different treatment to solve the question of classification. With the rules grouped together in this section, I have created for my work the essential matrix of guiding principles. I have held myself strictly to them for yet undescribed soil forms. With regard to earlier soil names, I have replaced them where it is possible without undue interference. In a case where a further investigation is required and in which useful synonyms are lacking, considering the practical aim of this book I have given priority to the best known and most used name. The common names are given alongside the international designations. The rules of nomenclature should not influence the common national names or infringe on their use, but serve purely for international communication.

I have tried therefore, by looking for rules in the works of my predecessors, to create a firm basis and find a traditional way for my work and build it up methodically; for the rest, I would like to avoid a quick, hasty solution. It is better, if the solution comes gradually and more completely. In this way I hope that the nomenclature of soil systematics will one day attain in all its parts the same level of order, uniformity and clearness as the Linnean system.

Rules of Nomenclature.

1.   The name of the s o i l   t y p e (DOKUCHAEV 1879, synonyms: global type, group = great soil group *)) is indicated by a noun. It can come from any language, may have any meaning, its only function is to be a name **). It ought not to be translated into others languages, but used entirely as a proper name.

a)   The type name should give no difficulties with regard to pronunciation, sound or subsidiary meaning for international use. It ought to be as neutral and as short as possible, not exceeding three syllables (e. g. dy, gyttja, rutmark, rendsina, solonetz, solod, podsol). Unprofitable furthermore are too highly descriptive names which cannot be transferred untranslated into other languages (e. g. Kalkhumusboden) or those which are for any other reason unsuitable for international use as proper names.

b)   To be avoided as unnecessary are additional nouns, which by themselves have no particular meaning but need an adjective for their completion, e. g. «soil», «forest soil», «mountain soil» ***) (not «anmoor-like soil» but «anmoor»).

c)   Names already used with some particular meaning, irrespective of whether they have since become entirely invalid or recognized as a synonym, should not be used again with a new meaning *).

2.   The designation of the s u b - t y p e (synonym: sub-group) **) has

---

*) The additions «great» and «soil» have no particular function and could easily be omitted.

**) All names derived from soil colour (chernosem, serosem, braunlehm, roterde) are nothing but names and not designations of colours (e. g. a chernosem with low humus content is never black but grey). They are therefore just as valid as names derived from some other or no characteristics.

***) A botanical nomenclature having the genus names with a general noun like «plant», «flower», «wood plant», in conjunction with a sense-giving adjective (perhaps resin secreting wood plant») is to us already inconceivable.

*) One thinks of a chemistry in which the following was decided one day: the compound hitherto known as quinine to be known in future as strychnine, while the compound previously called strychnine to be given name veronal.

**) Instead of «great soil sub-group».

always to be done in conjunction with the type name either by an adjective, a prefix, or a noun in the genetive or in word combination. Examples of the use of adjectives are: degraded chernosem, wet solotchak, lateritic roterde; of prefixes: cryptopodsol, nanopodsol, pararendsina; of nouns: gleypodsol, humuspodsol, dygyttja. These attachments to the type name ought as far as possible to express something of the nature of the sub-type.

a)   While the type name remains untranslated, the adjective denoting the sub-type can be taken over translated into the other language (e. g. English: degraded chernosem; Spanish: chernosem degradado). It is advantageous to use adjectives which alter little in traslation.

b)   Prefixes are not to be translated and will remain the same in all languages.

c)   Nouns remain partly untranslated (especially as combinations of two soil names, e. g. dygyttja, solontchak-solonetz, gleypodsol), or partly translated in the same way as adjectives (e. g. English: peatpodsol; German: Torfpodsol; Spanish: podsol de turba).

d)   To be avoided are names for the sub-types which do not show their relation to a particular global type (e. g. suglinok instead of degraded chernosem, popylucha instead of xerorendsina).

e)   With sub-type names which consist of a combination of a sub-type designation with an indefinite ending such as -soil, -earth etc. the latter to be replaced by the type name (e. g. not «eilag soil» but «eilag-ranker»; not «tundra soil» but «tundra-anmoor» and «tundra-ranker»).

3.   The names of v a r i e t i e s , which are variations of the sub-type are produced by similar additions to the name of the soil type as in the case of the sub-type.

a)   The designation of the variety can be used either together with the sub-type designation or only with that of the soil type, especially if the name is unequivocal or for other reasons a mistake is very unlikely (e. g. sub-type: Central European braunerde; variety: eutrophic Central European braunerde or eutrophic braunerde).

b)   If the name is given in entirety, it always starts with the designation of the variety, followed by that of the sub-type (e. g. sub-type: pararendsina, variety: mull pararendsina; sub-type: xerorendsina, variety: mull--like xerorendsina).

c)   In the romance languages the order of adjectives and translated compound nouns is reversed (Spanish: braunerde centroeuropea oligotrofa, pararendsina de mull, xerorendsina mulliforme).

4)   The *Local Form* (soil series) is a unit of soil systematics in which is manifested the influence of local soil forming factors *). It corresponds there-

*)   A Webster and Carrington occur only on the prairies of the U. S. A., and not in Europe; an Iwatoka or an Um Berembeita occur only in the Anglo-Egyptian

fore to the local forms, geographical varietes or races in Botany or Zoology and is subordinated to the above categories. The designation of the local forms is generally derived from the local name of some place in their area of occurrence. It is advantageous to use it either in conjunction with the name of the global type (Greenville rotlehm, Caribou podsol, Fargo chernosem) or, especially for agricultural survey, in conjunction with the texture of the surface soil (Greenville clay, Fargo silt loam *).

5. In order to avoid subjective influence as much as possible, the name which is to have international recognition, is to be the oldest among the existing synonyms conforming to the rules of nomenclature. The requirement that the name should be formed according to the rules is indispensable in the interest of the uniformity, clearness and ease of comprehension of the nomenclature.

a) The *Principle of Priority* **) can only be used on such names where the corresponding soil formations are sufficiently described and defined.

b) The corresponding concept of the soil must furthermore conform to present day standards of soil science.

c) The principle of priority does not apply if by this a name obeying the rules of nomenclature, which has been in general usage for several decades, must be rejected.

C. The Soil Profile

Horizon Formation. A soil profile is arrived at by a vertical section through the soil mantle. This shows in most cases a series of horizontal zones, which are designated h o r i z o n s . The horizons are not layers in the geological sense, that is, are not formed by sedimentation, but are built up according to the particular kind and intensity of soil life, the weathering and other chemical and physical transformations in the soil. Of great influence further are translocations of material of all kinds, both those which reach beyond a horizon or sub-horizon into another part of the profile and also

---

Sudan and not in Puerto Rico or elsewhere; but on the contrary global types, subtypes and varieties are units which are found in all parts of the world under similar soil forming conditions.

*) This primarily cartographic unit, created from a practical point of view, has received the name «soil type» or «soil unit». It would be of great advantage if it were possible to use only the second, the soil unit, in order to fit it into the international nomenclature, as well as on grounds of priority. See also global type and local type.

**) A far-reaching consideration of the principle of priority is also requested by a sense of justice as well as by general scientific custom. Considering the little competition among names in soil systematics, the difficulties which have appeared in Botany and Zoology (which by no means outweigh the advantages) are scarcely to be expected.

those which take place in a limited area (as formation of flecks, concretions, streaks, bands, waterlogged zones, etc.). At the same time the horizons are floors of different living conditions which strongly influence the kind and composition of soil life (including the intensity of plant root development). The kind of horizon formation is remarkably varied and is always especially characteristic of a particular kind of soil formation. The characteristics of profile development belong therefore to the most important elements of soil systematics and diagnosis.

General Designation of Horizons. The nature of horizon description has considerably changed since the introduction of nomenclature using letters by representatives of the Russian school about fifty years ago and is at present undergoing still further developments. The causes of this lie in the demand for a more exhaustive characterization of the manifold possibilities of horizon structure, than that of the turn of the century. For soil diagnosis, the following general rules are considered to be most advantageous [1]).

Following the letters of the alphabet, A H o r i z o n s , the characteristic humus horizons, are those which show the highest population of organisms and the strongest enrichment of organic matter. The unweathered or little changed parent materials in the soil profile are called C H o r i z o n s . In normal terrestrial soils (i. e. not influenced by water-logging), further horizons can be located between the A and C Horizons which are designated as B H o r i z o n s . They contain compounds of iron in oxidized form and are therefore brown, ochre-yellow to red coloured. Profiles of pronounced underwater or ground water soils have no B Horizons, but show grey, grey-blue, grey-green to olive green coloured G H o r i z o n s (Gley Horizons). These are characterised by a deficiency in oxidation (the colour is due in the first place to ferrous oxide compounds), predominately reduction processes and anaerobic conditions for soil organisms. Rust-brown to rust-red coloured horizons, derived by secondary oxidation in ground water soils (gley soils) are known as F e H o r i z o n s (BLÜMEL 1949). Horizons with strong precipitation of finely divided calcium carbonate in land soils and dried out ground water soils, generally strongly contrasting with their white hues, are called C a H o r i z o n s . Analogous layers which are formed by the concentration of water soluble salts are called S a H o r i z o n s , Y H o r i z o n s [*]) in the case of gypsum accumulation. A further geological layer below the C Horizon is known as the D H o r i z o n , which is able to influence the profile perhaps as a base (e. g. in regard to its water relations) but cannot be considered as the parent material for soil formation.

General Division of A Horizons. When several sub-horizons can be distinguished in the A Horizons, they can generally and without closer characterization be designated as A $_1$, A $_2$, A $_3$ H o r i z o n s . Mineral defi-

---

[1]) See notes at the end of the keys.
[*]) From Spanish yeso = gypsum.

cient humus layers, lying with a sharp boundary on the mineral soil, with slight decomposition and humification are called A_o Horizons (e. g. the raw humus layer of most podsols). This is, however, not to be used for the highest, undecomposed litter layers of forest profiles (Förna), which are separated as A_{oo} Horizons. They are not «raw humus», i. e. no form of humus, but (similar to the C Horizon) more or less raw material for the soil formation. The designation by numerical indices will be also particularly necessary whenever the exact character of a horizon is still not clear. Transitional formations which have characteristics both of the A and B horizons are called A/B horizons. Correspondingly there are A/C horizons in the A/C-soils and A/G horizons in the gley soils.

Special Terms for A sub-horizons. Accumulations of undecomposed and more or less uncomminuted organism residues on the soil surface are called F ö r n a (HESSELMANN) or litter (L-layer, French: litière). The name is used not only to characterize the A sub-horizon of forest soils (forest litter) but also of soils under water, whose humus is derived predominately from residues of higher plants. The following F L a y e r (HESSELMANN, Swedish: förmultningskiktet = fermentation layer, German: Vermoderungsschicht) is distinguished from the litter layer by the beginning of comminution, decomposition and humification of the organism residues. Soils with considerable F layers can show a further division into F_1 and F_2 layers. This is followed by the H L a y e r (HESSELMANN, Swedisch: humusämneskiktet, humic substance layer, German: Humusstoffschicht), the zone of strongest decomposition and humification in which only few plant residues are recognisable while enrichment of humic substances and their intimate mixing or binding with the mineral constituents of the soil is strongly in evidence. The various sub-horizons can have, however, very variable development and thickness in the different soil types, sub-types, and varieties, which is treated in more detail in the section on humus forms. Layers in the region of A horizons which consist more or less of bare and therefore light coloured mineral sand, owing to the washing out of all the finely dispersed particles, are called bleached layers. They are extreme eluvial horizons or impoverished horizons.

If one is to describe the above sub-horizons, so that they can be clearly recognised as parts of the A-horizon, the following notation can be adopted: A_{oo} (litter), A_F (F-layer, if necessary, A_{F1}, A_{F2}), A_H (H-layer), A_e (eluvial or bleached layer).

Definition of (A) Horizons [*]. Raw soils are soils which, to the naked eye, have as yet no recognisable development of humus horizons, and therefore no A horizons. However, they are already colonized by organisms and can also show a particular kind of humus formation, generally only recogni-

---

[*] Pronounced A-bracket-horizon.

sable microscopically (raw soil humus, syrosem humus). The most strongly colonized zone is always the well aerated superficial soil layer, which by its strong through-rooting or other characteristics contrasts markedly with the deeper soil layers. This characteristic layer in raw soils, which although not yet a humus horizon indicates already the future humus horizon, is called the (A) horizon.

Definition of Äfja (TRYBOM 1888, SERNANDER 1918, Swedish folkname). This name describes the predominately green coloured, superficial layer of underwater soils, containing living plants, mostly algae, and scarcely decomposed, almost uncomminuted plant remains. It differs essentially from the förna (underwater förna), which consists of the remains of higher plants (mainly shore litter).

Closer Characterization of B sub-horizons. The B sub-horizons can be designated in the same general way as the sub-horizons of the A horizons, if sequence only, and not individual character is defined. In this case they are called B_1, B_2, B_3 H o r i z o n s, etc. Transitional horizons to the parent rock can be designated as B / C H o r i z o n s, to the chalk enriched horizons, B/Ca H o r i z o n s, etc. Those showing slight marks of gleying are called B/G H o r i z o n s. The B horizons of podsols can be named after the preponderance of the particular kind of illuvial material concentrated in them from which they derive their characteristic colour. The enriched horizons in iron podsol in which the sesquioxides of iron and aluminium predominate, showing a rust-yellow to rust-brown colour due to highly hydrolysed iron, are called B_s H o r i z o n s (B sesquioxidic) after PALLMANN (1933), the sepia brown horizons enriched predominately by organic matter in humus podsols are called B_h H o r i z o n s (B humous). In iron humus podsols, both layers can occur simultaneously.

Definition of (B) horizons *) (LAATSCH 1938). If one wishes to give prominence to a B horizon, which is not an enriched horizon of illuviated substances, but purely a layer built up by deep reaching chemical weathering and simultaneous oxidation of the iron complexes (e. g. in brown earths, red earths, or un-bleached braunlehms and rotlehms), it is called a (B) horizon.

B/A horizons. In contrast to the A/B horizons, these are not transition formations between humus horizons and underlying B horizons, but are formed by strong enrichment and irreversible fixing of illuvial material on the soil surface or in the uppermost soil layer. This is typical of certain crust soils as well as of the rinds of certain desert soils. With extreme humus deficiency it can be described as a B/(A) horizon.

g-Horizon **), **gley-like horizon** (G. KRAUSS 1928). This describes horizons which have a similar external appearance to gley horizons, but have

---

*)   Pronounce B-bracket-horizon.
**) Pronounce small g-horizon.

a different genesis and dynamic. The light colour (grey, yellowish-grey, violet grey to whitish) is due either only partly or not at all to the presence of iron in less oxidized form. As the iron in soils with g-horizons is also highly mobile in oxidized forms, it becomes either concentrated in small, often microscopic to pin-head sized concretions and the ground mass, due to the lack of colouring substances becomes a lighter colour, or undergoes lateral eluviation.

As a rule these occur generally with silty to silty-loamy horizons. The peptization of the iron is due to tannic substances or humus sols. Soils with g-horizons were called «gley-like» soils by G. KRAUSS. Gley-like formations occur, either in combination with braunerde, podsolic brown earths or podsols. Those which are peptised by tannins are called «marbled soils» (marmorierte Böden) after LAATSCH.

Profile Diagrams. The profile diagrams in the figures 1, 2 and 3 are an attempt to facilitate a comprehensive view of the above possibilities of horizon description. In each diagram, the attempt was made to include all the different horizons and sub-horizons.

Grouping of Soils by their Profile. The following grouping makes it possible to obtain an overall view of the feasibility of profile morphology for the classification of soils. It allows the tendency of soil development to be easily recognized, which consists of a progression from the simple to the more complex. It confirms further the logic in the arrangement of the natural system, which starting with sub-aqueous soils, progresses through semi-terrestrial to true terrestrial soils, in particular by the absence of the more complex profile types in the first two groups.

The grouping of soils by the nature of their profile is simple, comprehensive and all-embracing. It is not satisfactory as the exclusive foundation of a natural system, because it is based on only a single characteristic, the profile diagram. However this important characteristic, which stands in close correlation with many others, is always of great importance also in a natural system, as will be shown later.

General Grouping of Soils by their Profiles
1. (A)C-Soils *) **)

With soil life, but without macroscopically distinguishable humus layers, and only with an upper layer colonized by organisms (with or without a plant root layer).

---

*) Pronounce: A-bracket-C Soils.
**) With sub-aqueous and semi-terretrial soils it may be also (A)G, or AG-soils.

Sub-aqueous: Underwater-raw soils (e. g. red deep sea clays, coral reefs, marine marl and marine chalk).

Semi-terrestrial: Raw gley soils.

Terrestrial: Raw soils (e. g. nival raw soils of the Alps, arctic raw soils, desert soils, white rendsinas).

2.   AC-Soils

With distinct humus horizon, but without B horizons.

Sub-aqueous: Underwater humus soils (e. g. dy, gytta, sapropel, reed peat).

Semi-terrestrial: Humus-gley soils (e. g. anmoors, gleyed grey warp soils, mull gley soils).

Terrestrial: Rendsina- and ranker-like soils (e. g. rendsinas, chernosems, rankers, para-chernosems).

3.   A(B)C-Soils *)

With pronounced B horizons which however are not real eluvial horizons built up by peptizable substances, but whose origin, in the first place, is due to deep reaching weathering with sufficient aeration and oxidation.

Sub-aqueous: –

Semi-terrestrial: –

Sub-aqueous: Brown earth and red earth like soils (e. g. brown earths, brown and red loams, red earths, terra rossa).

4.   ABC-Soils

With B horizons which are at the same time developed illuvial horizons, i. e. having a strong enrichment of peptizable substances.

Sub-aqueous: –

Semi-terrestrial: –

Terrestrial: Bleached soils (e. g. podsols, bleached brown and red loams, soloti).

---

*)   Pronounce: AB-bracket C-soils.

5. B/ABC-Soils

With strong enrichment of illuvial substances transported to the surface layer in peptized state by intensive capillary rise and irreversible precipitation.

Sub-aqueous : —
Semi-terrestrial : —
Terrestrial :   Rind and surface crust soils.

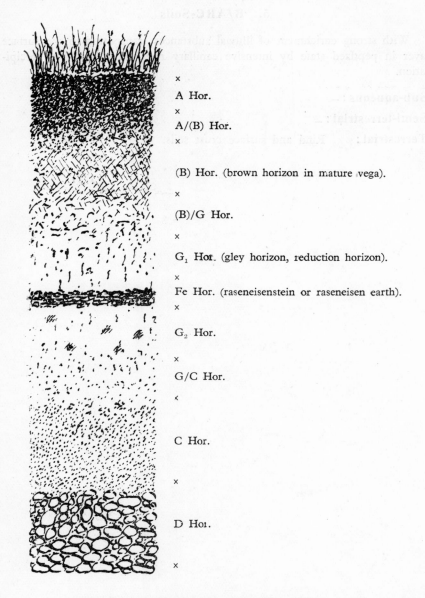

    x

A Hor.

    x

A/(B) Hor.

    x

(B) Hor. (brown horizon in mature vega).

    x

(B)/G Hor.

    x

G_1 Hor. (gley horizon, reduction horizon).

    x

Fe Hor. (raseneisenstein or raseneisen earth).

    x

G_2 Hor.

    x

G/C Hor.

    x

C Hor.

    x

D Hor.

    x

Fig. 1. — Profile Diagram for Warp Soils.

Note: Furthermore can be distinguished (A) horizons in raw warp soils (*ramblas*), mineral deficient A_0 horizons with peat humus layers, A_{00} horizons (förna, litter) in soils under wood vegetation.

Designation after sequence by numerical indices		Designation after the character of the horizon

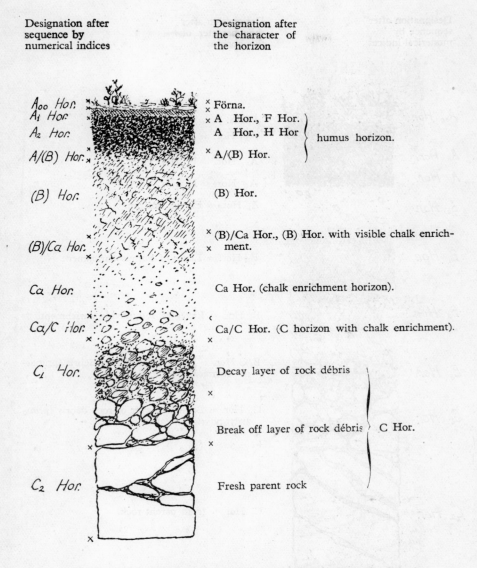

A₀₀ Hor. — ˣ Förna.

A₁ Hor. — ˣ A Hor., F Hor. ⎫

A₂ Hor. — A Hor., H Hor ⎬ humus horizon.

A/(B) Hor. — ˣ A/(B) Hor. ⎭

(B) Hor. — (B) Hor.

(B)/Ca Hor. — ˣ (B)/Ca Hor., (B) Hor. with visible chalk enrich-
ˣ ment.

Ca Hor. — Ca Hor. (chalk enrichment horizon).

Ca/C Hor. — Ca/C Hor. (C horizon with chalk enrichment).

C₁ Hor. — Decay layer of rock débris ⎫

⎪

Break off layer of rock débris ⎬ C Hor.

⎪

C₂ Hor. — Fresh parent rock ⎭

Fig. 2. — Profile Diagram for Soils of the Brown Earth Region.

Note: Furthermore can be distinguished: (A) horizons with raw soils, (B)/C horizons with chalk deficient soils, G, (B)/C and G/C horizons with gleyization of the subsoil and g horizons with gley-like soils.

Designation after sequence by numerical indices		Designation after the character of the horizon

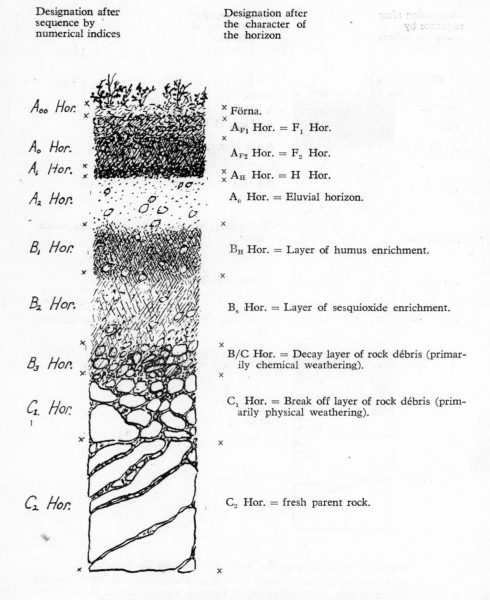

A_{oo} Hor.		Förna.
		A_{F_1} Hor. = F_1 Hor.
A_o Hor.		A_{F_2} Hor. = F_2 Hor.
A_1 Hor.		A_H Hor. = H Hor.
A_2 Hor.		A_e Hor. = Eluvial horizon.
B_1 Hor.		B_H Hor. = Layer of humus enrichment.
B_2 Hor.		B_s Hor. = Layer of sesquioxide enrichment.
B_3 Hor.		B/C Hor. = Decay layer of rock débris (primarily chemical weathering).
C_1 Hor.		C_1 Hor. = Break off layer of rock débris (primarily physical weathering).
C_2 Hor.		C_2 Hor. = fresh parent rock.

Fig. 3. — Profile Diagram for Soils of the Podsol Region.

No. 1: Key for the Identification of the most important Humus Forms with their description.

General. An exhaustive investigation of humus forms is one of the most important requirements for the development of useful comprehensive soil systematics. The tendency for «simplicity» was just as detrimental here, as for soil systematics in general. The knowledge of the most important humus forms belongs, with profile morphology, to the indispensable aids in soil diagnosis. There are very many ways of humus formation in nature. The fundamental unit of systematics of humus formation is the h u m u s f o r m (P. E. MÜLLER 1879). The designation humus form refers always to the humus formation as a whole, i. e. with it is meant, not only particular chemical or physical characteristics, but also a particular profile development with all its horizons, their internal structure and the totality of their life. In primitive soil formations with very simple profiles, which are already characterized by their kind of humus formation, the name of the humus forms is identical to that of the soil type. On grounds of simplicity they are not described here, but later under the soil types. The finding of the appropriate places will be made easier by the following key. The construction of humus profiles and the designation of humus horizons were dealt with in the preceding section.

Key for the Humus Forms

1.	Always covered with water … … … … … … … … … … … … … … …	2
1*.	Never or only intermittently covered with water … … … … … … …	6
2.	Without the formation of a macroscopically distinguishable humus horizon.	

1. Sub-aqueous raw soil humus.

2*.	With distinct formation of a humus horizon … … … … … … … … …	3
3.	Humus layer, loose, muddy … … … … … … … … … … … … … … …	4
3*.	Humus layer, coherent, peaty.	

6. Low moor peat (underwater form).

4.	Humus layer brown, composed almost entirely of humus flocks, generally occurring in brown coloured waters.

2. Dy.

4*.	Humus layer blackish, grey to grey brown, not occurring in brown coloured water and only rarely occurring in water containing humus sols.	5

5.   Without or only with slight smell of putrefaction, rich in animal excreta.

3. **Gyttja.**

5*.   With strong to unbearable smell of putrefaction, deficient in animal excreta.

4. **Sapropel.**

6.   Always or for the greater part of the year completely or partially water-logged   7
6*.   Not or only very exceptionally temporarily water-logged   10
7.   Peaty and mineral deficient   8
7*.   Not peaty, very rich in minerals, earthy, when wet muddy, blackish to grey coloured.

8. **Anmoor.**

8.   Peat masses composed either predominately of grasses (reeds) or false grasses, of brown moss or wood fragments, leaf remains, and cones of alders.

5. **Low moor peat** (drained form).

8*.   Peat masses of different composition, not formed under water   9
9.   Peat masses composed primarily of wood, cones, needle, and leaf residues of forest trees (primarily pines or beeches).

6. **Transition moor peat.**

9*.   Peat masses formed, above all, by the remains of peat mosses, extremely acid

7. **High moor peat.**

10.   Without the formation of a macroscopically distinguishable humus horizon.

9. **Raw soil humus.**

10*. With well marked humus horizon   11
11.   F-horizon strongly developed, consisting predominately of strikingly little decomposed or comminuted plant residues, easily recognizable, often matted together like peat   12
11*. Humus with no plant residues recognizable with the naked eye   13
12.   Humus strongly acid, more or less browned, if almost mineral free, then lying with a sharp boundary on the mineral soil, or containing bare, polished, «bleached» mineral grains. By percolation, acid humus sols are formed (brown coloured leachings). The influence of the humus cover on the underlying mineral soil, which is strongly eluviated, is always considerable and leads in general to the formation of bleached sand layers which consist of smooth washed, bare mineral grains.

10. **Raw humus.**

12*. Humus containing no bleached grains, forming no brown humus sols; its influence on the underlying mineral soil is small and in no way «bleaching». The upper humus layer, consisting primarily of little decomposed, strongly browned and mostly stalky to needle shaped plant residues, contains also large quantities of droppings of small animals in most cases even earthworm casts. It transforms gradually and without a sharp boundary into the humus-rich mineral horizon. Mostly occurring on limestone in the sub-alpine region.

11. **Tangel humus.**

13. Humus loose, forming few or no aggregates, for the most part consisting of droppings of small animals (Arthropoda).

13*. Humus layer with very good humification forming compact or loose aggregates   15

14. Deficient in lime, low in bases, of acid reaction, with an intense moder smell, occurring on soils on silicate rocks.

*12. **Moder** (silicate moder).*

14*. Occurring on limestone, of slightly alkaline to neutral reaction (mineral rich forms effervescing with HCl), when dry powdery to dusty.

*14. **Rendsina moder.***

15. Humus formation always dense and compact, when wet deep black, pitch-like, fabric almost entirely mineral free, occurring in the high Alps on limestone.

*16. **Pitch moder.***

15*. Humus formation with coherent, porous, spongy structure or consisting of loose aggregates   16

16. Organic matter proportionately well humified, humus formation low in clay to clay free, however mineral rich, forming mostly very small irregular to clearly cylindrical aggregates   17

16*. Organic matter thouroughly humified, humus formation with moderate to high clay content, in most cases distinct clayey or typical earthy smell, the brownish grey humus substances are contained as finely divided dyes in the clay fraction.

*17. **Mull.***

17. Soils occurring on silicate rock, acid in reaction, always with moder smell.

*13. **Mull-like (silicate) moder.***

17*. Occurring on limestone, chalky to rich in chalk, effervescing with HCl.

*15. **Mull-like rendsina moder.***

Description of Humus Forms.

I. Sub-aqueous Humus Forms

1. **Sub-aqueous raw soil humus.** A very young humus formation in which the decomposition of plant residues proceeds very slowly, primarily due to low colonization by the soil fauna. The plant residues, which are separately imbedded in the mineral soil mass show only slight mechanical comminution and little chemical decompositon. Coprogenic elements do occur frequently, but only in small quantities. With aeration a gradual browning of the plant residues begins as in peat. It is distinguished from low moor peat by the absence of a matted layer of plant residues and the isolated plant remains represent only a small fraction of the total, primarily mineral soil mass.

Explanation to Plate I.

(Micromorphology of the humus-forms)

1. **Gyttja.** Preparation in waterdrop. Detritus of droppings of small soil animals, residues of plants, shells of diatoms.
2. **Turf Peat Moor** (*Phragmites-Fen*), unprepared, incident light. Remains of leaves and roots.
3. **Sedge Peat Moor** (*Carex-Fen*), unprepared, incident light. Remains of leaves, between them gyttja-like humus flocks.
4. **Hypnum Peat Moor** (*Hypnum-Fen*), unprepared, incident light.
5. **Sphagnum Peat Moor** (*Sphagnum-Fen*), unprepared, incident light. Undecomposed remains of *Sphagnum*.
6. **Old Sphagnum Peat Moor** thin section. Remains of dark brown coloured mosses which are little decomposed but strongly pressed and impregnated whith acid humus sols.
7. **Syrosem Humus** (raw soil humus) of a chalk raw soil, thin section. Sand rich in calcite and poor in humus with imbedded splinters of undecomposed plants remains with feeding cavities of mining animals. In the cavities very small, short cylindric droppings of Oribatides.
8. **Raw Humus,** thin section. Accumulations of little decomposed plant remains with very few feeding cavities and accumulations of droppings of small animals. Mineral content very low.

---

2. **Dy,** description see type II, page 86.
3. **Gyttja,** description see type III, page 87.
4. **Sapropel,** description see type IV.
5. **Low moor peat,** description see type V.

II. Semi-terrestrial Humus Forms

6. **Transition moor peat,** description see type XI.
7. **High moor peat,** description see type XII.
8. **Anmoor,** generally a mineral rich, gyttja-like humus form, always or mostly waterlogged, in which immediately higher plants root and at the same time serve as parent material for humus formation. Anmoor shows no f o r m a t i o n o f p e a t but consists principally of a blackish or dark grey mixture of mineral substance with mechanically decomposed, finely divided, constantly enriched, well humified, excretal remains of aquatic animals. The smell is characteristically «inky», with a muddy structure in excessively humid conditions, becoming earthy in moderately humid state (plate IV).

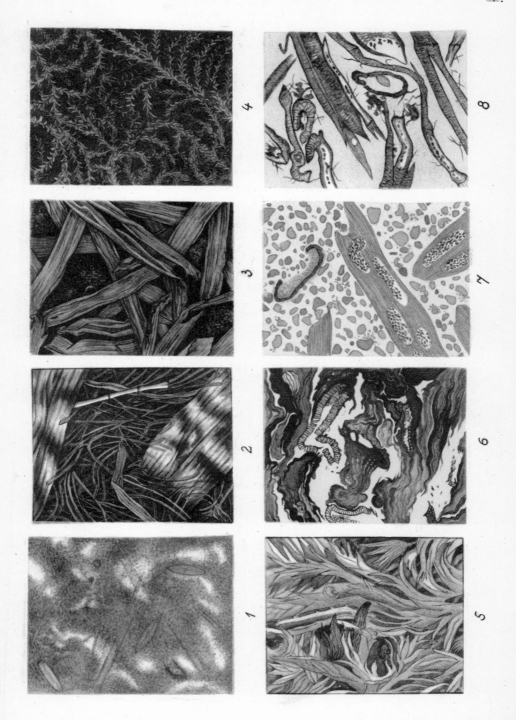

I.

III.   Terrestrial Humus Forms

9.   **Raw soil humus** (Syrosem humus). This very young humus formation
(which must not be mistaken for raw humus) has no humus horizons but
consists of isolated little decomposed plant residues imbedded in the mineral layers of the biologically little active raw soils. It shows a typical
individual pioneer fauna. Microscopic examination generally reveals chop-
ped straw like plant splinters, with well preserved cell structures, in which
cavities are formed by mining animals and filled with their well preserved
droppings (plate I). From the forms of the droppings those of Oribatides
predominate. The low humification of the raw soil humus is not due to
unfavourable environmental conditions but to the low stage in development
of the humus formation and soil life.

10.   **Raw humus** (Rohhumus FRICKE 1905, RAMANN 1911), synonyms:
mor *) (P. E. MÜLLER, 1879), «torf» (MÜLLER 1884) [2]), duff (Ro-
MEL 1931) rahumus (Swedish), Trockentorf (ERDMANN 1904) [2]). The
humus formation is characterized by the preponderance of structurally
well preserved, little decomposed and generally also little comminuted
plant residues and always high acidity leading to the development of
acid humus sols (brown effluents). The humus sols usually produce
a strong eluviation of the peptisable substances from the top soil and
the formation of a bleached sand layer consisting of bare mineral granules. The formation of raw humus is strongly encouraged by the development of certain plants rich in crude fibre forming a large mass
of residues (so-called raw humus plants). Further these contain usually
substances which obstruct the decomposition by plant micro-organisms.
The plant residues are also reluctantly absorbed in the raw undecomposed condition by the soil fauna. The plants are undemanding, showing luxuriant growth in soils poor in nutriants and crowd out other
more valuable species. The low rate of decomposition by plant organisms is also accentuated by the cool soil climate and the strong acidity
of the litter and humus layers. Examples of raw humus plants are
Calluna and *Erica* spp., mat-red rhododendrons, crowberry, also in
many cases conifers, especially spruce, stone pine and others pines.
Microscopic examination shows a preponderance of little decomposed
plant residues against the very sparse of the droppings and remains
of droppings of the soil fauna (plate I). Raw humus is formed in a
cool and humid climate on poor acid soils, very deficient in chalk,
bases, nutrients and mineral colloidal material. It is the most unfavourable form of terrestrial humus formation. In forests the raw humus profile is characterized by a thick förna in which the litter of

---

*) Pronounce: mœr as in förna, not moor.

several years has accumulated owing to the low decomposition. Next
to it the F-layer is always very strongly developed but the H-layer is
scarcely perceptible or completely missing in very unfavourable raw
humus formations. In transitional forms to moder, the H-layer enters
more into the picture. A particular variety of raw humus (especially
in spruce forests) is the «Auflagetorf» (VATER 1904), in which the humus layer consists of a trick, compact, easily cut blanket of plant residues. Microscopic examination shows little decomposed plant-frag-
ments of varying size, which are glued to each other by blackish-
brown, peptized coprogenic humus masses. The strongly comminuted
plant remains are derived generally from the bulky, undecomposed
fraction of the droppings, while the brownish black amorphous masses
are produced by the strongly humified, peptized fraction of the droppings. These are the reasons for the occasionally rather high tenacity
shown by «Auflagetorf» [3].

11. **Tangelhumus.** A necessary condition for this humus formation is
the pre-existence of a mull or mull-like moder rich in humus (rendsina moder). In these humus layers in open sub-alpine forests (Pine-Erica
and Fir-Erica) or in the alpine dwarf-shrub region on limestone, humus plants are developed which produce a large accumulation of fibre-
rich plant residues. Of such humus plants (tangel plants) the following
are the most important; *Erica carnea, Rhododendron hirsutum, Juniperus communis, Pinus mugho,* etc. Since the residues of these plants
are laid down in very activ humus layers, in spite of their very low
decomposability they do not produce raw humus but a product which
contains besides nearly undecomposed plant remains large quantities
of droppings of small animals which in most tangel formations consists of calcareous earthworm casts (plate II). These casts are formed
of the soil material of the mull horizon, on limestone (dolomite) as
parent material also of the underlying Ca-horizon. Therefore the surface
layer consisting of raw plant remains (tangel layer) is constantly enriched
by chalk and earth. In this way the tangel layer gradually loses all characteristics reminiscent of a raw humus layer and its lower part becomes increasingly like a mull layer into which it is eventually turned.
Tangel humus formations at the lower boundary of the sub-alpine
region or in the hill region with very active mull layers always show
a severely diminished tangel layer, while those on high laying northern
slopes with a lasting snow cover have tangel layers of much greater
thickness and lower content of droppings. The latter is called d y s t r o -
p h i c   t a n g e l   h u m u s, and approaches more closely the character
of raw humus. However, it also does not produce an eluviation or
bleaching of the mineral soil. The complete humus formation may oc-

casionally attain a thickness of up to 1 m. Tangel humus has been found in the Alps only on limestone and not as yet on silicate rock, while on the Spanish high mountains (Sierra de Guadarrama, Sierra Nevada) it is beautifully developed on silicate rock. The name a l p i n e m o d e r (LEININGEN) seems partly to be a synonym for tangel humus i. e., only so far as formation on limestone and dolomite with connecting mull horizons, but excluding formations on primitive rock or of other origin. The following table may help to show up clearly the difference between tangel and raw humus:

Raw Humus	Tangelhumus
The eventual H-horizons are formed from the raw humus itself.	The mull layer (H-horizon) is always formed beforehand.
Is always very acid.	Is usually only moderately acid.
Forms acid humus sols (brown percolations).	Forms no acid humus sols.
Causes eluviation and formation of bleached layers (plate XXIV).	Causes no eluviation or formation of bleached layers.
Lies generally with a sharp boundary on the mineral soil.	Always passes over gradually into the mineral soil (mull layer) (plate XIV).
Contains only raw, little decomposed, and in most cases also little comminuted plant remains.	Constains besides raw, mostly stalky to needle shaped dark brown plant remains also increasing deposits of calcareous droppings.
Shows no tendency towards mull formation.	In favourable location converted into mull or mull-like rendsina moder.
Is always an unfavourable humus formation.	Is for forest vegetation generally a favourable humus formation.

12. **Moder (silicate moder).** Synonyms: insect mull (P. E. MÜLLER 1879)[4], mull-like mor (MÜLLER)[5], mull-like peat (MÜLLER)[5], moder (RAMANN 1906), mar (HESSELMANN 1926), twin mull (ROMELL and HEIBERG 1931), duff mull (WILDE 1948). By moder formation one has meant a kind of decomposition and humus formation which produces a far-going but not complete humification of the remains of organisms due to excellent aeration. The product of that kind of humus formation is clearly distinguishable from raw humus and from what was called moder. What the nature of moder is, may easily be shown and defined by any comparative microscopic examination. While in raw

Explanation to Plate II.
(Micromorphology of the Humus-forms)

1. **Tangel Humus** of a *tangel-rendsina*, thin section. Undecomposed strongly browned plant splinters with remains of earthworm droppings.

2. **Moder** (silicate moder), thin section. Loose mixture of bitten through plant remains, mineral fragments and numerous droppings of small Arthropodes (predominately Oribatides and Collembolas).

3. **Pitch Moder** of an alpine *pitch rendsina,* thin section. Striking accumulation of very small cylindric droppings of a very homogeneous fabric, extremely poor in minerals and good humification. The mass shows a few splinter-like plant residues and numerous cracks produced by shrinking.

4. **Mull-like Rendsina Moder**, thin section. Loose mixture of mineral-rich aggregates (predominately droppings and fragments of small animals and little decomposed plant remains). In the aggregates little chemical decomposition of the mineral substance, relatively good humification (the humic substances act mainly as binding substances) but also existence of little decomposed plant splinters with well preserved cellular structures.

5. **Mull** with typical spongy fabric, thin section. Complete decomposition and humification of the organic substance, lack of recognisable plant remains, good clay formation, binding of the finely dispersed humic substance by the clay substance (formation of clay-humus complex and other minero-humus complexes). The spongy fabric is formed by fusing of the aggregates (in prevalence dropping complexes of earthworms).

6. **Pitch Peat Anmoor**, thin section. More or less homogenous humus mass poor in mineral matter, strongly peptized, breaking down by shrinkage into sharp edged brittle aggregates, low in plant splinters.

7. **Humus Ortstein**, debris preparation. The mineral grains show coatings of sepia brown humus substances which produce a characteristic network of cracks by drying.

8. **Coated Humus Ortstein**, thin section. The coated sand grains (coatings visible only in form of a thin dark line) are combined with each other at the junction points. The spaces between the grains are empty.

---

humus only very few animal droppings are found and these generally only of mites, in moder coprogenic elements become very important. These originate not only from mites and insects [4]) but innumerable other soil animals. In general the excreta of Oribatides and Collemboli (spring tails) predominate. Moder contains besides greater or lesser quantities of browned plant remains broken down by plant microorganisms, but still with well-preserved cell structure. However, these are eaten through, extensively comminuted and mixed-up together, not matted as in raw humus. Moder further is permeated more or less strongly by loose, incoherent mineral particles (plate II).

Although moder has been introduced as a decomposition product primarily of bacteria and fungi, moder occurs in nature in formations in

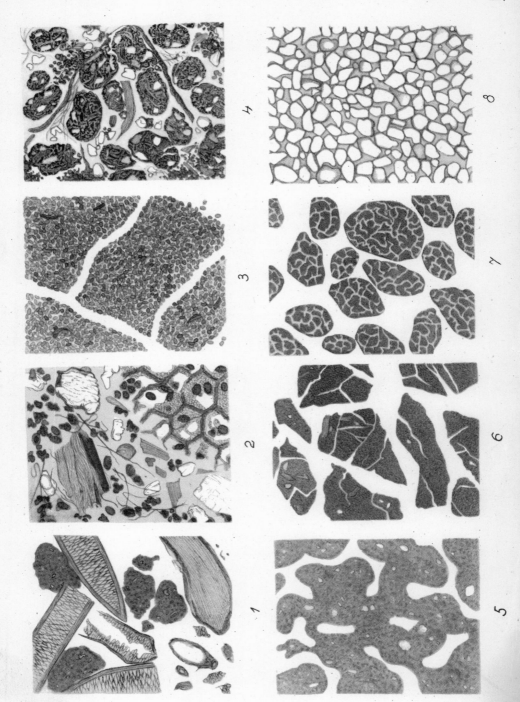

which the small animals have a decisive influence on the development of humus. A moder, little attacked by the soil fauna, has still a raw humus character. How moder is to be distinguished from mull will be shown by the description of the mull.

Moder formations are to be found principally in deciduous and coniferous forests, but can also occur outside forests especially on young soil formations. There they are easy to recognise because they are l o o s e , fairly well to very well humified, chalk deficient, rich in organic matter, with typical somewhat obstructive smell (moder smell), while those in forests are determined by having neither an excessively developed F-layer nor a strong accumulation of litter (förna). As the H layer is always well developed there is a humus profile of förna, F and H layers of approximately equal thickness.

For soil diagnosis, the difference between coarse and fine moder as sub-forms is of particular importance. The c o a r s e m o d e r contains very many plant remains, consisting mainly of the coarser parts, and comes close to raw humus. In f i n e m o d e r the coprogenic elements predominate by far and may even practically compose the entire humus form. Also in this case, it is always a moder and not a mull formation (also in the sense of P. E. MÜLLER, cf. note [5])).

13. **Mull-like moder.** Synonyms: mull-like silicate moder, moder earth. This humus formation is a mineral rich, chalk deficient, generally acid fine moder, consisting predominately of animal droppings and their residues. The humus has a similar external appearance to mull, but is distinguished from a true mull in that the humus and mineral particles are present as distinctly separable elements. They are well mixed up but present only in comparatively looser binding. The binding however is sufficient for soil crumbs to be formed. These consist almost entirely of droppings or dropping fragments of small soil animals (Julidi, Glomeridi, insects, small earthworms, etc.) which are capable of taking up with their food a large quantity of mineral fragments as well. The binding substances of the soil aggregates are almost completely of organic matter. This humus form occurs mostly in soils where the chemical weathering and clay formation are not sufficiently advanced for the formation of a true mull. The smell is typically moder-like. Externally the similarity to mull can be so strong that they can only be distinguished microscopically. Generally the mull-like moder can easily be distinguished from common moder by its high mineral content and from mull by its usual sandy texture, also by a certain rawness and ununiformity in its humus formation (compare smell). If kneaded when moist it shows a certain plasticity but its formability is quite different from that of mull. Mull-like moders occur frequently in forests and are favourable humus formations for them, but often are to be found as well in young soil formations outside forests.

14. **Rendsina moder.** Synonym: chalk moder. On young, shallow and easily dried out rendsinas, humus formations are found which consist to a great extent of loose, mostly deep black coloured droppings of soil animals well preserved in form. The bulk of the blackish substance consists of calcium humates, which is the main difference between it and the morphologically similar silicate moder. Between the droppings, numerous loose, almost unweathered mineral grains are found, mainly of calcite or dolomite. In addition, there are present bitten through, strongly comminuted but structurally little distorted plant splinters. The droppings are mainly very small, deep black, mineral deficient, short cylinders, originating almost entirely from Oribatides (the *proto-rendsina* in which rendsina moder is primarily to be found demands drought resistant animals). All the various constituents above form a mixture which is loose and very dusty in the dry state.

15. **Mull-like rendsina moder.** Synonyms: moder marl (RAMANN 1911). This humus form is essentially more mature, in the dry state no longer powdery. It is characterized as well by the formation of chalk humates and has a similar external appearance to mull. Microscopically it is distinguished from the previous form, by the larger, more or less mineral rich aggregates (i. e. droppings of Julidi, Glomeridi, Engerlings and other insect larvae, ants, earthworms, etc.). The mineral grains (predominately calcite or dolomite) are not found loose between the droppings and dropping fragments but are contained in them. Undecomposed plant splinters are of little distribution, but are as typical constituents still distinctly recognisable (plate II 4). The droppings are mainly of cylindrical form of about 2-5mm in length. The humus form is active, rich in organisms and shows good humification but is always easily dried out in hot summers with low rainfall. Owing to the low chemical weathering and low clay content and to the insufficiently balanced water relations, the conditions are not ripe for the formation of a true mull (plate XV).

16. **Alpine pitch moder** (n. f.). This very striking humus form occurs in the grass heath region of limestone high mountains, and consists when moist, of a deep black pitchy humus layer of 15-20cm, characterized by the almost complete absence of mineral particles. The appearance of a thin section is extraordinarily typical showing a very homogeneous fabric of well formed, sepia brown cylinders about 30-50μ long. Other forms of droppings are rare. Mineral fragments as well as undecomposed plant splinters are almost completely missing as the plant remains have been completely decomposed (plate II 6). Pitch moder layers are formed

in locations where snow lies to a great depth in winter, generally below moist Firmeta. They never completely dry out even in the hottest summers. Yet they never suffer from waterlogging (except some anmoor-like varieties). They are particularly rich in Collembola so it must be assumed that the very uniform dropings are produced mainly by them. The humus form is typical for the *alpine pitch rendsina* and developes from the mineral rich chalk moder humus of the *alpine protorendsina*, as with strong wetting, high biological activity and therefore high carbonic acid production all the fine chalk fragments go gradually into solution. Thus from an extremely water deficient soil dominated by drought resistant Oribatides there arises a moist, mineral deficient Collembola soil (plate XIII).

17. **Mull** (P. E. MÜLLER 1884). Synonyms: muld (Danish, P. E. MÜLLER 1879), mull earth, crumb mull (ROMELL 1931), earth mull (WILDE 1948). Mull is not simply a humus formation similar to the above, characterized only by a more advanced humification, but it is a completely new humus form with particular characteristics, particular genesis and particular biology. It is found only in favourable places with mild to warm soil climate on soils sufficiently high in clay and nutrients with balanced water conditions and aeration and under plant covers which yield easily decomposable plant remains of higher biological value. Externally it appears as a grey, dark grey, brown grey to blackish, well crumbling plastic mineral soil, coloured by diffuse humus substances generally with a typical earthy sometimes clayey smell. Microscopic investigation show not only that remains of organisms with still recognisable cell structures are almost completely missing, but also that there are practically no large humus particles. All the organic substances have been turned into browny grey finely divided true humus substances which are adsorbed like a dye by the clay fraction (plate II 5). Humus substances and clay cannot be separated at all mechanically and only very inadequately by chemical methods. Thus new bodies are formed which are designated as clay-humus complexes *) which are characteristic of every true mull formation. Mull is rich in very diverse organisms. It is extremely suited for colonization by certain very productive kinds of earthworms which exert a strong influence on its morphology. Practically all the aggregates are earthworm casts or residues of them. According to the results of the investigation work of L. MEYER (1943), the formation of the clay-humus complex occurs in the intestines of the earthworm. For this the presence of suitable clay substances is essential. Exact boundaries of the concept of mull

---

*) Partly also iron hydroxide-and silica- humus complexes.

are very important for humus research as well as for soil systematics and practical soil science. If the concept had not been attached by MÜLLER already in this form, making it easy to recognize from its description, then it would now have to be created. In cultivated soils only the clay-humus complexes provide a lasting accumulation of humus while humus in other forms is more or less rapidly used up. Herein lies the great importance of true mull for agriculture, and its formation and intensification is to be striven for by all methods.

No. 2: Simplest Keys for the Easy Identification of the most frequent Forest and cultivated Soils of Central and Northern Europe.

a. Starting from the Soil Colour *)

Soil colour light grey to whitish grey.	1. Soil continuously, or for the greatest part of the year, w a t e r l o g g e d r i g h t t o t h e s u r-f a c e, soil mass occasionally permeated by flecks and channels of rust colour, frequently with bluey to greeny tint 2
	1*. Soil not or in another way water-logged ... 3
	2. To the naked eye no distinguishable humus horizon. **Raw gley soil** (*syrogley*), type VIII.
	2. With generally strongly water-logged humus horizon of a light grey colour. (Humus deficient) *anmoor*, type IX.
	3. The soil shows continuous or long period water-logging only below the grey humus horizon. The humus layer itself is free from water-logging and represents a land humus form. The subsoil colour is frequently tinted blue to green ... 4
	3*. Soil with strongly varying moisture content or with normal water economy 5
	4. Soil with mull formation (page 41). (Humus deficient) *mull gley*, No. 36.
	4*. Soil with moder or mull-like moder formation (page 37 and 39). (Humus deficient) *moder gley*, No. 35.
	5. Soil very compact even in the upper layer, little permeable, fine-sandy with dark brown concretions. Strong alternation of drying out and water-

*) The starting point is always the colour of the surface layer of the naturally moist soil.

Soil colour light grey to whitish grey.

logging in the upper to surface layers. Subsoil strongly flecked or more or less uniformly brown with light marbling (plate xxiv).

Pseudogley (gley-like soil), type xxxviii.

5*. Soil with good water penetration ... ...　6

6. Soil occurring near the banks of rivers, however not continuously water-logged but at most showing periodic flooding by high waters.　7

6*. Soil not periodically flooded and not occurring near river banks ... ...　9

7. Soil without distinct humus horizon but at best with a strongly through-rooted surface layer (plate iv).

Raw warp soil *(rambla)*, type vi.

7*. Soil with distinct humus horizon even if it is very lightly coloured due to low humus content or due to mixing by cultivation with the subsoil ... ...　8

8. Soil calcareous, effervescing with dilute HCl.
(Humus deficient) rendsina-like warp soil *(borovina)*, type xviii.

8*. Not effervescing with HCl (plate vi).
(Humus deficient) grey warp soil *(paternia)*, type xvii.

9. Without distinct humus horizon or brown coloured subsoil ... ...　10

9*. With distinct humus horizon ... ...　11

10. Effervescing with HCl.
Chalk raw soil *(chalk syrosem)*, No. 50

10*. Not effervescing with HCl.
Silicate raw soil *) *(silicate syrosem)*, No. 49

11. Effervescing with HCl.
(Humus deficient) *rendsina,* type xxv.

11*. Not effervescing with HCl ... ...　12

12. Top soil generally sandy, mineral granules bare, washed smooth (bleached sand mixed by cultiv-

*) The colour of the silicate raw soil depends strongly on the colour of the parent material and therefore in most cases but not always is grey coloured.

Soil colour light grey to whitish grey.

ation with the humus layer), with poor, strongly acid humus formation. Subsoil ochre yellow, rust brown to coffee brown coloured (plate XXV and XXVI).

Podsol, type XL.

12*. Without ochre yellow to brown coloured subsoil. Soil moderately raw, showing little chemical weathering (plate XI).

Grey ranker, No. 57.

Soil colour dark grey to blackish.

1. Soil permanently or during the greatest part of the year water-logged r i g h t t o t h e s u r-
f a c e , subsoil generally with bluey to greeny tinting, frequently permeated by brown rust flecks and channels. The generally very moist humus formation is muddy in wet state (plate IV).

Anmoor, type IX.

1*. Soil not or in another way water-logged ... 2

2. Continuous or long duration water-logging commences only below the humus horizon, while the humus horizon itself is free from water-logging and shows the development of land humus forms. The subsoil colour has a bluish to greenish tint, frequently interspersed with rust channels and flecks 3

2*. Soil with strongly varying moisture content or with normal water economy 4

3. Soil with mull formation (page 41).

Mull gley, No. 36.

3*. Soil with moder or mull-like moder formation.
Moder gley, No. 35.

4. Soil very dense even in the upper layer, with low permeability, fine-sandy to silty, frequently with dark brown pin-head concretions of ferric hydroxide. Strong alternation of drying out and water-logging in the superficial to surface layers. Humus formation mostly raw and unfavourable, subsoil strongly flecked (plate XXIV) or brown with light marbling.

Pseudogley (gley-like soil), type XXXVIII.

4*. Soil with high water permeability 5

Soil colour dark grey to blackish.

5. Soil occurring near the banks of rivers, however showing no continuous water-logging but only periodic flooding by high waters. The soil material is generally raw, predominately sandy, showing little chemical weathering   6

5*. Soil not periodically flooded nor occurring near the banks of rivers   7

6. Soil calcareous, effervescing with dilute hydrochloric acid.

     Rendsina-like warp soil (*borovina*), type XVIII, [plate VII.

6*. Not effervescing with hydrochloric acid.

     Grey warp soil (*paternia*), type XVII, plate VI.

7. Soil effervescing with hydrochloric acid already in the always well developed humus horizon, or at least at its lower edge   8

7*. Soil not effervescing with hydrochloric acid.

     Grey ranker, type 57, plate XI.

8. Soil mostly with deep humus horizon almost only formed on level surfaces primarily of loess or calcareous loess-like sediments (plate XVII).

     Chernosem, type XXX.

8*. Soil generally shallow, occurring chiefly in mountains or hill-lands, predominately on hard limestone, marl, calcareous sandstone, dolomite, gypsum, but also on loose marly to calcareous sandy sediments (plate XV).

     Rendsina, type XXV.

Soil colour brownish grey to blackish dark brown grey.

1. Soil humic to humus rich, only occurring in the alluvial flats of streams or rivers. The brownish grey to dark-brown grey humus horizon is followed by a humus deficient brown mineral layer (plate VIII).

     Brown warp soil (*brown vega*), No. 38.

1*. Soil not occurring in the flats of streams and rivers   2

2. Soil consisting only of a humus layer or at best with a thin brown seam on its lower edge, without the addition of a strongly developed

Soil colour brownish grey to blackish dark brown grey.

brown coloured humus deficient subsoil layer ((B)-horizon); parent material always calcareous   3

2*. Soil always with a strongly developed brown subsoil layer under the humus layer   4

3. Soil in most cases with a proportionately deep humus horizon only occurring on plains, especially on loess or calcareous loess-like sediments (plate XVII).

Degraded chernosem, No. 7ι.

3*. Soil generally shallow, occurring in mountainous or hilly land especially on hard, calcareous parent rock (plate XIV).

Brown rendsina, No. (42).

4. Soil usually neutral to slightly acid with good humus formation, free from any unweathered plant remains and the humus intimately bound with the mineral substance (mainly mull formation, page 41). Brown mineral subsoil not essentially heavier and richer in colloidal material than the surface soil (plate XXI and XXII).

Brown earth (*braunerde*), type XXXVII.

4*. Soil acid to strongly acid, with an inert, unfavourable humus formation, generally rich in undecomposed plant remains, with ochre yellow to brown subsoil which is not essentially heavier, more compact, denser or richer in colloidal material than the top soil   5

5. The dark brown colour is exclusively conditioned by the usually raw humus particles, while the mineral grains of the surface layer are uncoloured. In undisturbed profiles the humus layer is followed by a strongly developed light grey to whitish, loose, bleached sand layer. The subsoil is ochre yellow, ochre brown to coffee brown coloured (plate XXV and XXV) and very often solidified like sandstone (ortstein formation).

Podsol, type XL.

5*. No strongly developed bleached sand layer below the humus horizon but only separate flecks of bleached sand or a thin seam of bleached sand. Often bleached sand granules are to be found only in the humus layer itself, as numerous characteristic constituents (examination with

Soil colour brownish grey to blackish dark brown grey.

magnifying glass). The brown subsoil is always heavier, loamier, denser than the top soil, but is never hardened like sandstone (plate XXII).

Podsolic brown earth, No. 85

Soil colour light ochre yellow, light ochre to grey ochre.

1. Colour generally very intense, extraordinarily bright, soil low in humus, strikingly easily silted up, tending to the formation of a dense structure, when moist strongly swelling, easily becoming pasty, on drying out becoming hard like stone or splitting up into sharp-edged fracture pieces down to the finest angular fragments.   2

1*. Soil not having the above characteristics.   3

2. Soil occurring on hard limestone, dolomite or gypsum (plate XVIII).

Limestone brown loam (*terra fusca*), No. 74.

2*. Soil occurring in deep deposits of soil formations of former (mostly tertiary) ages.

Brown loam (*braunlehm*), type XXXIV.

3. Soil light ochre coloured, calcareous, without humus horizon and with little chemical weathering, occurring on deposits of loess.

Loess raw soil (*loess syrosem*), No.(31).

3*. Soil not formed on loess   4

4. Soil generally with shallow humus deficient mull formation (page 41), which with cultivation frequently disappears by mixing with the underlying humus deficient mineral soil. The soil mass is never strongly acid and the similar coloured subsoil is never essentially heavier, loamier or richer in colloidal material than the top soil (plate XXI).

Brown earth (*braunerde*), type XXXVII.

4*. Soil always acid to very acid, subsoil always considerably heavier, richer in colloidal material and denser than the top soil   5

5. The cultivated soil shows in the surface layers a high content of smooth washed sand grains («bleached» grains), often whole pockets, lenses, and layer remains of grey to whitish bleached sand. The subsoil frequently shows dark brown flecks and colourings of eluviated humus

Soil colour light ochre yellow, light ochre to grey ochre.

often together with a sandstone-like hardening (ortstein formation). The colour and character of the generally sandy surface layers are produced by mixing of humus, bleached sand and iron enriched layers.

Podsol, type XL (plate XXVI).

5*. The cultivated soil shows in the (frequently loamy) surface layer, only a comparatively low content of bleached sand grains. The subsoil is not hardened like sandstone, but is always heavier, loamier and richer in colloidal substances than the top soil.

Podsolic brown earth, No. 85 (plate XXIII).

Soil colour intense brown to reddish brown.

1. Soil mass dense, low in humus, easily silted up, strongly swelling when moist, easily becoming pasty. Drying out produces a stone like hardening or break down into sharp edged fractional pieces or finest fragments. The soil occurs on hard limestone, dolomite or gypsum. **Limestone brown loam** (*terra fusca*), No. 74 (plate XVIII).

1*. Soil as above, not however formed on hard limestone, dolomite or gypsum.

Brown loam, type XXXJV.

Soil colour dark brown to rust coloured.

1. Occurring in the flats of streams and rivers. Soil either very low in humus or the humus horizon has become unrecognizable in mixing by cultivation with the subsoil.

Brown warp soil (*brown vega*), No. 38 (plate VIII)

1*. Soil not occurring in river and stream flats.　2

2. Soil neutral, slightly acid to moderately acid, generally with good crumb structure, subsoil is not essentially heavier, richer in coloidal substances and has similar colour as the top soil.

Brown earth (*braunerde*), type XXXVII.

2*. Soil always acid to very acid with very poor crumb structure. Subsoil always distinctly heavier, denser and richer in colloidal material than the top soil ... ...　3

Soil colour dark brown to rust coloured.	3. The cultivated soil *) in the surface layer is distinctly lighter coloured than the subsoil and contains a great amount of smooth washed sand grains (bleached sand grains), often white packets and layer remains of grey to whitish unmixed bleached sand. The soil is often hardened like sandstone.

Podsol, type XL.

3*. The bleached sand content in the surface layer is low and the colour difference between it and the subsoil less marked. The subsoil is never compacted like sandstone.

Podsolic brown earth, No. 85 (plate XXIII).

Soil colour red to brown red.	1. Soil strongly swelling when wet, easily silted up. Almost only occurring on pure limestone. *Terra rossa* (limestone red loam), No. 75 (plate XVIII).

1. Soil as above, however not occurring on limestone but on silicate rocks (e. g. basalt) or in the form of deep sedimentary deposits of soil formations of former ages.

Red loam, type XXXV (plate XX).

b.   Starting from Chalk Content and Reaction

Soil highly calcareous to calcareous. With dilute HCl **) effervescing in the surface layer or on the lower edge of the hu= mus layer.	1. Soil water-logged continuously or during the greater part of the year, bluish to greenish grey, in parts with a few brown rust channels or flecks 2

1*. Soil not or in another way water-logged.   3

2. Without distinct humus horizon to the naked eye.

Calcareous raw gley soil (*syrogley*), type VIII.

2*. Generally with strong water-logging, generally blackish humus horizon is with muddy appearance when wet.

Calcareous anmoor, type IX.

*)   Almost only cultivated soils come into consideration.
**)   One starts always from the characteristics of the top soil. The given pH ranges represent approximate not absolute boundaries, serving only for a general orientation. Local factors within the individual types, can produce a certain (often only temporarily effective) fluctuation above or below.

Soil highly calcareous to calcareous. With dilute HCl *) effervescing in the surface layer or on the lower edge of the humus layer.

3. The soil shows continuous or long period water-logging only under the humus horizon, while the humus layer characterized by mull formation is free from stagnant water. The subsoil is mostly bluish-grey to greenish-grey with few rust channels or flecks.

    Calcareous mull gley, No. 36.

3*. The soil is free from water-logging   4

4. Soil occurring in the flats of streams and rivers with high permeability, however often periodically flooded by high waters   5

4*. Soil not occurring in the flats of streams and rivers   6

5. With no definite humus horizon apparent to the naked eye, low chemical weathering, subsoil whitish to grey, mostly sandy.

    Calcareous raw warp soil *(rambla),* type VI.

5*. In most cases with shallow grey to blackish humus horizon. Subsoil as above (plate VII).

    Rendsina-like warp soil *(borovina),* type XVIII.

6. To the naked eye no distinct humus layer or other horizon formation   7

6*. With humus layer or other soil horizon ...   8

7. Occurring on deposits of loess.

    Loess raw soil *(loess-syrosem),* No. (31).

7*. Occurring on other calcareous parent material.

    Chalk raw soil *(chalk-syrosem),* No. 50

8. Humus layer not coloured brownish by ferric hydroxide, without distinctly developed brown subsoil   9

8*. Humus layer when occurring (in arable soils where the surface layer has not become indistinguishable by mixing with part of the subsoil) is coloured brownish by ferric hydroxide, subsoil ochre, ochre brown or brown coloured (plate XXII).

    Chalk brown earth, No. (60).

9. Soil mostly with deep humus horizon, formed

*) HCl, 1:1 by volume.

Soil highly calcareous to calcareous. With dilute HCl **) effervescing in the surface layer or on the lower edge of the humus layer.

almost only on plains primarily on loess or calcareous loess-like sediments (plate XVII).

Chernosem, type XXX.

9*.   Soil generally shallow, stony, chiefly occurring in mountains or hilly land, primarily on hard limestone or dolomite.

Rendsina, type XXV (plate XV).

Soil neutral (pH 7.2 to 6.5) to slightly acid (pH 6.5 to 5.5) not effervescing with dilute HCl.

1.   Soil water-logged continuously or for the greatest part of the year right to the surface. Subsoil grey with generally strong bluish or greenish tinting (occasionally almost pure turquoise blue or olive green), with in general numerous intense brown coloured rust channels and flecks.   2

1*.   Soil not or in another way water-logged ...   3

2.   With no distinguishable humus horizon to the naked eye.

Raw gley soil (*syrogley*), type VIII.

2*.   With generally strongly water-logged humus horizon, when wet with muddy appearance.

Anmoor, type IX (plate IV).

3.   The soil shows continuous or long period water-logging only below the humus horizon, while the humus layer free from stagnant water, is characterized by terrestrial humus forms. Subsoil mostly grey, with strong bluish or greenish tinting and intensive formation of rust channels and flecks   4

3*.   Soil with strongly varying moisture content or normal water economy   5

4.   Soil with mull formation (page 41).

Mull-gley, No. 36.

4*.   Soil with formation of moder (page 37) or mull-like moder (page 39).

Moder-gley, No. 35.

5.   Soil very dense even in the upper layer, with low permeability, fine sandy to silty, light grey coloured, almost always without rust channels or flecks. Instead of this, frequently with (pinhead to pea-size) dark brown concretions. The surface layer is subjected to strong alternation of superficial to shallow water-logging and drying

Soil neutral (pH 7.2 to 6.5) to slightly acid (pH 6.5 to 5.5) not efferves= cing with dilute HCl.

out. The subsoil is strongly flecked or more or less uniformly brown with light marbling. *Pseudogley* (gley-like soil), type XXXVIII (plate XXIV).

5*. Soil with high water permeability   6

6. Soil occurring in the flats of rivers, showing however continual water-logging but at the most only periodical flooding by high waters ...   7

6*. Soil not subjected to flooding and not occurring in alluvial flats   9

7. Soil colour brown (with abundance of humus, dark brown grey) with brown subsoil.
Brown warp soil (*brown vega*), No. 38 (plate VIII).

7*. Soil colour mostly grey, soil material generally raw, chemically still little weathered, generally sandy.

8. Soil without distinct humus horizon but fre- quently with a strongly through-rooted surface layer (plate IV).
Raw warp soil (*rambla*), type VI.

8*. Soil with distinct humus horizon (plate VI).
Grey warp soil (*paternia*), type XVII.

9. Soil without distinct humus horizon and without brown coloured subsoil.
Silicate raw soil (*silicate-syrosem*), No. 49

9*. Soil with distinct humus horizon or with brown to ochre coloured subsoil   10

10. Soil with intense ochre yellow, ochre brown to reddish brown colour extraordinarily easily silted- up and becoming dense, with thorough wetting pasty, on drying out hard like stone or breaking down into sharp edged angular pieces or finest fragments   11

10*. Soil of different nature   12

11. Soil occurring on limestone, dolomite or gypsum.
Limestone brown earth (*terra fusca*), No. 74 (plate XVIII).

11*. Soil not occurring on the above parent rocks but generally in the form of deep deposits of (tertiary) soil formations of former ages.
Brown loam, type XXXIV.

Soil neutral (pH 7.2 to 6.5) to slightly acid (pH 6.5 to 5.5) not effervescing with dilute HCl.

12.   Soil with generally slightly browned proportionately thick humus layer sometimes with a thin brown seam on its lower edge, on loess or loess-like sediment. No distinct well marked ochre to brown coloured subsoil (plate XVII).

Degraded chernosem, No. 71

12*.   Soil including the subsoil down to the parent material usually dull brown to light ochre coloured (with abundance of humus top soil dark-brown grey). Soil mass generally with good crumb structure, in every case without extreme silting-up or erodability and without rock-like hardening or easy break-down into sharp edged fracture pieces to finest angular fragments on drying out plate XXI and XXII).

Brown earth (*braunerde*), type XXXVII.

Soil acid (pH 5.5. to 4.5) to strongly acid (pH<4.5)

1.   Soil completely and almost continuously water-logged right to the surface layer. Subsoil bluish to greenish grey, mostly with numerous brown rust flecks and channels. The humus formation has a muddy appearance but contains many small, strongly browned, however, still little decomposed small plant splinters, which cause its slight brown colouration.

Dystrophic anmoor, type IX and No. 18.

1*.   Soil not or in another way water-logged ...   2

2.   Soil with very dense, fine sandy to silty upper layer with strong alternation of drying out and stagnation of water above the surface or in the surface layer. The humus is a slowly decomposing moder (page 37) or raw humus (page 35) and is followed by a dense light grey to whitish layer, usually containing numerous brown pin-head concretions of ferric hydroxide (plate XXIV). These change over into a strongly flecked or more uniform brown subsoil with light marbling.

Pseudogley (gley-like soil), type XXXVIII.

2*.   Soil with high water permeability and distinct translocation of the colloidal substances into the subsoil by percolating water   3

3.   Soil with inert humus formation, generally rich in undecomposed plant remains followed by a strongly developed, loose, light grey to whitish

Soil acid (pH 5.5. to 4.5) to strongly acid (pH <4.5)	bleached sand layer (plate XXV and XXVI), which also in cultivated soil either strongly dominates or exists in the form of pockets and layer remains, or can be recognized as a strong admixture in the surface layer. The ochre yellow, rust brown to coffee brown coloured subsoil frequently shows a sandstone-like compaction (Ortstein formation). *Podsol*, type XL

3*. Soil even in undisturbed profiles always without bleached sand layer, but at most with isolated bleached sand flecks, thin seam like formation or only numerous bleached sand grains in the humus layer. The ochre yellow to brown (never coffee brown) subsoil is always heavier, loamier, denser than the top soil. However there is never any sandstone-like compaction (plate XXIII).

Podsolic brown earth, No. 85.

C. Starting from the Parent Material.

Key for the forest, meadow and cultivated soils which frequently occur on the given parent rock groups un Central and Northern Europe, and for which the parent material is specially characteristic.

Acid granite, acid gneis, muscovite schist, quartzite, siliceous schist and siliceous sandstone.	1. Humus continuously or almost continuously, strongly water-logged, very acid, when wet muddy, blackish with numerous browned plant splinters. (*Dystrophic*) *anmoor*, type IX and 18
	1*. Humus not continously nor almost continuously water-logged 2
	2. Humus form moder (page 37), mull-like moder (p. 39), or very shallow humus deficient mull *) (page 41). Soil very stony, shallow, generally of a light ochre colour. The subsoil is not essentially richer in colloidal substances, heavier, loamier or denser than the top soil (plate XXI). It occurs primarily in deciduous and mixed forest areas. **(Oligotrophic) brown earth,** No. (59).

*) Humus layer in arable soils generally unrecognizable due to mixing with the subsoil.

Key No. 2 (Central and Northern Europe)

Acid granite, acid gneis, muscovite schist, quartzite, siliceous schist and siliceous sandstone.

2*. Subsoil essentially richer in colloidal material, heavier, loamier and denser than the top soil. Soil very stony, shallow, generally light ochre yellow coloured, strongly acid to acid 3

3. Soil usually with raw humus or acid coarse moder, with strongly developed light grey to whitish bleached sandlayer under the humus layer, which with cultivation only leaves residues (bleached sand pockets, high bleached sand content of the surface soil). Ortstein-like hardening rare.

Podsol, type XL

3*. Humus form generally acid moder *), no bleached layer but only bleached sand flecks or thin seam-like zone of bleached sand, often only numerous bleached sand grains in the humus layer itself. In cultivated soil no remains of a bleached sand layer.

Podsolic brown earth, No. 85 (plate XXIII).

Serizite phyllite, graphite phyllite, grey clay schist, phonolite.

1. Soil grey coloured, raw, rich in grit, chemically little weathered showing no distinct humus horizon to the naked eye.

Silicate raw soil (*silicate-syrosem*), No. 49.

1*. The profile already shows the formation of a humus layer or other soil horizons 2

2. Soil with humus layer. The subsoil in spite of far-going (often even earthy) physical breakdown, owing to the low chemical weathering, is still grey coloured.

Grey ranker, No. 57 (plate XI)

2*. Subsoil mostly bright ochre coloured 3

3. Subsoil not essentially heavier or richer in colloidal substances than the soil.

Brown earth, type XXXVII.

3*. Soil strongly acid, with bleached flecks or often below the humus horizon only with strongly brownish coloured illuvial zone of humus sols (plate XXIII). Subsoil generally light ochre coloured, essentially heavier, richer in colloidal substances and denser than the top soil.

Podsolic brown earth, No. 85.
(Not known on phonolite.)

*) In cultivated soil generally unrecognizable due to mixing.

Basalt, gabbro, diabase, melaphyr, dark diorite, amphibolite, basalt=tuff, base=rich pumice sand.	4. Soil generally dark brown to almost sepia brown colour, good crumb structure, loose, with humus rich mull formation, generally relatively deep humus horizon and deep reaching chemical weathering (plate XXI). The vegetation usually indicates a high level of fertility. **(Eutrophic) brown earth *)**, No. (58).
Limestone, dolomite, mag=nesite, marl schist, gyp=sum.	1. Soil little weathered and without well marked humus horizon. **Chalk raw soil** (*chalk-syrosem*), No. 50.
	1*. Soil well weathered or at least with distinctly developed humus horizon 2
	2. The soil consists only of a humus horizon without a transition zone of a brown subsoil between it and the parent material, but at best with a formation of a thin brown seam on the lower side of the humus horizon 3
	2*. Soil with distinctly developed brown subsoil. 4
	3. Humus grey to blackish coloured (plate xv). *Rendsina*, type XXV.
	3*. Humus brownish grey to blackish brown grey coloured, with or without a brown seam on its lower side (plate xIV). *Brown rendsina*, No. (42).
	4. Soil usually free from lime, strikingly easily silted-up, tending to the formation of a dense structure, colour a striking intense ochre yellow, ochre brown to reddish brown. Soil mass swelling strongly, on drying out either hardening like stone or disintegrating into sharp edged angular fractures or finest fragments. **Limestone brown loam** (*terra fusca*), No. 74 (plate xVIII).
	4*. Soil not capable of swelling strongly, usually loose with good crumb structure, colour generally a dull brown. **Chalk brown earth**, No. (60) (plate XXII).

*) As the phase of development of the ranker on the above parent rocks as a cultivated soil is very rare, for it is easily weathered and the soil due to its high reserve of bases is also little liable to podsolization, there needs to be considerer here almost only the determination of the above brown earth in Central and Northern Europe.

Fine grained sandstone, decalcified dust loess, silty morainic boulder loam, loose fine sandy, silty sediments.

1. Humus continuously or almost continuously water-logged, very acid, when moist muddy and blackish coloured.

Anmoor, type IX (plate IV).

1*. Soil not continuously water-logged 2

2. Soil with strong alternation of heavy drying-out and stagnation of water above the surface or in the surface soil. Under the humus layer a light grey to whitish dense horizon, which frequently contains numerous pin-head shaped dark brown concretions of ferric hydroxide, and gradual changes over into a flecked or marbled subsoil with a generally brown coloured ground mass (plate XXIV).

Pseudogley (gley-like soil), type XXXVIII.

2*. Soil with acid raw humus (page 35) or coarse moder formation (page 39), dense, light grey to whitish bleached layer, with distinctly determinable vertical translocation of colloidal substances, especially humic substances, which are precipitated in a uniform dark brown illuvial layer of humus immediately under the bleached layer (plate XXIV).

Molkenpodsol, No. 87.

Chalk and base-deficient dune sand.

1. Soil without distinct formation of a humus horizon.

Silicate raw soil (*silicate-syrosem*), No. 49.

1*. Soil with humus layer and other soil horizon. 2

2. Subsoil light ochre yellow to reddish brown. The soil profile shows essential displacement of colloidal substances.

Sandy (oligotrophic) brown earth *), No. (59)

2*. Soil profile with distinct displacement of colloidal substances and their precipitation in the subsoil 3

3. Profile with distinctly developed bleached layer below the humus horizon. Frequently sandstone like hardening in the subsoil (ortstein formation) 4

3*. Profile at most with bleached sand flecks or a thin seam-like bleached sand zone, or only with

*) See also rostbraunerde.

Chalk and base-deficient dune sand.

numerous bleached sand grains in the humus layer itself. Subsoil light ochre yellow to rust brown coloured (plate XXIII).

Podsolic brown earth, No. 85.

4. The subsoil consists only of coffee brown humus enriched layers (plate XXV).

Humus podsol, No. 88.

4*. The subsoil is divided into a more or less coffee brown humus enriched zone and a light ochre yellow to rust brown iron enriched zone (plate XXV).

Iron humus podsol, No. 89

Loamy tertiary sediments.

1. Soil extraordinarily vivid ochre yellow, ochre brown, reddish brown to red coloured, strongly silting-up, tending easily to subsoil compaction, when wet strongly swelling, on drying-out stone-like hardening, with low water penetration after strong rainfall and in level areas often stagnant water above the surface   2

1*. Soil mostly dull brown coloured with good crumb structure, not capable of swelling strongly and on drying-out, not becoming hard like stone.

Brown earth, type XXXVII.

2. Soil colour intense red to brown red.

Red loam (rotlehm), type XXXV.

2*. Soil colour intense ochre yellow, ochre brown to reddish brown.

Brown loam (braunlehm), type XXXIV.

Alluvial stream and river sediments.

1. Soil raw, generally light grey coloured, very slightly weathered, mostly sandy, often fine pebbly to coarse pebbly, with high water permeability, generally exposed to periodical flooding by high water   2

1*. Soil more strongly weathered, mostly loamy, either continually water-logged or with normal water and air relations   4

2. Profile without distinct humus horizon (plate IV).

Raw warp soil (rambla), type VI.

2*. Profile with distinct humus horizon   3

Alluvial stream and river sediments.

3. Soil containing chalk, effervescing with dilute HCl, under the humus horizon generally a white chalk enriched layer.

     Rendsina=like warp soil(*borovina*), type XVIII (plate VII).

3* Soil low in chalk, not effervescing with HCl, always without chalk enriched layer in the soil profile (plate VI).

     Grey warp soil (*paternia*), type XVII.

4. Soil continually water-logged or with stagnant water right to the surface, subsoil bluish grey to greenish grey, generally permeated by brown rust flecks and channels   5

4*. Soil with normal water and air relation ...   6

5. Profile without distinct humus horizon.

     Raw gley soil (*Syrogley*), type VIII.

5*. Profile with blackish humus formation, when wet muddy (plate IV).

     Anmoor warp soil (*Auanmoor*), No. 16.

6. Soil consisting only of a dark grey to blackish humus horizon (often reaching a considerable thickness) and a whitish chalk enriched horizon. The profile shows no water-logging due to continually lowered ground water level, the soil changes over in many places to moist anmoor-like or semi-anmoor-like soil formations. The humus formation is an excellent mull (page 41). The soil is always calcareous to highly calcareous (plate VII).

     Chernosem=like warp soil (*smonitza*), type XIX.

6*. The soil shows under the brownish grey humus layer a brown subsoil (plate VIII).

     Brown warp soil (*brown Vega*), No. 38.

No. 3: Simplest Keys for the Easy Identification of the most frequent Forest and Cultivated Soils of Southern Europe.

a. Starting from the soil colour *).

Soil colour very light to almost pure white.	1. Soil calcareous, effervescing with dilute hydrocloric acid **2**
	1*. Soil low in chalk, mostly sandy, not effervescing with dilute HCl. The light surface layer (bleached sand layer) changes gradually into a very dense ochre yellow, intense ochre, ochre brown to red-ochre coloured subsoil (plate xx). In spite of humus deficiency mull formation (page 36) is usually found and there are usually numerous earth-worm tubes in all parts of the profile. **Bleached brown loam, No. 77.**
	2. Soil with no distinguishable humus horizon to the naked eye **3**
	2*. In spite of the humus deficiency, with distinctly recognizable humus horizon **4**
	3. The upper surface layer consists of an extraordinarily hard, tenacious, limestone-like crust which can only be split with a hammer (plate IX). In cultivated soils where it was possible to destroy it owing to its comparatively low thickness, it shows itself in the surface layer as numerous large platy fractions of the crust, which contrast strongly by their white colouring with the usually light ochre coloured subsoil **). On level surfaces with undisturbed profiles and where strong wind erosion prevails, the crust layer is often covered with a light ochre coloured wind-born sediment. **Chalkcrust soil,** (*chalkkrust-yerma*), No. 48.
	3*. Surface not hard like limestone and easily dug with a spade. **Carbonate raw soil** (white rendsina) (*chalk syrosem*), No. 50.

*) The starting point is always the colour of the uppermost layer of the dry soil, only with *anmoor* is it the colour of the wet humus formation.

**) With rainfall becoming deep ochre to brown ochre coloured.

Soil colour very light to almost pure white.	4.	Occurring on hard limestone, marl schist, gypsum, or gypsum rich marls primarily in hilly or mountainous land under open, drought resistant vegetation (plate XVI).
		Xerorendsina, No. 61.
	4*.	Occurring on loess or loess-like chalk rich sediments in dry steppes (plate XVI).
		Serosem, type XXVII.

Soil colour grey, dark grey, to blackish.	1.	Occurring in the flats of streams and rivers. 2
	1*.	Not occurring in flats of streams and rivers. 5
	2.	Soil without distinct humus horizon, soil mass raw, little weathered (plate IV).
		Raw warp soil (*rambla*), type VI.
	2*.	Soil with distinct humus horizon 3
	3.	Soil continuously or for the greatest part of the year water-logged, with blackish muddy humus formation. Subsoil greenish to bluish grey, frequently permeated with brown rust flecks and channels (plate IV).
		Anmoor warp soil (*Auanmoor*), No. 16
	3*.	Soil not continuously nor for a great part of the year water-logged 4
	4.	Soil low in chalk, not effervescing with dilute hydrochloric acid. The subsoil is generally light grey, little weathered, predominately sandy (plate VI).
		Grey warp soil (*paternia*), type XVII.
	4*.	Soil calcareous to highly calcareous, generally with proportionately deep humus horizon characterized by excellent mull formation, to which is connected a strongly developed, whitish chalk enriched horizon (plate VII).
		Chernosem-like warp soil (*smonitza*), type XIX.
	5.	Profile with distinct humus horizon, however without ochre to brown coloured subsoil. 6
	5*.	Soil with well developed brown subsoil ... 11
	6.	Soil low in chalk, not effervescing with hydrochloric acid, with good humus formation, free

Soil colour grey, dark grey, to blackish.

from undecomposed plant remains and well bound with the mineral substances (mull, p. 41).

Mull ranker, No. 56.

6*. Soil calcareous to highly calcareous, either effervescing with HCl in the surface layer or at least in the lower side of the humus layer   7

7. Soil mostly occurring in mountainous or hilly land predominately on hard parent rocks ...   8

7*. Soil occurring in the area of steppes, generally on loess or loess-like calcareous sediments.   10

8. Soil occurring on strongly weathered basalt, basanite, tephrite and other basic volcanic rocks which with weathering form much calcium carbonate, further on calcareous silicate rocks, calcareous sandstone, chalk conglomerates.

Pararendsina, type XXVI.

8*. Soil predominately formed on limestone, dolomite, marl schist or gypsum   9

9. Soil highly calcareous, occurring in areas of low rainfall under sparse, open drought resistant vegetation. The humus layer changes on top generally into a lighter surface layer (plate XVI).

Xerorendsina, No. 61.

9*. Soil not occurring in extremely low rainfall areas but principally in humid mountains, with more intense, darker (often blackish) humus formation with higher humus content, which does not change into a lighter, more calcareus surface layer (plate XV).

(Typical) rendsina, type XXV.

10. Soil low in humus and with shallow humus layer formed under sparse vegetation in the extremely dry steppes (plate XVI).

Serosem, type XXVII.

10*. Soil generally rich in humus and with deep, in the upper part mostly decalcified humus horizon; in grass steppes with a wet spring or in the corresponding cultivated areas (plate XVII).

Chernosem, type XXX.

11. The soil colour is produced by strongly acid generally mineral rich (sandy) moder of grey to blackish colour. Under the humus layer there is a light grey to whitish bleached lay-

Soil colour grey, dark grey, to blackish.

er consisting of smooth washed sand. By the strong eluviation of colloidal material very distinct illuvial layers are formed in the sub-soil. Generally there is a sepia brown humus enriched layer and an ochre yellow to rust brown iron enriched layer (plate xxv).

Podsol (iron humus podsol), No. 89.

11*. The soil shows no bleached sand layer but at best isolated bleached sand flecks or a very thin seam-like bleached sand zone, and the acid mineral-rich (sandy) moder of the grey to blackish grey humus layer is mostly rich in bleached sand grains. The subsoil is an ochre yellow to rust brown iron enriched horizon, while there is usually no humus enriched horizon (plate xxiii).

Podsolic brown earth, No. 85.

Soil colour brownish grey, dark brown grey, to blackish dark brown grey.

1. Soil in the areas of the steppes derived predominately from loess or loess-like highly calcareous sediments 2

1*. Soil occurring chiefly in mountain or tree-rich or wooded districts 4

2. Generally effervescing with dilute HCl in or near the surface layer 3

2*. Soil not effervescing inside the humus layer. In the lower part of the humus horizon there is frequently a humus deficient brown seam coloured only by ferric hydroxide, to which generally is joined a strongly developed chalk enriched horizon (plate xvii). The soil shows always an unbroken cover of vegetation and is found geographically on the humid side of grass steppes in the so-called forest steppe.

Degraded chernosem, No. 71.

3. Soil is low in humus, brownish grey, with shallow humus horizon, which always passes however into a more or less well defined chalk enriched horizon without a brown seam. It always occurs in the dry steppes, in natural conditions under open dwarf shrub (usually Arthemisia species) vegetation.

Brown desert steppe soil (*burosem*), type xxviii.

3*. Soil usually dark brown grey, when wet having the colour of a dark, wet chestnut. The usually

Soil colour brownish grey, dark brown grey, to black= ish dark brown grey.

relatively deep humus horizon passes gradually into parent material or a distinctly developed chalk enriched horizon. The soil is characteristic of the grass steppes very strongly drying out in summer, and occurs in natural conditions under generally unbroken grass-rich plant covering.

Chestnut-coloured soil (*kastannosem*), type xxix.

4.   The chalk deficient acid soil consists only of a humus horizon lying immediately on the parent rock. The latter may be loose but not browned by ferric hydroxide. It occurs primarily in coniferous woods rich in litter. The dark brown grey (often almost blackish) colour is conditioned exclusively by the humus fraction, in the first place by coprogenic elements (droppings of small soil animals), but also by numerous deep brown, little decomposed plant splinters *).

(*Dystrophic*) *ranker*, No. 52.

4*.   Soil consisting not only of a humus horizon but also a brown subsoil   5

5.   The dark brown grey (to almost blackish brown) colour is due entirely to the humus fraction. Besides a large quantity of animal droppings numerous deep brown, little decomposed plants remains. Between the humus layer and the brown subsoil there is a strongly developed grey to whitish bleached sand layer. The subsoil usually shows besides a sepia brown humus enriched layer, an ochre to rust brown iron enriched layer (plate xxv).

Podsol (*iron humus podsol*), No. 89.

5*.   Soil without strongly developed bleached sand layer   6

6.   Without strongly developed bleached sand layer, but only with bleached sand flecks, or a thin seam-like bleached sand zone. The ochre yellow to rust brown subsoil shows a strong enrichment of illuvial material and has the character of an iron enriched horizon, but there is no humus enriched zone (plate xxiii).

Podsolic brown earth, No. 85.

*) In the absence of plant splinters and with the presence of very mineral-rich humus layers, see also *brown ranker*, No. 59.

Soil colour brownish grey, dark brown grey, to black= ish dark brown grey.

6*. The brownish colour in the humus is derived primarily from the admixture of ferric hydroxide, the humus form is almost always mull (page 41). The soil is mostly loose and crumbly. The transition from the humus layer to the underlying dull brown to ochre coloured subsoil, which shows no essential enrichment of illuvial material, occurs gradually and without a sharp boundary. The soil indicates good chemical weathering and is formed in humid regions.

Central European brown earth, No. 80.

Soil colour light ochre, drab to light brown.

1. Soil occurring in the flats of streams and rivers, with an extraordinarily intense colour, strikingly high swelling, strong silting-up and tendency to dense structure, with rock-like hardening on drying out. High waters produce usually marked signs of erosion in the form of channels and pools and strong deposition of erosion sediments with far going grain separation *) (plate VIII).
Brown loam warp soil (*braunlehm vega*), No. 39

1*. Soil not occurring in the flats of streams and rivers 2

2. Soil with low chemical weathering, generally sandy to fine sandy silty, with low swelling capacity 3

2*. Soil strongly weathered, with high swelling capacity, generally vivid colour, easily eroded, with tendency to silting-up and rock-like hardening. It generally occurs in high rainfall areas. 4

3. Without distinctly recognizable humus horizon, formed on deposits of loess.
Loess raw soil (*loess-syrosem*), No. (31).

3*. Soil low in chalk, drab to light brown coloured with sparce humus formation, which with cultivation or erosion can be completely lost. Generally occurring under open herbacious and dwarf shrub drought resistant vegetation as well as in dry woods on hard silicate rocks (plate XXII).
Meridional brown earth, No. 81.

4. Formed on limestone or dolomite (plate XVIII).
Limestone brown loam (*terra fusca*), No. 74.
4*. Formed on silicate rock or on deep deposits of fossilized (tertiary) soils.
Brown loam (*braunlehm*), type XXXIV.

*) The rivers are generally turbid even at low water.

Soil colour ochre brown, brown to reddish brown.

1. Occurring in the flats of streams and rivers. 2

1*. Not occurring in the flats of streams and rivers 3

2. Soil intense ochre brown to reddish brown coloured, strongly swelling, easily silted-up, tending to form a dense structure. High waters produce various signs of strong erosion. The erosion sediments show strong grain separation (plate VIII). The soil occurs primarily in the flats of great rivers in plains rich in loamy tertiary sediments.
Brown loam warp soil (*braunlehm vega*), No. 39

2*. Soil mostly dull brown, crumbly, not strongly swelling and highly erodable (plate VIII). Occurring in particular in the vallies of wooded mountains consisting predominately of hard silicate rocks.
Brown warp soil (*brown vega*), No. 38.

3. Soil occurring in humid areas 4

3*. Soil occurring in dry areas 7

4. Soil colour generally very intense, soil strongly swelling, when moist becoming pasty, tending to a dense texture, on drying-out hardening like rock, or breaking-up in to sharp-edged angular fragments or finest debris 5

4*. Soil with none of the above characteristics. 6

5. Soil occurring on limestone or dolomite (plate XVIII).
(Typical) limestone brown loam (*terra fusca*), No. 74.

5*. Occurring as relic soil on silicate rock (often buried) or in deep deposits of soil formations of former (tertiary), ages.
(Typical) brown loam (*braunlehm*), type XXXIV

6. Colour usually dull brown, soil neutral to slightly acid, generally with good crumb structure, neither eroding strongly nor hardening like rock on drying-out. No strong translocation of colloidal substances into the subsoil (plate XXI).
Central European brown earth, No. 80.

6*. Soil mostly rust brown coloured, always considerably acid, frequently containing numerous bleached sand grains in the surface layer while the subsoil is heavy and distinctly richer in colloidal substances.
Podsolic brown earth (plate XXIII), No. 85.

Soil colour ochre brown, brown to reddish brown.	7. Soil on deep deposits, with intense colour, strongly swelling and tending to a dense structure (see point 4, above). In the surface layer, however, dull brown, becoming loose, earthy crumbling and not breaking-up into sharp edged fragments. It occurs on silicate rock or on (generally tertiary) loose sediments. **Earthy brown loam**, No. (51). 7*. Soil as in 7, occurring however on limestone or dolomite. **Earthy limestone brown loam** (*earthy terra fusca*), No. (47).
Soil colour red to brown red.	1. Occurring in the flats of streams and rivers, generally strongly swelling and strongly silting-up with a tendency to form a dense structure. **Red warp soil** (*red vega*), No. 40. 1*. Not occurring in flats of streams and rivers. 2. Occurring on limestone (mostly in conjunction with terra fusca) (plate XVIII). *Terra rossa* (limestone red loam), No. 75. 2*. Occurring as a soil on silicate rocks (often covered by recent soil formations) or in the form of deep deposits of soils of former (mostly tertiary) ages. **Red loam** (*rotlehm*), type XXXV (plate XX).

b. Starting from Reaction and Lime Content. *).

Soil strongly a l k a l i n e (pH 8.5). Drops of Phe= nolphtaleïn solution give a strong reddening.	1. The soil shows efflorescenses of salts in the surface on drying-out. By the drying of surface soil samples taken when moist, the efflorescences can be produced artificially. Humic soils are mostly blackish coloured when moist, the structure is generally compact and when moist pasty. *Soda-solonchak*, No. 28. 1*. The soil shows with natural drying in the field or by artificial drying of surface soil samples

*) One starts always with the characteristics of the top-soil. The *p*H-ranges given, do not represent absolute boundaries, but serve only for a general orientation. Locally conditioned or temporary fiuctuations above or below cannot be taken yet as a sign for the change of the soil type.

Soil strongly alkaline (pH 8.5). Drops of Phe=nolphtaleïn solution give a strong reddening.	very few or no salt efflorescences. The structure is very dense, when dry hardening like stone. The soil profiles frequently show in the middle to the lower part of the humus horizon columnar cleavage when dry (plate v). *Solonchak-solonetz*, No. 34.

Soil alkaline (pH 7.6 to 8.5) to slightly alkaline (pH 7.2 to 7.6) however low in chalk and not effervescing with HCl.

1. The dried out soil shows in or near the surface strong efflorescences of salts which can also be produced by artificial drying-out of wet samples. The soil is not extremely dense and hardened, but generally has a good crumb structure (plate v).

    Solonchak, type XIII.

1*. The soil remains without salt efflorescences, is extraordinarily dense, strongly swelling, on drying-out hardening like stone, carrying little or no vegetation. In the middle to the lower part of the humus horizon there is frequently columnar (prismatic) cleavage when drying (plate v).

    Solonetz *), type XIV.

Soil alkaline (pH 7.6 to 8.5) to slightly alkaline (pH 7.2 to 7.6) however calcareous to highly cal=careous, effervescing with dilute HCl, at the same time rich in salt or occur=ring in the region of salt soils or former salt soils.

1. Surface or surface soil samples showing efflorescences of salts when dry, soil usually well crumbling.

    Chalk solonchak, No. 31.

1*. Soil without efflorescences of salts, soil mass swelling, tending to a dense structure, hardening on drying-out, however generally not showing the degree of silting-up and tenacity of a typical solonetz.

    Chalk solonetz, No. 33.

Soil calcareous, efferves= cing with dilute HCl in the surface layer or near it.

1. Occurring in the flats of streams and rivers.   2

1*. Not occurring in the flats of streams and rivers   4

2. Soil continuously or at least for the greater part of the year water-logged right to the surface. The humus when moist is muddy, usually blackish coloured.

    Calcareous anmoor warp soil, type IX.

*) The pH values of this soil can occasionally go over into the slightly acid range.

Soil calcareous, efferves=cing with dilute HCl in the surface layer or near it.

2*.   Soil not water-logged   3

3.   Soil without distinctly developed humus hori-zon, but frequently with a strongly through-rooted upper layer.
      Calcareous raw warp soil (*calcareous rambla*), [No. 12.

3*.   Soil with excellent humus formation of mull form (page 41), generally relatively deep humus horizons, which are followed usually by strongly developed whitish, chalk enriched horizons (pla-te VII).
      Chernosem=like warp soil (*smonitza*), type XIX.

4.   Soil without distinctly developed humus ho-rizon   5

4*.   Soil profile with distinctly marked humus layer or other soil horizons   7

5.   The surface layer consists of a hard, limestone-like crust (plate IX). With cultivation this crust remains in the form of compact platy fragments strewn over the surface.
      Chalk crust soil No. 48.

5*.   Soil without stony chalk crust   6

6.   Soil formed on loess.
      Loess raw soil, No. (31).

6*.   Soil formed on other calcareous parent material.
      Carbonate raw soil (white rendsina), No. 50.

7.   Soil of an intense ochre, brown, brown-red, or dazzling red colour or with a subsoil which is coloured in this way   13

7*.   Soil not coloured as above, consisting only of a humus horizon, which generally changes through a whitish, chalk enriched horizon into the parent material   8

8.   Soil occurring predominately on loess or loess-like calcareous loose sediments   9

8*.   Soil predominately occurring on limestone, marl schist, dolomite and gypsum   12

9.   Occurring in the desert steppe under open to sparce, drought resistant vegetation   10

9*.   Occurring in the wet spring grass steppe or in the climatically corresponding cultivated land   11

Soil calcareous, efferves-cing with dilute HCl in the surface layer or near it.

10. Soil with shallow, light grey humus horizon, which is poor in humus and often scarcely distinguishable from the lower mineral horizons. It often contains gypsum and occurs in the extreme desert steppe (plate XVI).

Serosem, type XXVII.

10*. The humus has a grey-brown colour, with generally a light grey surface layer.
Brown desert steppe soil (*burosem*), type XXVIII.

11. The humus has a distinct chestnut colour when moist. It occurs in the extremely summer-dry grass steppes or in the corresponding cultivated land.
Chestnut=coloured soil (*kastannosem*), type XXIX.

11*. The soil often occurs in association with deep black earths in grass steppes with a very wet spring or in the corresponding cultivated land. Soil formation however is generally still young, shallow, low in humus, of a light grey to dark grey colour *). Frequently nothing else than truncated profiles in which the upper part of humus layers has been removed by erosion.

(Shallow) chernosem, type XXX.

12. Occurring in humid areas (plate XV).

(Typical) rendsina, type XXV.

12*. Occurring in dry areas under open to sparce drought resistant vegetation consisting mainly of herbs and dwarf shrubs. Humus layer shallow, low in humus, light grey coloured, with light, whitish, strongly dusty surface layer (plate XVI).

Xerorendsina, No. 61.

13. Soil brown-red to red coloured, generally stony or lying on marl layers.

(Calcareous) red loam **)   type XXXV.

13*. Soil ochre, brown to brown-red coloured, generally rich in limestone shingle and pebbles laying on marl layers or mixed with them.

(Calcareous) brown loam *) type XXXIV.

---

*) Mature chernosems generally do not effervesce in the upper part of the humus horizon.

**) Occasionally *terra rossa* (No. 75) and *terra fusca* (No. 74) can also become secondarily enriched with chalk.

Soil effervescing with dilute HCl only below the humus layer, or with deep humus horizon in its lower part.

1.   Soil mostly blackish to dark brown-grey coloured, rich in humus, consisting only of a humus horizon with perhaps a chalk enriched horizon under it. Occurring usually in humid areas, especially in mountainous or hilly areas on limestone and dolomite.

            (*Typical*) *rendsina*, type xxv (plate xv).

1*.   Soil with mostly thick humus layer, occurring in the first place on the plains or low hilly steppes on loess or loess-like calcareous loose sediments   2

2.   Humus blackish to dark grey coloured, generally changing only through a whitish, chalk enriched horizon into the parent material.

            Chernosem, type xxx.

2*.   Humus mostly brownish grey to dark-brown grey, with or without a brown coloured seam, due to ferric hydroxide, on its lower side (plate xvii). It occurs on the humid side of grass steppes (or the corresponding cultivated lands.

            Degraded chernosem, No. 71.

Soil neutral (pH 7.2 to 6.5) to slightly acid (pH 6.5 to 5.5) not effervescing with dilute HCl.

1.   Occurring in the flats of streams and rivers.   2

1*.   Not occurring in the flats of streams and rivers   7

2.   Soil without distinct humus horizon, soil mass raw, little weathered, generally sandy, pebbly to shingly (plate iv).
     Chalk deficient raw warp soil (*chalk deficient* [*rambla*]), No. 11.

2*.   With distinct humus layer or other soil horizons   3

3.   Soil water-logged continuously or for the greater part of the year up to the surface, with blackish, muddy humus formation. Subsoil greenish to bluish grey, generally permeated by brown rust flecks and channels (plate iv).

            Anmoor warp soil, type ix.

3*.   Soil without long continued water-logging.   4

4.   The soil consists of a grey to dark grey humus horizon and a likewise chalk deficient, generally light grey, loose, little weathered, predominately sandy subsoil (plate vi).

            Grey warp soil (*paternia*), type xvii.

Soil neutral (pH 7.2 to 6.5) to slightly acid (pH 6.5 to 5.5) not effervescing with dilute HCl.

4*.   Soil otherwise coloured   5

5.   Soil generally dull brown, crumbly, neither swelling nor eroding strongly, occurring principally in the valleys of tree-rich or wooded mountains on hard silicate rock (plate VIII).

Brown warp soil (*brown vega*), No. 38.

5*.   Soil vividly coloured, generally strongly swelling, easily silted-up with tendency to a dense structure, occurring principally in river vallies of large plains rich in tertiary loamy sediments or in the vallies of limestone mountains ...   6

Red warp soil (*red vega*), No. 40.

6*.   Soil colour an intense ochre yellow, ochre brown to red brown (plate VIII).

Brown loam warp soil (*braunlehm vega*), No. 39

7.   Without distinct humus horizon, soil mass raw, with little chemical weathering, generally light grey coloured.

Silicate raw soil (*silicate syrosem*), No. 49

7*.   Soil with distinct humus layer or other soil horizon   8

8.   Soil light ochre yellow, ochre brown, brown to red brown coloured   9

8*.   The soil consists only of a humus horizon, in addition perhaps of a raw, little weathered, generally light grey coloured subsoil. Occurring on silicate rock or chalk deficient sands (plate XI).

(*Grey*) *ranker*, type XXIV and No. 57.

9.   The soil colour is a dull drab to light brown, soil little weathered, sandy to gritty, occurring predominately under open drought resistant vegetation consisting of herbs and dwarf shrubs or in dry woods on silicate rocks (plate XXII).

Meridional brown earth, No. 81.

9*.   Soil strongly weathered, soil colour always intense to dazzling   10

10.   Soil colour brown red to dazzling red   11

10*.   Soil colour ochre yellow, ochre brown, brown to red brown   12

11.   Soil formed on hard limestone (plate XVIII).

Terra rossa (limestone red loam), No. 75.

Soil neutral (pH 7.2 to 6.5) to slightly acid (pH 6.5 to 5.5) not effervescing with dilute HCl.

11*. Soil occurring on silicate rock or in the form of usually deep deposits (plate xx).
Red loam, type xxxv.

12. Soil formed on hard limestone, marl or dolomite. *Terra fusca* (limestone red loam), No. 74.

12*. Soil not or only rarely occurring on hard limestone, marl or dolomite *) 13

13. Soil colour usually a dull brown, soil generally with good crumb structure, never strongly silted-up or eroded, occurring generally in mountains, rainfall areas, primarily on hard silicate rock.
Central European brown earth, (plate XXI), No. 80.

13*. Soil colour usually in the surface or at least in the subsoil an intense, shining ochre yellow, ochre brown to red brown. Soil capable of swelling strongly, occurring on silicate rock or in deep deposits.
Brown loam, type xxxiv.

Soil acid (pH 5.5 to 4.5) to strongly acid < pH 4.5.

1. Soil occurring in coniferous woods, rich in litter, on acid silicate or silica rocks, with raw humus formation, rich in brown little decomposed plant remains without an ochre yellow to rust brown subsoil.
(Dystrophic) ranker, No. 52.

1*. Soil profile with ochre yellow to rust brown subsoil 2

2. Humus formation raw, often with many browned, little decomposed plant remains or with predominately grey colour rich in smooth, washed mineral grains. The humus layer lies on a distinctly developed light grey to whitish bleached sand layer, wich is usually followed by a sepia brown humus enriched layer and an ochre yellow to rust brown iron enriched layer (plate xxv).
Podsol (iron humus podsol), No. 89.

2*. Soil similar to the above, without however a distinctly developed bleached sand layer but only with bleached sand flecks, a thin film-like bleached sand zone, or only numerous bleached sand grains in the humus layers itself. There is no sepia brown humus enriched layer in the subsoil (plate xxiii).
Podsolic brown earth, No. 85.

*) It has not been possible for me to find brown earth in southern Europe on limestone, marl or dolomite but almost always earthy terra fusca instead.

c. Starting from the Parent Material.

Key for forest, arable, meadow and pasture soils which frequently occur in southern Europe on the given parent rocks of which they are particularly characteristic.

Granites and gneisses.	1.	Soil resulting only by mechanical loosening with slight chemical weathering, without formation of a distinct humus horizon. **Silicate raw soils,** No. 49.
	1*.	Soil profile with humus layer or other distinctly developed horizons 2
	2.	The soil profile consists only of a humus horizon with perhaps at most a grey sandy transition layer, between it and the parent rock, without the formation of a brown subsoil. *Ranker,* type XXIV.
	2*.	Soil grey-brown or brown coloured with brown subsoil 3
	3.	Soil light brown to almost drab coloured, generally sandy to gritty, little weathering with low humus formation, occurring predominately under open drought resistant vegetation or in dry woods (plate XXII). **Meridional brown earth,** No. 81.
	3*.	Soil strongly coloured, generally dull brown, highly weathered, with good clay and humus formation, good crumb structure and water relations. It occurs primarily in humid woods or wooded to tree-rich areas. **Central European brown earth,** No. 80.
Cindery basalts, basanites, tephrites and others, calcium silicate rich, easily weathered lavas and tuffs.	1.	Soil little weathered and without formation of a distinct humus horizon. **Silicate raw soil,** No. 49.
	1*.	With a humus layer or other distinctly developed horizons 2
	2.	With a humus and white chalk enriched horizon, but without a brown or red subsoil. Both horizons are rich in calcium carbonate and effervesce strongly with dilute HCl. *Pararendsina,* type XXVI.

Cindery basalts, basanites, tephrites and others, calcium silicate rich, easily weathered lavas and tuffs.

2*. With brown or red subsoil   3

3. Soil very dry, light brown, with low clay content and generally sparse humus formation.
Meridional brown earth, No. 81.

3*. Soil strongly coloured, with strong chemical weathering   4

4. Soil loose, with strikingly good crumb structure, loamy, deep brown to almost sepia brown coloured, occurring as a recent soil formation in humid forests or woody to tree-rich areas (plate xxi).
(Eutrophic) Central European brown earth,
No. 80 and (58).

4*. Soil capable of swelling strongly, easily silted-up, tending to the formation of a dense structure. Occurring, as relic soil (often in the form of buried layers)   5

5. Soil of an intense ochre brown colour.
Brown loam, type xxxiv.

5*. Soil of a dark red brown to red colour.
Red loam, type xxxv.

Grey clay schists, serizite and graphite phyllite.

1. Soil uniform grey coloured without distinct humus horizon.
Silicate raw soil, No. 49.

1*. With a humus layer or other horizon coloured by ferric hydroxide   2

2. Soil dry, very shallow, consisting only of a humus layer and grey coloured subsoil.
Grey ranker, No. 57.

2*. Subsoil red brown ochre to brown coloured.   3

3. Soil of a light colour, often a pale ochre brown. It is very dry, highly powdery, and occurs generally under bare, drought-resistant vegetation, consisting mainly of herbs and dwarf shrubs.
Meridional brown earth, No. 81.

3*. Soil always strongly coloured   4

4. Soil dull brown coloured, well crumbling, with good humus formation, occurring in humid woods or wood to tree rich districts.
Central European brown earth, No. 80.

4*. Soil of an intense and vivid colour, soil mass capable of strong swelling and silting-up, with tendency to form a dense structure. It occurs as relic or fossil formations   5

Grey clay schists, serizite and graphite phyllite.	5.	Soil of a vivid brown ochre colour. **Brown loam,** type xxxiv.
	5*.	Soil of a dazzling red colour (plate xx). **Red loam,** type xxxv.

Siliceous sandstone, quart= zite, silica schist a n d other extremely base and nutrient deficient rocks.	1.	Soil without a humus layer or other distinct horizon formation. **Silicate raw soil,** No. 49.
	1*.	With humus layer or other distinctly developed horizon ... ... :.. ... 2
	2.	Soil consisting only of a humus horizon, without ochre yellow to rust brown coloured subsoil. The humus is always acid, usually rich in browned but otherwise undecomposed plant remains. (*Dystrophic*) *ranker,* No. 52.
	2*.	With ochre yellow to brown subsoil 3
	3.	Soil profile with distinctly developed light grey to whitish bleached sand layer under the humus horizon (plate xxv). The vegetation is mostly rich in heather especially Erica especies. *Podsol,* type xl.
	3*.	Soil profile without a distinct bleached sand layer, but only with bleached sand flecks, a thin seamlike bleached sand zone or only numerous bleached sand grains in the humus layer (plate xxiii). **Podsolic brown earth,** No. 85.

Pure limestone.	1.	The profile consisting only of a superficial loose layer rich in grit and rock fragments, without the formation of a distinct humus horizon. **Carbonate raw soil,** No. 50.
	1*.	Soil distinctly differentiated into horizons, which differ in colour and chemical composition from the parent rock 2
	2.	The soil consists only of a humus horizon and shows no strong coloration by iron 3
	2*.	Soil with strong iron coloration, generally low in humus 4
	3.	Soil occurs in dry areas under sparse, xerophytic

Pure limestone.

vegetation. It is strongly powdery with a light grey, thin humus layer which changes over on top into a whitish superficial layer strongly enriched with chalk (plate XVI).

Xerorendsina, No. 61.

3 . Soil occurring in humid areas, with tendency to humus enrichment and eluviation of calcium carbonate. The humus is mostly blackish often low in minerals (plate XV).

(Typical) rendsina, type XXV.

4. Soil vivid ochre yellow, brown ochre, ochre brown to brown red coloured (plate XVIII).

Terra fusca (limestone brown loam), No. 74.

4*. Soil dazzling red to brown red coloured (plate XVIII).

Terra rossa (limestone red loam), No. 75.

**Loess and loesslike cal=
careous loose sediments.**

1. Soil profile without distinct humus horizon.
   Loess raw soil (carbonate raw soil), No. (31).

1*. With distinct humus layer 2

2. Occurring in the desert of dry steppes ... 3

2*. Occurring in the grass steppes or wet spring but summer dry cultivated areas 4

3. Soil very low in humus, humus layer of little thickness, light grey, occurring in the extreme desert steppes (plate XVI).

Serosem, type XXVII.

3*. Soil grey brown coloured, generally with a light grey surface layer.
   Brown semi=desert soil (*burosem*), type XXVIII.

4. Humus chestnut brown coloured, humus depth up to about 1/2 m.
   Chestnut=coloured soil (*kastannosem*), type XXIX

4*. Humus dark grey to blackish coloured, humus depth up to about 1 m. (plate XVII).

Chernosem, type XXX.

Loamy tertiary sediments.	1. Soil dazzling red to brown red coloured. **Red loam**, type xxxv. 1*. Soil ochre yellow, ochre brown to red brown coloured ... ... 2 2. Soil predominately in humid areas, occurring also however in dry areas with vivid colour, strong swelling, easy silting-up and tendency to form a dense structure. **Brown loam**, type xxxiv. 2*. Soil occurring in dry regions, surface layer loose, earthy, usually deep brown coloured, with good crumb structure. Subsoil or basic layer usually not crumbly, easily silted-up and dense as in 2. **(Earthy) brown loam**, No. (51).
Chalk and base deficient dune sands.	1. Soil profile without horizon formation or distinct humus layer. **(Sandy) silicate raw soil**, No. 49. 1*. With distinct horizon formation ... ... 2 2. Soil profile consisting only of a humus horizon, without brown subsoil. *Ranker*, type xxiv. 2*. Profile with generally brown however very light coloured subsoil, with sparse chemical weathering. **Meridional brown earth**, No. 81.
Alluvial stream and river sediments.	1. Soil waterlogged continuously or for the greater part of the year, with blackish, and when moist muddy humus formation (plate iv). **Anmoor warp soil**, type ix. 1*. Soil without waterlogging ... ... 2 2. Soil raw, very little weathered, with low clay formation, generally sandy-pebbly to shingled, usually light grey coloured ... ... 3 2*. Soil with good to excessive clay enrichment. 4 3. Profile without distinct humus horizon (plate iv). **Raw warp soil** (*rambla*), type vi). 3*. Profile with a humus horizon and grey subsoil. (plate vi). **Grey warp soil** (*paternia*), type xvii.

Alluvial stream and river sediments.

4. Soil calcareous to highly calcareous, fertile, with excellent dark grey to blackish humus formation and humus horizon of frequently considerable thickness. Under the humus layer there is generally a strongly developed whitish chalk enriched horizon. The soil is never coloured by iron (plate VII).
    Chernosem=like warp soil (*smonitza*), type XIX.

4*. Soil with strong iron colouration   5

5. Soil generally dull brown coloured, good crumb structure, permeable, not strongly swelling nor easily silted-up (plate VIII). It occurs primarily in the vallies of wooded mountains of predominately hard silicate rocks.
    Brown warp soil (*brown vega*), No. 38.

5*. Soil generally strongly swelling easily silted-up and tending to form a dense structure. It occurs predominately in the river vallies of wide plains and hilly areas rich in loamy tertiary sediments   6

6. Soil vivid ochre yellow, ochre brown to reddish brown coloured (plate VIII).
    Brown loam warp soil, No. 39.

6*. Soil dazzling red to brown red coloured.
    Red warp soil (*red vega*), No. 40.

No. 4: Simple Key for the Easy Identification of the most frequently occurring European Alpine Soils.

1. Occurring on primitive rock   2

1*. Occurring on limestone or dolomite   10

2. Soil raw, chemically very little weathered, sandy, gritty to gravelly, without formation of distinct humus horizons   3

2*. Soil profile with distinct horizon formation or at least with development of a distinct humus layer   4

3. Occurring in high elevated small snow basins with a snow covering, lasting far into the summer and subsequent waterlogging, under a plant cover of mosses with slight gleying but generally distinct formation of polygon fissures in the frozen stage.
    Nival snow basin soil (*rutmark of nival snow basins*), No. 15.

3*. Not occurring in small snow basins.
    Alpine silicate raw soil (*rawmark*), type XXI (plate IX).

4. Soil with humus layer, without however an ochre yellow to rust brown coloured B-horizon   5

4*. Soil with ochre yellow to rust brown coloured B-horizon   8

5. Soil occurring in small basins, with anmoor-like humus formation and a bluish grey to greenish grey subsoil generally with many rust flecks.
    Alpine snow basin soil (*snow basin anmoor*), No. 19.

5*. Soil without anmoor-like humus formation   6

6. The soil shows the formation of tangel humus (page 36) with generally a strongly developed tangel layer of brown plant remains over a blackish mull-like moder. It occurs in the dwarf shrub region of southern high mountains (plate XII).
    Tangel ranker, No. 55.

6*. Soil without tangel humus   7

7. Soil very shallow, particularly on summits within the alpine grass heath region consists essentially of a mat, rich in roots, easily cut like peat, but not waterlogged, which contains more or less loose blackish coloured droppings of small soil animals (plate x).
    Eilag ranker, No. 54.

7*. Humus mostly earthy, with good decomposition, humification and good mixture with the mineral substances. The generally dark grey humus layer can reach the thickness of 25 to 40 cm. and more (plate XI).
    Alpine mull-like ranker (humus silicate soil), No. (32).

8. Soil without a bleached sand layer, loose, mostly sandy, with low clay formation, however plentiful precipitation of free ferric hydroxide. Profile generally very shallow with strongly reduced, rust brown to ochre yellow (B) horizon. The soil occurs in the grass heath or bunch grass region.

Alpine sod braunerde, No. 82.

8*. Soil profile with distinct bleached sand layer   9

9. Profile generally well developed, subsoil containing distinctly marked usually sepia brown humus enriched layer and an ochre yellow to rust brown iron enriched layer. Soil occurs in the dwarf shrub region.

Sub-alpine iron humus podsol, No. (67).

9*. Profile with usually strongly reduced irregularly running horizons, soil with little chemical weathering, loose, sandy to gritty but frequently with strong tendency to form blackish humus layers, rich in animal droppings.

Alpine sod podsol, No. 91.

10. Soil raw, gritty to gravelly without formation of a definite horizon.

Alpine carbonate raw soil (*calcareous rawmark*), No. 42.

10*. Soil profile with distinct humus horizon formation or at least with development of a distinct humus layer   11

11. Soil profile with humus layer but without an ochre yellow to reddish brown (B)-horizon   12

11*. Soil usually low in humus, with vivid ochre yellow, brown ochre, ochre brown to reddish brown coloured, generally dense, strongly swelling, easily silted-up (B)-horizon. Primarily it occurs as a relic soil on slightly sloping or flat locations on old land surfaces (plate XVIII).

Terra fusca (limestone brown earth), No. 74

12. Soil occurring only in the dwarf pine and dwarf shrub region, with formation of tangel humus (page 36) with strongly developed tangel layer rich in brown plant remains, above a blackish mull-like chalk moder (plate XIV).

Tangel rendsina, No. (39).

12*. Soil not or not only occurring in the dwarf pine and dwarf shrub region.   13

13. Soil of cushionlike form, occurring only in the cushion vegetation region, with a raw humus-like external layer and well humified blackish (mineral deficient) to light grey (mineral rich) inner layer (plate XIII).

Alpine cushion rendsina, No. (38).

13*. Soil occurring primarily in the alpine grass heath region   14

14. Soil striking deep black to brownish black coloured, pitchy, extraordinarily low in minerals, almost always moist but almost never waterlogged, with good humification, primarily occurring on limestone (plate XIII).

Alpine pitch rendsina, No. (37).

14*. Soil mineral rich, generally light grey, only coloured dark grey in transition formations, sandy, with a silted-up structure, in summer completely loose, easily removed by wind.

Alpine protorendsina, No. [3].

No. 5: Universal key for the Identification of the most frequent European Soils, with their Descriptions, arranged after the Natural System.

In the natural system *) soils are not ordered after a single or a few, but after all characteristics (insofar as they are essential) and also after their mutual inter-relations. The decisive characteristics are never settled in advance but arise only from an exact comparison of the different forms. They are never fixed for all soil formations, but undergo a continual change, by which first this, then that group of characteristics becomes the most important. As with all natural systems, the arrangement of soils proceeds form the simplest to the most complex. In this way, groups arise of their own accord corresponding essentially to the natural phases of development. Besides the arrangement according to levels of organization (phase of development) it is however also necessary, for a better overall view, to create larger or smaller closed associations of forms in order to avoid overlapping of the different groups and unprofitable separation of certain members. Thus the entire kingdom of soil formation may be grouped into the following three great ranges of forms or divisions:

Division A, Sub-aqueous or Underwater Soils.

This division is composed of two sub-divisions. The first consists of primitive soil formations *always covered with water and not forming peat*, in which primarily lower plants (algae) serve as parent material for humus formation. They are always characterized by a very simple profile structure in which B horizons are usually completely missing. The possibilities of profile development are limited to (A)C, AC and AG. Further mull humus formation, being the most highly developed humus form, is completely missing in these soils. They are characterized too, by a very low variety of form (which is essentially limited to four main types), further also by low exchange of form i. e. a low transformation of type (generally only raw soils into *gyttja* or eventually *gyttja* into *sapropel*). They are the oldest forms of soil formation, which already may be found in the Cambrium, where besides terrestrial

---

*) As to the fundaments of the natural system, the establishment of the various categories of the system and their arrangement, see KUBIENA 1948, Entwicklungslehre.

life, also terrestrial soil formations, as well as semi-terrestrial formations were entirely lacking. (Begin with the key of division A-1, page 85.)

The second sub-division of soils consists of *sub-aqueous soils with peat formation*, a type of soil formation which is geologically considerably younger than the above mud soils, whose origin nevertheless, also goes back to palaeozoicum (Upper Devonian, Carboniferous). Formed originally from the remains of pteridophytes, to-day they arise in the first place from the residues of higher plants which root under water but which develop leaf and flower organs above the water surface. The humus formation still takes place completely below the water level. (Begin whith the key of division A-1 *), page 85.)

Division B, Semi-terrestrial Soils or Flooded and Groundwater Soils

Not or only temporarily covered with water, however *generally completely or partially waterlogged, peaty or non-peaty soil formations*, which altogether stand distinctly higher than the previous ones. The main sources of parent material for humus formation are higher plants, a few types already show mull formation. The profile structure starts with simple forms but increases considerably in complexity. Also B horizons may appear in the more mature phases. With increasing maturity the soils become drier, lose gradually the characteristics due to waterlogging and develop into dry terrestrial soils *). The humus formation is more varied, the number of forms distinctly larger and the change of form more pronounced than with the sub-aqueous soils.

They represent the second oldest kind of soil formation appearing as embryonic formation in the Carbon and in full development considerably later. (Begin with the key of division B.)

Division C, Terrestrial or Land Soils.

Soil formations practically never covered with water or waterlogged but at worst in a few transition formations showing stagnant water in particular horizons. In the highest phases of development they show a rich profile division up to seven or more horizons or sub-horizons. The parent material for the humus formation consists primarily of the remains of higher plants. There is an extraordinary variety of humus formations in which mull predominates by far. The soils also show an unusual variety of forms (great number of types) and a strong change of forms (sequences of development with up to seven and more members.

The highest development forms are geologically proportionately young.

---

*) Individual warp soil types strictly taken already as belonging to terrestrial soils (like the brown warp soil without G horizon, *smonitza, ganynyatcha* among others) in order not to break the class warp soils are described in the division of flooded and groundwater soils.

They are not only conditioned by an atmosphere which has become to a high degree perfected as a biosphere but also by the presence of a plant cover which is suitable for the formation of highly developed humus forms. The development of true, deep, mull soils (as the *chernosems, para-chernosems, smonitsa, eutrophic braunerde*, etc.) depends on the presence of a luxuriant grass flora or angiosperm woods, so that the first appearance can be taken at the earliest in the upper Cretaceous and Tertiary. (Begin with the key of division C.)

A. Sub-Aqueous or Underwater Soils (Ramann 1918)

Key for the Determination of the Types and certain particular Sub-types.

1.	Soil without peat formation … … … … … … … … … … … … …	2
1*.	Soil with distinct peat formation … … … … … … … … … … …	8
2.	Soil without macroscopically distinguishable humus horizon … … … …	3
2*.	Soil with macroscopically distinguishable humus horizons … … … … …	6
3.	Low in chalk, not effervescing with HCl … … … … … … … … … …	4
3*.	Calcareous to highly calcareous, effervescing with HCl … … … … … …	5

4. Extremely rich in iron, intense rust yellow, rust brown, or rust red coloured.

> 2. *Dystrophic lake iron protopedon.*

4*. Not extremely rich in iron and otherwise coloured.

> 1. *Chalk deficient protopedon.*

5. Containing clay to rich in clay.

> 3. *Lake marl protopedon.*

5*. Low in clay to free from clay, extremely calcareous.

> 4. *Lake chalk protopedon.*

6. Very acid, consisting almost entirely of brown humus flocks, occurring only in acid brown waters.

> II. *Dy.*

6*. Colour blackish, grey, to grey brown not occurring in brown waters, but in humus free or at most moderately humus containing waters … … 7

7. Humus layer without or with only slight smell of putrefaction, ric in animal excretions.

> III. *Gyttja.*

7*. With strong to unbearable smell of putrefaction, poor in animal excretions.

> IV. *Sapropel.*

8. Peat composed predominately of the remains of grasses or false grasses.   9

8*. Peat composed predominately of remains of other plants   10

9.   Peat predominately composed of the remains of roots, stems, rhizomes
     and leaves of reeds recognisable by their size, as well as with strong
     peat decomposition by the visible stalk nodes.

(10). *Phragmites-Fen* (Reed peat moor).

9*. Peat consisting predominately of the remains of sedge species recognisable
     by their fineness as well as almost always by the presence of lustrous dark
     seeds of the marsh trefoil.

(11). *Carex-Fen* (Sedge peat moor).

10. Peat thin layered, loose, relatively little decomposed, consisting predomin-
     ately of the remains of Hynum mosses almost always easily recognisable,
     besides carex residues   18

(12). *Hypnum-Fen* (Hynum peat moor).

10*. Peat consisting predominately of the leaves, fruits, soft easily cut woody
     remains of alders and willows.

10. *Wood-Fen.*

Description of Sub-Aqueous soils

AA. Sub-Aqueous Soils not forming Peat.

I. Protopedon
Sub-Aqueous Raw Soil

1. Chalk deficient Protopedon
Chalk deficient sub-aqueous raw soil

Synonyms: Minerogener Seeboden (WASMUND).

General Specification: Embryonic underwater soil formation on chalk
deficient clastic sediments with colonization by organisms but without formation of a macroscopically apparent humus horizon.

Characteristics:

Profile: The (A) horizon consists often of an algal layer (Äfja) or a
root layer of higher plants. The profile structure is either (A)C, if the subsoil
is composed of little weathered sediments, or (A)G, if it is a strongly weathered,
more or less coloidal rich and gleyed lake soil layer (sub-aqueous gley soil).

Humus Form: Sub-aqueous raw soil humus with low decomposition
and humification and transitions to gyttja.

Dynamic: Underwater weathering increased in acid waters. Gleying.
With local increase in oxygen content and by the activity of iron bacteria,
oxidation and irreversible precipitation of ferric hydroxide.

Texture *): From the finest clays through loam, silt, pebbles to coarse

---

*) Used in the sense of particle size distribution.

shingle, which can be expressed also by the name (e. g. lake sand raw soil, lake clay raw soil, in the case of marine formations schlick raw soil, etc.).

Chalk Content : Not effervescing with HCl 1:1. Transitions to chalk sand and marl raw soils can be separated as moderately calcareous s. a. raw soils.

2. *Dystrophic Lake iron Protopedon*
Dystrophic lake iron raw sol

Synonyms : Erzseeboden.

General Specification : S. a. raw soil formation on extremely limonite rich sediments, resulting by flocculation from acid, iron rich waters deficient in electrolytes.

Characteristics:

Profile : Colonized by organisms but no development of humus horizon. The (A) horizon consists mostly of a poor Äfja. The underlying Fe horizon (iron enriched layer) is due entirely to sedimentation and consists predominately of rust brown to rust yellow flocks and concretions of ferric hydroxide, partly also of manganese hydroxide.

Humus Form : S. a. raw soil humus with tendency to dygyttja formation.

Occurrence : Frequent in northern Europe and known particularly from its occurrence in Fennoskandia, namely areas of acid igneous rocks and crystalline schists with predominance of terrestrial soils with raw humus or acid coarse moder formation. From these come the acid substances, to which is due the strong weathering and the strong solution (peptization) of the ferric hydroxides.

3. *Lake marl Protopedon*
Lake marl raw soil

Synonyms : Weisserde, Seeziger (Swiss), subhydrous chalk raw soil, white marl (American), maremud (Dutch); on land utilization: meadow marl, meadow chalk.

General Specification : Lake soil rich in chalk and clay, superficially colonized by plants and animals without macroscopically distinguishable humus horizon. Its chalk is mostly organic in origin. For its differentiation from lake chalk raw soil and alm-raw soil, see page 88.

Characteristics:

Profile: Generally thin (A) horizon which consists of an algal cover
(Äfja) or root layer of higher plants, above a whitish coloured C horizon.

Humus Form: S. a. raw soil humus with transition to gyttja.

Chalk Content: 20-70 % CaCo₃.

Texture: Presupposes a certain clay content. Soils consisting of chalk-
sand, chalk-pebbles, or chalk shingles, have to be designated specifically
(e. g. chalk sand raw soil).

4. *Lake chalk Protopedon*
Lake chalk raw soil

Occurrence: In all zones with sufficient content of chalk and clay, substances in the feeding waters.

Synonyms: Soblage, Sjöblecke, Wysse (Swiss), Kalkmudde (C. A. WE-
BER), weisse Leber (Swiss); with higher shell content: Schill (unbroken
shells), Schnecklilehm (Swiss), Bruchschill (mechanically and coprogenically
comminuted); if formed by chalk precipitating stoneworts = characeae chalk,
crai lacustre (French).

General Specification: Extremely calcareous sediments low in clay,
superficially colonized by organisms, however showing still no humus horizon
formation; the chalk fraction is of organic origin (decomposed shells of
mussels and other shell remains, formation by chalk precipitating plants).

In comparison to the *lake marl protopedon* low in clay and to the alm raw
soil *) predominence of organogenic chalk. Phytogenic sub-aqueous chalk
under the influence of higher plants is easily transformed into gyttjas as the
plant litter is decomposed in the autumn.

Characteristics:

Profile: Above the whitish coloured C horizon mostly an (A) horizon
in the form of a thin algal cover (Afja) or a characeae sward or of a root
horizon of higher plants. Raw soil of phytogenic lake chalks have therefore
a particular profile structure, which underneath the (A) horizon shows a
layer containing the little decomposed remains of Characeae, Nitellea and
chalk encrusted higher plants, which may be designated as (A)/C horizon.

Humus Form: S. a. raw soil humus with transition to gyttja.

Chalk Content: 70-90 % CaCo₃.

---

*) *Alm* (SENDTNER 1854) or spring chalk appears rarely as soil forming sediment
in larger areas and is purely inorganogenic, precipitated by supersaturation.

Structure : Dense to powdery, permeated by shell residues and a few plant remains. With characeae chalks occasionally tubular structure.

Plant Cover : Generally algae (with characeae chalk and under water meadows of stoneworts), as well as also pondweeds, Myriophyllae, chickweeds etc.

Occurrence : Typical of smaller lakes and ponds rich in chalk of almost all zones. It reaches a great thickness in the littoral of great lakes. Northern boundary about 55° latitude, highest altitude about 1.100 m.

II. Dy
(Swedish folk name, H. v. Post 1862)

Synonyms : Braunschlamm, Tyrfopel (NAUMANN), Helopel (GAMS); in high moor regions : Torfmudde (C. A. WEBER), limnic peat (FRÜH and SCHRÖTER), liver peat (EISELEN, 1802), peat mud. The last five designations are not always exact synonyms.

General Specification : Muddy acid AC-soils, biologically extraordinarily inert, occurring at the bottom of brown waters which consist to a great extent of an amorphous precipitation of humus gels.

Characteristics :

Profile : The dark liver brown to blackish brown A horizon is not a pure sediment layer, but shows the marks of products of an autochtonous (although sparse) soil life. There is generally no Äfja. C horizons with infiltrated organic matter are designated A/C.

Structure : Amorphous, fragmentary, crumbly, fine-fibred to floccular. Occasionally the mass contains fragments of pure dopplerite (precipitates of pure humus gels) which are translucent as dark glass and show a jelly-like to glassy consistency with conchoidal fracture.

Micromorphology : As well as pure precipitates of humus substances also excrement balls of aquatic animals and thin broken-up fragments of the recognizable remains of organisms, remains of chitin predominate. Plant residues are almost completely absent.

Chemical Characteristics : Low base content, strong acidification and nutrient deficiency.

Dynamic : Strong weathering of the mineral particles, reduction and continual loss of O_2 in the region of humus precipitates. Occasionally translocation of colloidal material into the subsoil.

Biology : Poor in life to inimical to life, therefore deficient in organisms and organism remains. Plant organisms rare, among the aquatic animals molluscs and fishes are generally completely absent.

Explanation of plate III.

1. **Dy** in a pool of a podsol and highmoor zone over granite below spruce forest (Bohemian Forest).
2. **Eutrofic Gyttja** with *Nymphea alba* and an äfja of green algae (Wies, Styria).

Quality of the Water : Colour brownish to brown with low depth of visibility, rich in humus sols, poor in plankton, acid, low in chalk and eletrolytes.

After Drainage : Strong shrinkage (up to $1/10$), often break down into hard fragments going into powder by frost action which is difficult to reunite on rewetting. As terrestrial soils, infertile, unsuitable for cultivation.

Occurrence : In the region of podsols and dystrophic rankers with strong raw humus formation, furthermore in highmoor areas. The humus sols originate from the leachings of these soil formations.

III. Gyttja[*]
(Swedish folkname, H. v. Post 1862)

Synonyms : Grauschlamm, Mudde : refers usually only to inactive *gyttja* but also *dy* formations transformed into peat.

General Specification : Active, muddy, predominately coprogenic, grey, grey brown to blackish coloured AC-soils, rich in organisms occurring in waters sufficiently rich in nutrients and oxygen, containing great quantities of organic food (partly in excess).

Characteristics :

Profile : A horizon of a very variable thickness, from a few centimeters to several meters. Several to numerous A horizons frequently occur, alternating with buried C or G horizons. With very rapid alternation and clay material, micro-horizons of a few millimetres may appear (band clays). The soil surface of *limnic gyttja* generally shows prolific growth (algal layer or sward of higher plants). The algal layer with its scarcely decomposed plant remains is called Äfja, little decomposed litter layer of higher plants derived from shore vegetation is called Förna.

Biology : Generally good decomposition and proportionately good humification of the plant residues which prevail, due predominately to the activity of the soil and water fauna. Coprogenic elements prevail strongly in the product of transformation which consists of a good mixture of the organic

---

[*] Pronounced : yuetya.

III.

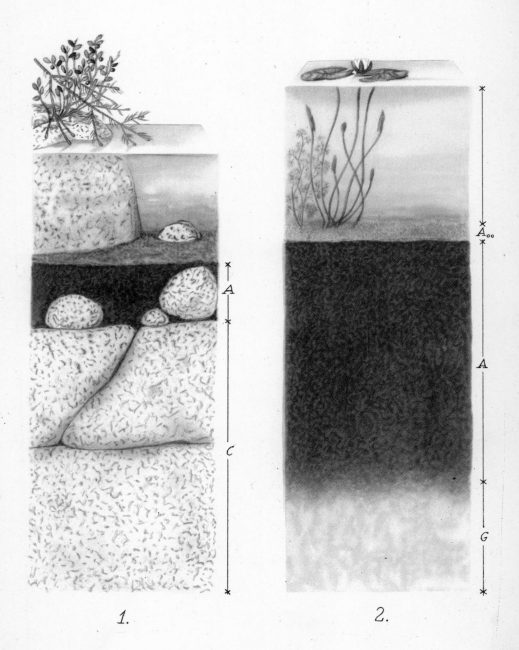

1.   2.

and inorganic substances; these are mostly well mixed but do not show the formation of clay humus complexes.

Structure: Loose, running easily through one's hand, very rich in water to semi-solid and elastic. On drying, shrinking strongly.

Colour: The colour changes with humus and mineral content. Mineral rich gyttjas are light grey. With a high humus content especially with eutrophic gyttja, the colour becomes almost black to brownish black.

Smell: Typical gyttja smell, slightly inky. In transition forms to sapropel slight smell of H_2S.

Micromorphology: Loose coprogenic particles, strongly eaten through corroded plant remains, silica shells of diatoms, chitin residues of crustaceae and rotiferi, maxillae of chironomidi larvae, rhizopod skeletons and mineral particles. The organic constituents, under the microscope, have preponderately a grey yellow, brown yellow, yellowish to greenish yellow colour.

Coprogenic Constituents: In general easily broken down, however, often the droppings of insect larvae, small crayfish, worms and molluscs are distinctly recognisable. A gyttja, rich in droppings and excrement residues is stable, less liable to erosion by water.

Occurrence: Outside the region of dystrophic terrestrial soils, in all zones in a level or slightly sloping foundation. If steep easily washed away and raw soil formation preponderate.

Key to the Identification of the Gyttja Sub-types and Varieties.

1. Occurring in inland waters ... ... 2 and 3
1*. Occurring in marine shallows 4
2. Luxuriantly developed humus layers in yellowish, nutrient rich waters with low depth of visibility.

(1) Eutrophic gyttja.

2*. Mostly poorly developed humus layers in nutrient and chalk deficient, very clear blue to grey waters.

(3) Oligotrophic gyttja.

3. Humus layer rich in chalk, effervescing strongly with HCl.

(2) Chalk gyttja.

3*. Humus layers generally brownish, raw, extremely chalk deficient and acid, already containing amorphic humus flocks in brownish waters.

(4) Dygyttja.

4. Generally bare, without äfja (algal growth layer) 5
4*. With Cyanophiceae cover.

(7) Cyanophyceae watt gyttja.

5. Formed of fine sediments in marine shallows.

(5) Schlickwatt gyttja.

5* Formed of coarse sandy sediments in marine shallows.

(6) *Sandwatt gyttja.*

Note: In addition gyttjas can be sub-divided according to *degree of division:* into
fine detritus gyttja (mostly formed from algae, consisting primarily of broken down
animal excreta and **coarse detritus gyttja** (many coarse tatters mainly of higher
plants; brownish colours predominate); *parent material:* in **algae gyttja, diatomaceae
gyttja, phanerogamae gytjja, leaf gyttja,**, etc.; *particular constituents:* in **chitin
gyttja** (recession of plant material), **pollen gyttja** or **fimmenit** (particularly rich in
flower pollen), **shell gyttja** (rich in mollusc remains), etc.

5. Limnic Gyttja
(1) Eutrophic Gyttja

General Specification : Generally luxuriantly developed *gyttja* in mature waters, rich in nutrients and plancton with prolific litoral plant production.

Characteristics :

Profile : A horizon generally of considerable thickness and in it well
developed vegetation.

Variability of Form : Proportionately great. Besides fine detritus gyttja, owing to richer vegetation in shallow waters many coarse detritus gyttja.
Slight tendency to form sapropel, so that there is almost always local sapro-
pelization, especially in deep waters.

Quality of Water : Rich in plancton and nutrients, yellowish to greenish colour with low depth of visibility.

Average Depth of Water : In temperate climates not over 18 m,
deeper in warm climates.

Hydroclimate : Formation favoured in temperate and warm hydroclim-
ates.

Chemical Characteristics : Many forms contain varying quantities of
iron sulphide, which appear as a powdery black pigment.

(2) Chalk Gyttja

Synonyms : Kalkmudde.

General Specification : *Gyttja* with high chalk content in calcareous
waters.

In comparison with other formations the nutrient deficient *chalk gyttja*
is well delimitated. The nutrient rich (*eutrophic*) *chalk gyttja* approaches

closely the foregoing *eutrophic gyttja* and generally differs little from it except for the high chalk content. However, it is important to distinguish between the two for pedological and agricultural reasons in regard to their different further development and cultivation in the drained state.

Characteristics:

Profile: Generally an easily recognisable whitish coloured C horizon. Also the chalk content of the A horizon is, in many cases, recognisable to the naked eye by its visible chalk fragments and amorphous chalk precipitates.

Dynamic: Chemical weathering, gleying and movement of material in the soil horizon is impeded by the high chalk content.

Chemical Characteristics: A and C horizons effervescing with dilute HCl.

Quality of Water: High in chalk, with oligotrophic forms, of intense blue to emerald green colour with considerable depth of visibility.

After Drainage: Easily transformed into *calcareous anmoor* and further to extraordinarily fertile chernosem-like warp soils (*Smonitsa*).

(3) Oligotrophic Gyttja

General Specification: Low in nutrients, generally with shallow horizons in acid, immature waters, low in electrolytes.

Characteristics:

Profile: A horizons generally of little thickness, usually with high mineral content.

Chemical Characteristics: Effervescing with HCl, acid reaction.

Biology: Due to plankton deficiency and low plant growth in shallow waters, low supply of plant material, therefore low humus production. Relatively strong oxidation and little reduction in the humus layer. The soil fauna is usually rich in species. Only slight tendency to fetid slime formation, almost never occurring in deep waters.

Variability of Form: Low, uniformity in profile structure and character of the humus formation.

Quality of Water: Chalk and nutrient deficient, of blue to green colour with considerable depth of visibility.

(4) Dygyttja

Synonyms: Dystrophic gyttja.

General Specification: *Gyttja* of low activity, in part containing precipitated humus gels in acid humic waters, transition formation to dy. (Dy contains predominately precipitates of displaced humus.)

Characteristics:

Profile: A horizons of brownish grey colour, generally of slight thickness, still with a distinct gyttja character.

Biology: Low in life, with low supply of plant parent material and a soil fauna, low in numbers of species. Acid humus soils and gels have a depressing effect on life.

Quality of Water: Very low in electrolytes, slightly brownish coloured due to humus soils.

Hydroclimate: Predominately cold.

6. Marine Gyttja

Synonyms: Marine shore gyttja (WESENBERG-LUND 1905); shallows soil, Wattboden; wad (Duch), kvelderboden: in those designations the marine sapropels (see 95) are also included.

(5) Schlickwatt Gyttja

Synonyms: Schlickwatt (WOHLENBERG 1931), Schlickwattboden.

General Specification: Soil formation of gyttja-like character on fine shallows sediment, whose organic fraction consists predominately of remains of droppings of small animals.

Characteristics:

Profile: Generally deep, blackish A horizons becoming light when exposed to air. The äfja is almost completely missing.

Structure: Characteristically tubular upper soil layer with dense, often honeycomb perforation of the surface.

Biology and Dynamic: Very rich in animals. Bare schlick shallows soils are colonized most strongly by small schlick crayfish (*Corophium volutator*), as well as by Annelida (in particular *Nereis diversicolor*). Decomposition of remains of organisms is carried out mainly by small animals. Owing to the numerous living tubes the upper soil layer is richly provided with oxygen at low water. The walls of the tubes are stabilized by oxidation of ferrous sulphides and the encrustation by ferric hydroxide.

Phenology: Characterized by a continuous alternation of draining and flooding with the ebb and flow of the water, which holds for all the following shallows soils.

(6) Sandwatt Gyttja

Synonyms: Sandwatt (WOHLENBERG 1931), Sandwattboden.

General Specification: Soil formation low in humus of gyttja-like character formed on coarse sandy shallows sediments.

Characteristics:

Profile: Generally deep in humus, very loose A horizons with äfja layer almost completely missing.

Biology: Dense colonization by animals, especially *Arenicola marina* which is absent in schlickwatt and whose heaps of worm casts are characteristic for the sandwatt. The walls of the numerous living tubes have a reddish concretion-like oxidation layer of ferric hydroxide several millimeters thick. Humus formation is primarily caused by soil fauna.

(7) Cyanophyceae Watt Gyttja
Cyanophyceae Shallows Gyttja

Synonyms: Blaualgenwatt (WOHLENBERG 1937).

General Specification: Gyttja-like schlickwatt with leathery cyanophyceae skin.

Characteristics:

Profile: Above the A horizon a dense äfja which can be removed like a skin and which is missing in other gyttja-like watts.

Biology: Not low in animals as the diatom watt, but richly colonized, particularly by *Bledius spectabilis* (Staphylinide) further by Enchytraidae (*Enchytraeus albidus*) various Carabidi (*Heterocerus flexuosus, Cillenus lateralis*), etc. The upper soil layer is well supplied with oxygen through the numerous living tubes of the *Bledius*.

IV. Sapropel
(Lauterborn 1901)

Synonyms: Fetid slime.

Key for the Determination of the Sub-types and Varieties.

1. Occurring in inland waters.
        7. *Limnic sapropel.*

1*. Occurring in marine shallows **2**

2.   Mostly thin pasty to fluid. Formed under a dense cover of seaweed or sea-grass.

(8) Muddwatt sapropel.

2*.   Not a thin pasty fluid. Formed under a dense, slimy algal skin.

(9) Diatomwatt sapropel.

7. *Limnic sapropel*

Synonyms: Limnic fetid slime.

General Specification: Stinking, strongly reduced soil in completely stagnant water with strong putrefaction due to complete loss of oxygen and copious formation of hydrogen sulphide and other foul gases.

Characteristics:

Profile: Primarily AG soils with generally deep black, seldom browned humus horizon with marked gleying in subsoil. There is no äfja.

Structure: The mass of the humus horizon is loose and flaky, sometimes dense and greasy, occasionally slimy.

Microscopic Characteristics: Usually presence of reddish flocks of sulfur bacteria, no excreta of small animals, presence of residues of a sparse characteristic sapropel fauna.

Chemical Characteristics: Always contains a significant quantity of ferrous sulphide partly in chemically very unstable forms. They form a blue-black pigment in the humus whose colour however is rapidly lost by removal and oxidation of the soil (often bleached completely). The presence of ferrous sulphide is easily shown by heating (stinging smell of SO_2 given) or by wetting a sample with dilute HCl (H_2S smell).

Biology: Primarily plant remains, partly protein rich, are decomposed up to entire destruction of the cell structure under almost complete absence of oxygen with strong action of anaerobic bacteria accompanied by strong development of hydrogen sulfide and other foul gases.

Smell: Foul smell which can become unbearable.

Quality of the Water: Yellowish, rich in nutrients, but containing putrefaction poisons. Usually formation of gas bubbles.

Hydroclimate: Formation strongly favoured in temperate to warm hydroclimate.

After Drainage: As iron sulphide is a heavy plant poison, the plant growth appears strongly impeded in former chalk deficient *sapropels*. In highly calcareous or heavily chalked soils with sufficient aeration (favoured by tillage) oxidation and complete transformation to harmless gypsum occurs.

Its abundant presence in the form of powdery precipitates and small crystals, pinacoids, lenses or grains becomes a diagnostic characteristic. The colour of the former blackish *sapropels* changes mostly into light grey by this transformation. Humus rich, calcareous *sapropels* may be transformed to *calcareous anmoor* with increasing mull formation and afterwards also to chernosem-like warp soils.

8. Marine Sapropel

(8) Muddwatt Sapropel

Synonyms : Mudd-Watt (Holstein folk name, WOHLENBERG 1937).

General Specification : Marine, very thin, partly almost fluid *sapropel* formation of great depth and strong evolution of gas with primarily luxuriantly developed seaweed and sea-grass as parent material.

Characteristics :

Profile : AG profile with mostly very deep humus horizons of blackish colour, which may be approached by boat at high water. Depth of humus horizons up to 130 cm. and more.

Structure : The humus has a high water content, being almost fluid even at low water. Animal droppings are rare, putrefaction products common.

Vegetation : Primarily dense seaweed meadows of *Fucus Mytili*, usually united with the sea mussel *Mytilus edulis* and sea grass vegetation of *Zostera angustifolia* and *Zostera stenophylla*.

Phenology : Never completely free of water. Even at low water, it is under a certain depth of water.

Biology and Dynamic : Strong putrefaction, greatly exceeding the formation of humus by animals, almost continuous evolution of gas bubbles if strong formation of H_2S. Strong reduction, precipitation of bluish black iron sulphide and of elementary sulphur in whitish yellow haze.

(9) Diatomwatt Sapropel

Diatom Shallows Sapropel

Synonyms : Diatomeen-Watt (WOHLENBERG 1931).

General Specification : Marine fetid mud formation produced by a complete closing up and covering of former *gyttja* formations by dense diatom skins.

Characteristics:

Profile : Above the blackish A horizon a strongly developed, usually olive brown coloured, extraordinarily slimy and smooth äfja layer *) composed principally of silicate algae. Generally there is a band structure of several diatom layers.

Biology and Dynamic : The algal skins are formed in particular by diatoms of the species *Pleurosigma, Pinnularia* and *Navicula,* living in the slimy mass which they secrete. If the skin is covered by a fresh layer of flood water sediment the algae for the most part, work their way to the surface. Owing to the soil being completely sealed by the slimy äfja, it is very deficient in fauna, and there is strong development of putrefying bacteria. The schlick crayfish disappears almost completely with increasing diaton growth. Due to the high production of H_2S, the iron in the soil solution is precipitated and concentrated as blackish blue amorphous iron sulphide of ferrous sulphide hydrate (hydrotroilite). Strongly reducing.

Occurrence : Greatest concentration on the North Sea coast 5-20 cm. under the average high water line.

Phenology : The strongest development of siliceous algae occurs in late summer to autumn.

AB. Peat-forming Sub-aqueous Soils

V. Fen **)

(Engl. folk name, Sir D. Hall 1903 Whittles 1928)

Synonyms : Sub-aqueous moor, infraaquatic moor, limnic moor, low moor, valley moor, basin moor, hard water moor, veen (Dutch) Fehn (North German) eutrophic moor (Germany): can only have real value in soil science if applied to nutrient rich low moor, while the nutrient deficient low moor to be consistent should be called oligotrophic, and further, the wood peat moor (page 117) and the high moor (page 118) dystrophic; meadow moor: refers only to the series of sub-types with the designation turf peat moor.

General Specification and Delimitation : Biologically inert soils below water with mineral deficient to mineral free humus forms, in which, due

---

*) This is so slippery that one can slide on it like a skater with bare feet.
**) The name corresponds to the Dutch veen and German Fehn. In England the term has been applied in recent years to calcareous soils high in organic matter and plant nutrients formed under stagnant water. According to the nomenclature of this book, soils which do not show real peat formation, but gyttja, anmoor or other non-peaty humus forms are excluded from peat soils. Therefore many soils with good humification formerly designated as *fens* belong to the *anmoor* type.

to the almost complete lack of oxygen, the generally acid reaction, the excessive production of organic matter and the unfavourable conditions for rapid humification, there is a strong accumulation of little decomposed plant remains.

The objects of study in soil science are primarily the recent «living» moor soils and the humus soils resulting from transformed former moor peats. The buried «dead» peat layers and former moor soils, whose humus formation owing to biological inertness of the environment are well preserved, are either parent material for new soil formations or mere substrata. It is however just as important to have knowledge of them as of any other parent material or substratum.

The most important recent soil formations derived from old moor peat are specially described in the division of semi-terrestrial soils in the appendix on hig moor soils (page 122). The characteristics of the old buried peats will be attached to the corresponding «living» form.

9. Turf Fen
Turf Peat Moor

(10) Phragmites Fen
Reed Peat Moor

Synonyms: Phragmites peat, rush-peat moor, darg = reed peat mostly rich in iron sulphide in the North Sea coast, originating in brackish water, permeated strongly by sand and silt.

Occurs frequently also as a buried peat layer under marsh soils (page 114). Other buried peat layers on coastlines have wrongly been described as darg.

General Specification: Soil formed under fresh or brackish water with peat humus composed mainly of the roots, steams and leaves of the reed cane.

Characteristics:

Profile: The reed peat cover is generally formed over a gyttja layer (page 90) and at first will not stand walking upon, but immediately gives way; it thus floats, so to speak, on the mud. When it is firm enough to bear one it forms the so-called *swing moor* which when trodden distinctly shakes. In the *stable moor* phase the heavier and thicker peat cover has compressed the mud layer up to the greatest possible extent. With buried reed peat or with that which has become land, lense-like water cushions may occur between it and the gyttja layer, and on penetration their contents are often explosively thrown out. The sub-soil is generally an impermeable gley layer, rich in colloidal material, or the gyttja horizon can lie directly on the dense rock (granite, basalt, clay schist). Under the moor, the chemical weathering and clay formation is sharply increased. With a permeable subsoil the stagnant water of the moor combines with the deeper dammed-up ground-water.

Characteristics of Peat Layer: Young reed peat consists of a light, felted, bulky, almost undecomposed mass of the plant remains given above and is easy to recognise by its broad leaves and the wide bands of flattened horizontal roots (rhizomes), further by hairless nodes occurring regularly 5-20 cm. apart. Root stalks and stems are only slightly compressed. Peat samples shrink little on drying and only reabsorb water slowly. The mineral content can occasionally be considerable.

Plant Cover: «Living» reed peat moor is always covered by a dense reed turf (*Phragmites communis*). In it are found numerous other swamp plants, like *Equisetum palustre* and *limosum, Scirpus lacustris, Sparganium ramosum*, etc.

Depth of Water: Its formation begins already at a depth of about 2.50 m., whereby it precedes all pure peat formations which require essentially shallower water.

Thickness: With mature formations, considerable (up to 3 m. and more).

Characteristics of Old Reed Peats: Older reed peat, buried under other moor covers, consists when strongly decomposed of a stramineous mass, but on being exposed to the air rapidly turns black and feels slippery. Morphologically it is composed of still recognisable rhizomes (with striking nodule formation) and remains of broad leaves which are imbedded in a fairly homogeneous, muddy ground mass. The decomposition is gyttja-like (*peat gyttja* No. [1], whereby the characteristics of this old peat approach those of *gyttja*. In this connection appears also the strong shrinkage of peat samples on drying, up to about a quarter of their original volume.

Decomposability: Even the young fibrous reed peats are decomposed easily after draining.

Appearance after Drainage: Reed peat moor is changed fairly quickly into a fertile, loose, blackish cultivated soil. For possible transformation forms see page 122.

Occurrence: Very widespread in Central and Northern Europe, rare in Southern Europe, absent in the sub-arctic.

(11) *Carex Fen*
Sedge Peat Moor

Synonyms: Carex peat, seggenmoor.

General Specification: Soils formed under stagnant freshwater, with peat humus form, composed primarily of the stalks, leaves, rhizomes and roots of sedges.

Characteristics:

Profile: Peat layer of proportionately slight thickness, which has ge-

nerally been found on a thick reed peat layer. These are followed generally
by more or less highly compressed gyttja layers lying on strongly gleyed
mineral horizons.

Characteristics of the Peat Layer : Young sedge peat consists of a
light yellowish coloured root felt containing, besides stalk and leaf remains,
numerous fruits of carex species, and usually the characteristically lens-
shaped seeds of marsh trefoil (*Menyanthes trifoliata*).

Depth of Water : Sedge grasses develop only in shallow water and
therefore the sedge peat is formed mainly in the margin of the waters made
shallow by the growing reed peat. If the pat formation by tall sedges has
reached the average height of the water surface, small sedges appear. With
their dense root mat the soil is further consolidated.

Biology :   Biological relations are considerable improved in the shallow
water by the greater air content and nutrient supply, whereby life can develop
more intensely.

Decomposability : Generally very easy.

Characteristics of Old Sedge Peats : In freshly cut condition dirty
yellow-grey mass which rapidly darkens in the air, containing stalk and root
remains of sedges in dark ground mass. With stronger (*gyttja*-like) decomposition (see page) becomes almost black by accumulation of muddy coprogenic
elements. Also in strongly decomposed peats, the smooth dark coloured, lens-
shaped seeds of marsh trefoil are often a striking constituent.

Appearance after Drainage : Generally almost deep lack coloured,
earthy, fertile cultivated soil. With regard to possible transformation forms
see page .

Occurrence : Very widely distributed in Central and Northern Europe.
Very frequently the highest layer of cultivated low moors in a transformed
condition.

(12) Hypnum Fen
Hypnum Peat Moor

Synonyms : Knotted moss peat moor, brown moss peat moor.

General Specification : Soil formed on old low moors under stagnant
water with peat humus composed mainly of the remains of various brown
mosses.

Characteristics :

Profile : The brown moss peat forms generally only thin layers or sometimes only isolated nests in the sedge and reed peat (see page 100).

Plant Cover : Brown moss meadows (low moor hypneta) i. e. sedge turf
with prolific development of *Hypnum* species.

Characteristics of the Peat Layer : Decidedly loose, easily crumbled yellow to red brown peat mass which never becomes as light coloured as the otherwise similar white peat (see page 118). The mosses which besides a few sedge remains form the main mass are well preserved and easy to recognise and by their prolific branching and other form characteristics sharply distinguished from the *Sphagnum*.

Decomposability : Considerably lower than the reed and sedge peats and therefore always easily recognized in old low moor profiles.

Characteristics of Old Hypnum Peat : Loose, very friable peat masses of blackish colour with brown moss remains always recognisable. Peat samples show a low shrinkage and have a far lower absorbing and retaining capacity for water than the Sphagnum peats.

Occurrence : On old low moors in the Alps, in Scandinavia, partly also frequently in Northern Germany, however generally in proportionately smaller formations. They are more important as buried layers in old peat profiles overlain by high moor covers.

10. Wood Fen

Synonyms : Alder swamp, swamp wood peat, low moor wood peat, Auwaldtorfmoor = variation in river valley characterized by the appearance of other woods, specially the pedunculate oak, Rüllenwaldtorf = variation which forms along the run-off channels (Rüllen) of high moor (type XII).

General Specification : Low moor soil formed in stagnant or frequently slowly flowing hard water under alder swamp woods, with peat, rich in leaf cone and wood remains.

Characteristics :

Profile : The swamp wood peat is formed either on old *turf fens* or it can be produced directly on *gyttja* becoming land, or also completely independently on gley horizons. In all cases this peat humus is formed below the water surface i. e. as a low moor formation.

Characteristics of the Peat Layer : When moist, soft and heavy peat of high mud content, when dry, becoming friable, breaking into fragments, shrinking strongly; it is characterized most distincly by its alder cones and brownish red woody remains.

Plant Cover : Principally alder woods (in particular *Alnus glutinosa*) interspersed with willows, with swamp plants, luxuriantly growing, shade and water-loving herbs and ferns below them. Gradually new species of trees appear, spruces, peduncular oaks, shaking aspens, etc. (stable low moor wood).

Thickness of Peat Layer: Low, as the rapidly growing soil soon allows colonization by other species of trees.

Biology: Higher oxygen content, better supply of nutrients (generally slow running water), more rapid warming up of the shallow water permits a better development of life than in other low moor peats. The decomposition of plant remains is gyttja-like and is done exclusively by water organisms.

Decomposability: Very easy.

Quality after Drainage: Well decomposed and humified, generally deep black coloured, earthy, particularly valuable cultivated soils.

Occurrence: Widely distributed in Central and Northern Europe, especially in Northern Germany, where amongst others it appears most frequently as a top layer of cultivated low moors.

Appendix to Peat- forming Underwater Soils

Sub-aqueous Transformation Forms of Peat

[1]. *Peat Gyttja* *)

General Specification and Delimitation: *Gyttja*-like transformation of peat layers of a most diverse kind underwater or with excessive waterlogging, without real addition of parent material for humus formation of fresh higher plants.

For differences from other transformation forms of peat see descriptions page 122.

Characteristics:

Profile: The transformation is generally fully shown within existing moor profiles, in which individual layers become more or less strongly decomposed according to their innate decomposability or biological conditions. This is shown especially strongly by the transformation of thin peat layers buried under mud or gyttja (e. g. darg covered by schlick on the North Sea coast).

Characteristics of the Peat Layer: Decrease of recognisable plant remains, together with growth of a muddy, strongly humified groundmass which consists predominately of the broken-down excreta of aquatic animals.

---

*) Forms in mature state according to their character are subvarieties of the *limnic gyttja*.

The entire peat mass becomes a darker colour (mostly blackish), feels slippery and shrinks more on drying. Occasionally the formation of methane and hydrogen sulphide is observed together with the precipitation of iron sulphide (generally as a black pigment), primary sulphur, vivianite (blue iron ore, $Fe_3(PO_4)_2$, white precipitates becoming an intense blue en exposure to air), white iron ore (colloidal ferrous carbonate, white cheesy masses rapidly becoming brown on exposure to air), etc.

Biology: The decomposition and humification is produced predominately by the activity of aquatic and mud fauna, bacteria in particular are important, primarily for fetid, mud-like varieties.

B. Semi-terrestrial or Flooding and Groundwater Soils

Key for the Determination of Classes and Types.

1.   Soils showing peat formation or produced directly from peats, generally underlain by raw peats.

BC. Semi-terrestrial peat soils.

1*.   Soils not showing peat formation … … … … … … … … … … … … …   2

2.   Soils with high salt content *) or occurring in conjunction with them and derived immediately from them.

BD. Salt soils.

2*.   Soils, low in salts and not derived from salt soils … … … … … … …   3

3.   Soils neither with macroscopically distinguishable humus horizon nor with ochre, brown or red coloured (B) horizons.

BA. Semi-terrestrial raw soils.

3*.   Soils with distinct humus horizon or failing that, at least with a distinctly developed (B)-Horizon … … … … … … … … … … … … … … …   4

4.   Soil with strongly gleyed, grey, blue-grey or green-grey sub-soil under the influence of impeded water … … … … … … … … … … … … …   5

4*.   Soils without strongly gleyed sub-soil … … … … … … … … … … …   8

5.   Humus muddy, blue-black to dark grey coloured, when moist muddy, black with inky smell. Soils, for most of the year, waterlogged up to the surface and beyond, or arising directly from such soil formations.

BB. Anmoor-like soils.

5*.   Humus layer never or only rarely temporarily waterlogged.. Humus not muddy nor with inky smell when moist … … … … … … … … … … …   6

6.   Profile with an unwaterlogged, brown (B) horizon between the humus horizon and the grey, blue-grey green-grey, gleyed subsoil.

37. Browned gley.

6*.   Profile without brown (B) horizon … … … … … … … … … … … …   7

7.   Humus loose, low clay content, rich in (mostly cylindrical) droppings of small animals as well as comminuted, in general still recognisable plant remains. Moder smell.

35. Moder gley.

7*.   Organic matter completely humified, absence of plant residues, humus

---

     *) Rougtly determined by the superficial salt efflorescences when dry (also on drying-out previously moistened soil samples).

formation with moderate to high clay content, plastic with crumbly or usually spongy structure; distinct clay or earth smell.

36. *Mull gley.*

8.   Soils with AC-Profile, i. e., consisting of a humus horizon and an ungleyed, little weathered sub-soil of mostly sandy (partly pebbly or shinghly) river sediments   9

8*.   Soil laid down in the alluvial region of a river, with distinct well, weathered (B) horizons, without a G horizon, or one only reached at a great depth.   11

9.   Soil calcareous, effervescing with dilute HCl   10

9*.   Soil deficient in chalk.

XVII. *Paternia* (grey warp soil).

10*.   Soil little developed, sandy, generally with shallow humus horizon, showing transition to calcareous raw warp soil (*rambla*), from which it has been derived.

XVIII. *Borovina* (rendsina=like warp soil).

10*.   Soil, similar to black earth, generally with deep humus horizon with high humus content derived from *calcareous Anmoor.*

XIX. *Smonitza* (cherno'sem=like warp soil).

11.   (B) horizon ochre yellow, ochre brown to brown coloured   12

11*.   (B) horizon red coloured

40. *Red vega* (red warp soil).

12.   Soil very easily silted up and eroded, with dense structure and generally a striking, shining, intense colour. In wet condition remarkably high stickiness (also with forms relatively rich in sand), on drying out hard and difficult to work.

39. *Braunlehm vega* (braunlehm warp soil).

12*.   Soil generally loose and easily worked, colour less intense.

38. *Brown vega* (brown warp soil).

Description of Semi-Terrestrial Soils

BA. Semi-Terrestrial Raw Soils

Key to the Determination of Types and some Sub-types.

1.   Essentially occurring only in the Arctic or high Alps   2

1*.   Soil occurring generally   3

2.   Arctic soil low in humus, with striking, individual peculiar cell structure in the superficial layer.

14. *Arctic rutmark.*

2*.   Cellular, mossy soil form of the high Alps free from snow only in mid-summer.

15. *Snow basin rutmark.*

3. Soil strongly gleyed, mostly strongly-weathered, grey, blue grey to green grey generally with rust channels, flecks, etc., of precipitated iron.

VIII. Syrogley (**raw gley soil**).

3*. Soil not, or only slightly gleyed, with low chemical weathering principally occurring on frequently flooded river banks near the water's edge.

VI. Rambla (**raw warp soil**).

VI. Rambla
Raw warp Soil *)

Synonyms : Rohauboden (German).

General Specification and Delimitation : Young, little weathered and altered river sediments, however already colonized by higher plants, but still not showing recognisable humus or other soil horizons.

With slight gleying, transition forms to raw gley soils may be found which are to be designated as slightly gleyed raw warp soils (*13. Slightly gleyed rambla*). To be further distinguished are chalk rich and chalk deficient forms (*11. Chalk deficient rambla, 12. Chalk rambla*).

Characteristics :

Profile : Raw warp soils have no humus horizons distinguishable to the naked eye, but a typical kind of humus formation. The beginning of the humus horizons is generally indicated by a layer of stronger through rooting and higher biological activity which is called the (A) horizon. In the immediate vicinity of the river bed, owing to the recurrent flooding and deposition, may be seen frequently a banded structure with several buried (A) horizons.

Humus Form : Raw soil humus (syrosem humus), consisting of little decomposed, structurally unaltered plant remains which are incoherently imbedded within the dense sediments.

Microscopic preparations reveal plant splinters unchanged in colour, intersected by isolated feeding cavities (containing droppings) of mining small animals (mostly mites).

Dynamic : Low chemical weathering of the generally smooth-washed mineral grains, deprived of all deposited colloidal material. Owing to the absence of cementing substances easily blown away and silted-up. The silty forms tend to become more easily gleyed and waterlogged.

Biology : Due to low colonization by organisms, biologically inert, containing few species and showing slow decomposition and humification.

Phenology : During periods of high water, generally covered with water, then rapidly drying up and due to the high permeability and low col-

---

*) See note on page 135.

loid content, no gleying. In summer usually strong drying out, in dry years
even leading to damage by drought.

Texture : Mostly pure sand or silt soils with low colloid content, partly
with admixtures of pebbles and shingle.

VII. R u t m a r k
(Swedish, Kjellmann 1879)
14. Arctic Rutmark

Synonyms : Rhomboid soil, cellular soil (Högbom 1914), fissure
network soil, polygonal fissure soil (O. Nordenskjöld), fissure polygons
(J. S. Huxley and Odall 1924) texture soil, tesselated soil (H. Kaufmann
1929) quarré soil, facet soil; polygon soil (Högbom): this name includes
both *rutmark* and *structure rawmark* (page 148).

General Specification : Mostly little gleyed, moist alluvial raw soil of
the Arctic with a remarkable cellular surface structure consisting of a network
of polygonal fissures.

Characteristics :

Profile : The fissure formation occurs primarily in the surface soil (fissure horizon), but can occasionally penetrate deeply into the soil. However,
in every case, they only go down to the permanently frozen underground layer
(tjäle layer, page 146). In spite of partial colonization by higher plants it forms
neither a humus nor (A) horizon.

Surface Structures : The soil surface is a web of strikingly regular polygonal (usually hexagonal) fissures. These are filled with ice in
winter and free of ice in summer. They absorb the melted snow water which
goes down in them, eroding the soil. The interior polygons are usually arched
in their centres. Their diameter varies from a few decimeters up to several
meters.

Plant Cover : Sparse vegetation. The insides of the polygons remain
bare, colonization by plants mostly following the fissures.

Texture : The soil is fine grained, homogeneous and contains only a few
or no stones.

Phenology : The soil is frozen right to the surface nearly all the year
round and covered with snow. It melts superficially only in the summer
months and therefore plants have a very short growing season.

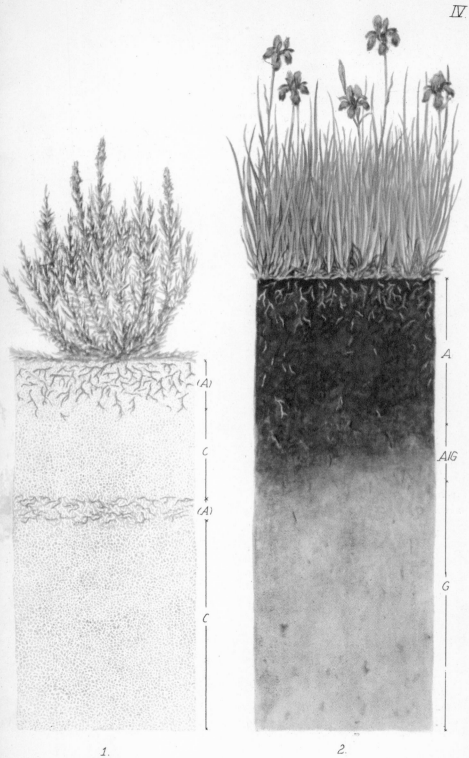

IV

(A)

C

(A)

C

A

AlG

G

1.

2.

15. Snow Basin Rutmark
Nival Snow Basin Soil

Synonyms: Nivaler Schneetälchenboden.

General Specification: Little gleyed alluvial soil of alpine high mountains in small basins in the nival and sub-nival regions with temporary frost polygon formation.

Characteristics:

Profile: A thin (A) horizon of about 2 cm., in which slight anmoor-like humus formation can be seen, followed by a very feebly gleyed or ungleyed generally grey coloured (C) horizon.

Phenology: The soil is frozen and covered with snow practically the whole year and the snow only starts to melt in the depressions (snow basins) in July or even at the beginning of August. The surface structures are a characteristic of the frozen soil and after the thaw and new surface colonization by mosses, they disappear and are only found again during the fresh complete freezing-up of the soil about the middle to the end of October.

Surface Structures: These are seen at their best if the surface is exposed in summer just before the thaw. One removes the remains of the by now thin snow cover with a spade and chisels (with a stone chisel or an ice pick) a window about 60 cm. wide out of the underlying layer of compacted ice. This ice window can be lifted off like a lid and shows on its underside a negative of the surface structure. This consists of a division of the soil into a net of polygons of about 10-15 cm. in diameter. They are usually hexagons, but a few pentagons and irregular rectangles may be found. The surfaces are arched in the centre, and separated by ice-filled fissures about 1-1 ½ cm. wide. As the soil is itself frozen, it can be cut off in slices with a knife. It is possible to cut off plates of about the thickness of one's finger even of parts intersected by ice-filled fissures. These are as transparent as clear glass and stand out strongly if the slice is held up to the light. After thawing, the soil absorbs a large quantity of snow-water and becomes almost fluid. The decrease in volume of the soil was caused by the migration of the soil water into the fissures and is followed by a strong volume increase, which closes the fissures. In the thawed soil in summer, the surface structure retains shallow polygonal grooves and slightly arched polygons. However, these gradually become indistinct and are soon covered completely by summer moss.

Plant Cover: The soil is almost exclusively inhabited by mosses particularly *Polytrichum sexangulare;* besides this, *Pohlia gracilis* is frequently to be found. The moss cover is almost completely destroyed by frost, so that only their few muddy deep black remains are found after the thaw. The fresh colonization, when the soil has melted and become sufficiently dry, begins first in the fissure grooves and spreads from them over the entire soil, which soon shows an unbroken moss cover.

Occurrence: Particularly in the Central Alps. In the Hohe Tauern already over 2700 m. altitude.

VIII. *S y r o g l e y*
Raw Gley Soil

Synonyms: The designation gley (Russian folk name, WYSSOTZKI 1900) referred originally to layers with ground-water precipitations but now refers to strongly waterlogged, reduction horizons in general. Gley soils are formations consisting of gley horizons.

General Specification: Soil of low pore space characterized by strong reduction and low oxidation without a distinctly differential humus horizon, with the continual or almost continual presence of impeded water within the soil right to the surface.

Characteristics:

Profile: Generally a thin, distinct (A) horizon followed by one or more G horizons of grey, bluish-grey to greenish-grey (olive green) colour, differentiated by the varying intensity of ferric hydroxide precipitation (rust flecks and channels). *Calcareous syrogley* can show one or more chalk enriched horizons (G/Ca horizons). Different levels of ground water can lead to the formation of brown rust horizons (Fe horizons).

Dynamic: Usually advanced chemical weathering with low oxidation. Iron is dissolved in the ferrous form in the carbonic acid rich soil water usually in the form of ferrous carbonate) and precipitated easily, either on contact with the air or by mixing with the high oxygen, low carbonic acid containing water, in the form of rust coloured ferric hydroxide (particularly in the plant root channels in contact with the surface soil and therefore rich in oxygen). Temporarily lower ground water levels can lead to the formation of rust horizons by allowing widespread contact with the air. Owing to the immaturity of the soil there is no structural hardening in the form of limonitic layers (page 112).

Structure: Usually dense with very low pore space. The occasionally looser structure is generally indicated by precipitations of ferric hydroxide.

Texture: Strongly gleyed soils are generally high in colloidal substances and the silt and raw clay fractions predominate.

Biology: The soil is very feebly colonized, cold and inert, and the production of organic substance is low. The humus formation is similar to raw soil humus (page 35), however the plant remains generally show peat-like browning with no cavities and no accumulation of excretal residues of arthropod sin their interiors.

BB. Anmoor-like Soils

Key for the Determination of Types.

1.   Formed on shallow sea coasts … … … … … … … … … … … … … …   5
1*.   Formed inland … … … … … … … … … … … … … … … … … … …   2
2.   Only occurring in the tundra.
                                            18.   Tundra anmoor.

2*.   Not occurring in the tundra … … … … … … … … … … … … …   3
3.   Occurring in small basins in the alpine region of high mountains covered
      with snow for a great part of the year.
                                            19.   Snow-basin anmoor.

3*.   Not confined to the alpine region of high mountains … … … … … …   4
4.   Occurring in river valleys or in the water-logged plains of meandering
      rivers or on shallow sea shores.
                                            16.   Warp anmoor.

4*.   Formed on mountain slopes on the spring line.
                                            17.   Hanging anmoor.

5.   Soil calcareous, loose with good crumb structure.
                                            20.   Chalk marsh.

5*.   Soil free from chalk, acid with one or more compacted horizons in the
      subsoil.
                                            21.   Knick marsh.

IX.   A n m o o r

16. Warp Anmoor

Synonyms: Muck, muck warp soil, river marsh soil, Wiesenboden
(cf. also page 134), lakovis (Murgoci), pitch earth (Hungarian) = for
heavy, clayey, highly dispersed forms of the Alfölds (derived from it: (13).
pitch anmoor); mineral. Bruchwaldboden (LAATSCH 1938) = for forms under
alder or mixed alder woods.

General Specification and Delimitation: Usually strongly waterlogged gley soil with blackish (often blue-blackish) to dark grey, muddy, gyttja-
like humus form with characteristic inky smell, occurring in river valleys,
on plains water-logged by meandering rivers, or on shallow lake shore.

Anmoor and peat moors are opposed formations and have therefore always
to be separated. Anmoors, excluding dystrophic transition forms (*dystrophic
anmoor*) are active, while peat moors are raw, inactive humus formations.
To be further distinguished are *chalk rich and chalk deficient warp anmoors.*
Sometimes secondary anmoor-like humus formations can occur on other soil
forms.

---

*) See note on page 135.

Characteristics:

Profile: In humid conditions, generally strikingly dark A horizons some-times of considerable thickness, which pass gradually over into grey, bluish or greenish gley horizons (AG soil). Earlier ground water levels can lead to the formation of extensive rust horizons (Fe horizons) which not infrequently can harden like stone into compact limonite layers (raseneisenstein) impe-netrable to roots.

Humus Form: Anmoor. Humus mineral rich, gyttja-like, whereby large quantities of residues from prolifically growing, moisture loving higher plants serve directly as raw material for humification. Microscopic examination shows that the humus layer consists of loose mineral granules and finely divided, continually enriched, well-humified excretal remains of aquatic animals. Dried-out anmoor changes gradually into mull, aided by a richly developed earthworm fauna (mull gley soils, also chernosem-like warp soils or brown warp soils).

Dynamic: Intense chemical weathering, particularly if acid. The iron complexes become freed by weathering and owing to lack of oxygen, go into solution in the form of ferrous iron; it is therefore very mobile and is precip-itated irreversibly on contact with oxygen rich water or with the air, in the form of brown ferric hydroxide (rusty channels, flecks, and layers).

Biology: With very wet oxygen deficient soils, anaerobic decomposition of the organism remains; among the soil fauna aquatic animals predominate. Chalk and nutrient rich anmoor ((14). *Eutrophic warp anmoor*) is particularly active and shows good decomposition and humification. In periods of less heavy water-logging their biology approaches that of land humus forms.

Phenology: The soil generally shows an alternation of water-logging and moderate water content. In the wet periods (especially in winter and spring) the level of impeded ground water or upper soil water reaches right to the surface and temporarily above. In mid-summer and autumn many soils dry up.

Texture: Easily silted up, loamy and clayey soils are frequent and usually the causes of the water-logging.

17. *Hanging Anmoor*

Synonyms: Springline anmoor, lush anmoor.

General Specification: Generally permanently waterlogged mineral soil with blackish anmoor-like humus formation in the region of ground-water outflow (spring-line) on mountain slopes.

Characteristics:

Profile: The A horizons only attain moderate depths (5-15 cm.) at first; the upper parts of the underlying gley horizons often show a considerable eluviation of iron, so that when dry, they are almost white.

Humus Form: In strongly water-logged soils with ground water permanently visible in small depressions in the surface, well developed anmoor almost approaching the gyttja form, and in less heavily water-logged soils transition formations to mull.

Dynamic: Iron goes into solution as ferrous iron and is highly mobile. With the outflow of the water there generally follows a considerable lateral movement of iron, which is precipitated as red ferrous hydroxide in pools and runnels, some distance from the point of outflow.

18. Tundra-Anmoor

Synonyms: Swampy tundra soil.

General Specification: Water-logged soil of the treeless tundra only free from ice in summer, with muddy dystrophic anmoor formation.

Characteristics:

Profile: The soil is formed above the permanently frozen layer (tjäle layer). Under the blackish, blackish-brown, bluish to bluish-grey, generally shallow A horizon one finds one or more usually light grey coloured gley horizons. Above the frozen layer they have such a high water content as to be almost fluid.

Vegetation: In very moist swampy places with dygyttja-like anmoor Carex species, *Comarum palustre, Menyanthes trifoliata,* which are later formed by mosses. Less swampy locations show strong mossy and lichen rich plant covers, in which however Sphagnum species are missing or unimportant. Frequent are *Betula nana,* arctic willows and other tundra shrubs.

Humus Form: Dystrophic anmoor, characterized by a less intense decomposition, and the presence of comminuted, undecomposed plant remains and by a much lower content of well humified coprogenic constituents than in the eutrophic anmoor of the temperate zone. Similar shallow dystrophic anmoors are found in swampy areas of the alpine region in the high mountains of Central and Southern Europe (Alps, Sierra Nevada).

Mud Explosions: The lower pasty-fluid part of the gley horizon lying above the permanently frozen tjäle layer, with rapid freezing of the upper topsoil can come under so much pressure, that it is forced out from the surface through weaker parts of the soil cover (so-called earth-springs, A. DE

W. L. KUBIENA

QUERVAIN 1920). The ejected soil mass is spread over the anmoor in striking, light coloured flecks.

19. Snow Basin Anmoor
Alpine Snow Basin Soil

General Specification: Slightly anmoor-like soil usually with espalier willows growing in it, in small basins of the upper grass heath region of the Central Alps, characterized by a long snow covering.

Characteristics:

Profile: The blackish to dark grey humus horizons are about 3-5 cms. in depth and are followed by several gley horizons usually blue-grey in colour with more or less numerous rust flecks. The profile frequently has a laminated structure, due to the frequent deposition of erosion sediments in the snow basins, arising from strong undercutting of the slopes.

Phenology: The soil is frozen and covered with snow for the greater part of the year, which remains longer in the basins than on the slopes. In early summer it becomes free from snow and only then begins to thaw out. This produces water-logging for some time and the humus is then pasty and muddy. After the soil has become completely free from ice, it almost always exhibits a certain excess of moistness but no lasting water-logging.

Plant Cover: Generally dense, very low, horizontal trelliswork of *Salix herbacea*. The plant cover does not die when the soil freezes up. In low lying snow basins the anmoor-like character of the soil is lost and the humus approaches a mull-like moder form, the vegetation altering to a rich, herbacious alpine turf.

Texture: Mostly silty to silty-sandy textures which may contain varying amounts of gravel and fine rock debris.

X. Marsh
Marsh Soil

Synonyms: Sea marsh soil, sea marsh earth, coastal marsh soil, polder soil, klei soil, Koogsboden, Marschboden (North German folk name, STELZNER 1828), Mar *) (Low German).

General Specification: Shallow sediments of the North European coast converted naturally or artificially into land, resulting in a more or less anmoor-like gley soil.

---

*) All the above names are derived from the same stem, the Latin word «mar» and therefore should refer exclusively to «marine soils».

20. Chalk Marsh

General Specification: Chalk, nutrient and humus rich, usually anmoor-like, fertile coastal marsh soil with good crumb structure.

Characteristics:

Profile: Humus horizon dark grey when wet, grey if dry, deep, loose, with stable crumb structure passing into a uniform light grey, calcareous, gley horizon with few rust flecks. Iron sulphide enriched underground layers are called Maibolt, exposed to air they pulverize to powder earth.

Dynamic: With the lowering of the ground water and the washing out of the sea salts, the marsh soils become very fertile. At the same time the chalk whose presence is due to the high content of mussel shell remains, begins to be dissolved and is washed down into the deeper soil layers. With increasing removal of the chalk there always follows a stronger precipitation of ferrous hydroxide in the form of rust flecks and channels.

Humus Form: Predominately anmoor, with progressive development of transitions to mull ((15). *Mull marsh*).

21. Knick Marsh
Knick Marsh Soil

Synonyms: Knick-Crack, (C. L. WHITTLES 1928).

General Specification and Delimitation: Chalk free, nutrient deficient marsh soils of low fertility with strong subsoil compaction due to deposition of colloidal material.

Transition formations to the *chalk marsh* are designated as moderately to completely *decalcified marsh*.

Characteristics:

Profile: In normal profiles besides a generally grey to brownish A horizon, there is an unusually dense, differently coloured subsoil, almost always strongly rust flecked, which can be up to 1 meter thick and is known as knick. The underlying soil is frequently calcareous and rich in nutrients and in this case is known as cooling earth, mixing earth, or with sandy texture, as blue sand *).

Dynamic: Generally accumulation of precipitates of ferric hydroxide is formed with age. The soil is further decalcified and acid to a considerable depth, the colloids peptize and form an extraordinarily dense subsoil known as knick. The *knick marsh* does not only preserve its gley character but the low aeration and water-logging may become considerably accentuated.

---

*) It is frequently mixed with the surface soil to improve it (cooling, blue sand amelioration).

Quality of the Top-Soil : The top-soil has a low capacity for crumb formation, easily silts up and hardens, shows low permeabilty to air and is only workable at a definite water content.

Kinds of Knick Formation : The knick producing water-logging has an extraordinarily dense structure, and when dry, is as hard as rock. Although it is very difficult for plant roots to penetrate, it is intersected by numerous old root channels encrusted with ferric hydroxide. Samples of knick give a highly peptized suspension in water, which settles very slowly. The various kinds of knick can be divided most easily according to colour and are named accordingly. The strongly oxidized **brown knick** contains a large amount of precipitated ferric hydroxide in the form of rust channels, flecks and nests. The **red knick** is a strongly iron-enriched band occasionally of a striking red colour, while the **grey knick** is characterized by low oxidation. Especially to be feared is the tenacious **blue knick** which is recognized by its particularly dense structure, low water permeability and lack of oxygen. The **white knick** is strikingly light coloured, with a ground mass of low iron content, but in which intense precipitation of iron has concentrated in the form of small rust flecks and rounded concretions. The **black knick** is coloured by colloidal humus. It too is dense, tenacious, penetrated by numerous root channels but with no living roots. Its colour is usually deep black, when dry it is hard and still of a black to dark grey colour. Frequently it appears as a thin layer in other kinds of knick and is then called **black tape.** Occasionally a variety of knick with light and dark laminations can be observed.

BC. Semi-Terrestrial Peat Soils

Key to the Determination of Types and Sub-types.

1. Surface layer of well preserved peat, humus formation either still living or without showing any real transformation 2

1*. Soils derived from old, «dead» peat formations 4

2. Occurring in the tundra.
                              23. *Tundra moss* (**tundra peat moor**).

2*. Not occurring in the tundra 3

3. Moor arising on dead low moor or nutrient-deficient mineral soils with a raw humus-like peat formation, generally produced from wood-bark and needle remains of coniferous woods. Occurring in region of podsols.
                              XI. Carr (**transition wood moor**).

3*. Moor with usually slightly convex or flat hill topped surface, built up primarily of white moss peat. Occurring in regions of podsols.
                  22. **Sphagnum high moor of the podsol zone.**

4. Peat layer relatively shallow, generally with dense vegetation cover of raw humus forming dwarf shrubs. Mineral subsoil consisting of a light grey

to whitish coloured bleached horizon and dark to blackish brown coloured humus enriched horizon (ortstein or orterde).

27. *Peat-podsol.*

4*. Mineral subsoil not consisting of bleached and humus enriched horizons. 5
5. Surface layer extensively decomposed, occasionally strongly water-logged and then pasty and impassable 6
5*. Ground water level continuously lowered. Surface layer not pasty, humus formation loose, always rich in well-formed droppings of terrestrial animals. Moder smell.

25. *Peat moder-ranker.*

6. When wet, gyttja-like, if dried-out, earthy, easily worked.

24. *Peat anmoor.*

6*. Peat strongly decomposed, consisting almost entirely of highly peptized humus substance. In semi-moist condition pitchy, on drying out breaking down into blackish brown, sharp-edged, brittle aggregates.

(16) Pitchy peat anmoor.

XI. Carr
(East Anglian, Whittles 1928, Fraser 1943)

Synonyms: Transition moor soil, intermediate peat moor.

General Specification: Moor soil with a peat formation similar to raw humus, usually rich in wood, bark and cone remains of coniferous woods. It generally arises as a transition form between low moors or dystrophic mineral soils and high moor.

Characteristics:

Profile: The soil is characterized by a drenched, very mossy A_0 horizon built up either on a dead low moor (page 98), a buried forest *podsol* (type XL), a *semi-podsol* (type XXXIX), or the A/C_1 horizon of a *dystrophic ranker* (No. 52).

Humus Form: In the initial stage similar to raw humus, but with increasing water-logging peat mosses develop. These exclude the air and produce an increasingly peat-like humus form, characterized by the well preserved fragments of bark, wood and branches and whole cones and at the same time by the increasing thickness of the A_0 horizon.

Biology: Low level of soil life, strong repression of land fauna due to excen of water, acidity and exclusion of air, starving and gradual dying of the woods with replacement by thick cushions of peat moss.

Plant Cover: It the first place Scots fir, spruce and mixed woods of birch and conifers, with a luxuriant dwarf shrub layer and dense soil layer rich in moss and lichen, in which Sphagnums gradually dominate.

Occurrence: Particularly in virgin forest podsol and wooded tundra regions of North and North-eastern Europe. In the podsolized regions of Central Europe, only in restricted areas.

Characteristics of old transition moor peats: Old transition moor peats, in general buried under thick Sphagnum peat layers, are usually little decomposed and sink little on drainage. They are easy to recognize by the numerous completely intact tree remains of the forests from which they were derived, the dominating species being very apparent. Pine forest peat has a bright reddish colour when fresh, after drying becoming dark brown to blackish and crumbling easily. Admixtures of birches are easily determined by their white bark residues which are difficult to decompose.

XII. M o s s
(High Moor. Whittles 1928)
22. *Sphagnum Moss of the Podsol Zone*

Synonyms: High moor, raised moss (FRASER 1943), white moss peat moor, bleached moss peat moor, supra-aquatic moss moor, soft-water moor, precipitation moor; Moos (Southern German, plural Möser), heath moor = = «dead» Sphagnum moor with raw humus cover of heather. Oligotrophic peat moor (Koppe): according to the usual soil science nomenclature the designation dystrophic peat moor would be more advantageous. See also the particular method of designation in limnology.

General Specification: A moor formation primarily due to the mossing over of woods, formed on dead transition wood peat by the accumulation of rain water, consisting predominantly of peat moss covers of unusually high water capacity. The resulting soil formation is extremely acid, very mineral and nutrient deficient, and very inert biologically.

Characteristics:

Profile: The profile varies enormously according to location, age and type of formation. Young profiles generally show a «living» peat moss layer over buried transition peat. Old profiles consist of a living peat moss layer often several meters thick over dead peat moss layers. These can be recognized by the upper light brown coloured white peat («younger moss peat») and deep brown to blackish coloured black peat («older moss peat»), which lie, in general, over transition moor peat. According to the kind of origin, immediately underneath are to be found either superficial remains of a buried dystrophic mineral soil, like a *podsol* (see also *peat podsol*, No. 27), a podsolic brown earth, a *dystrophic ranker,* etc., or buried layers of a low moor. On «dead» *) superficially dried out Sphagnum peat moors, raw humus plants

---

*) «Dead» means here only the cessation of development of the peat moss layer, not of soil life and soil development in general.

develop (*Erica tetralix, Pinus montana, Pinus silvestris, Calluna vulgaris*, etc.) which lead to the formation of raw humus horizons.

Vegetation : On «living» wet high moor, this consists almost exclusively of peat mosses, together with usually only a few flowering plants such as *Menyanthes trifoliata, Comarum palustre, Scheuchzeria palustris*, a few Carex species, later clumps of cotton grass (*Eriophorum vaginatum*), etc. In many high moor types (East European) there remains a thin stand of trees (white pine).

Biology . «Living» high moor peats owing to their low aeration, strong soaking, coldness, nutrient and base deficiencies and extreme acidity, belong to the most inert and lifeless of humus forms. The decomposition and humification not only of the Sphagnum plants, but of all the organism and residues contained in the moor, is extremely slow.

Dynamic : With regard to movements of substances, the primary one in old, less strongly percolated peat profiles is that of acid, deep brown coloured humus sols. The downward movement of the percolating water produces eluviation in the upper part of the profile and a strong enrichment in the lower black peat layers (which does not always show any appreciably higher rate of decomposition than the white peat layers). Old, usually thin peat layers but still producing considerable quantities of humus sols, which if on sandy mineral soil, can exert a strong bleaching effect (see *peat podsol*, No. 27).

Phenology : The high moisture content reaching to a considerable depth produces a colder soil climate, a later spring and, in the warm part of the year, a retardation of night frosts. Also the thawing out of the soil frozen in winter occurs late, which, with the surface water-logging of the moor, produces a considerably delayed start to the growing season. The severest water-logging of the moors is seen in spring; the relatively strongest drying out in early autumn. The occurrence of a series of extremely dry or wet years can have a distinct influence on the water content, vegetation and external appearance of the moor.

Surface Forms : Most Sphagnum moors have a watch glass arched to flat hill-topped surface with strongly articulated micro-relief. This is the basis primarily of the different rates of growth of the peat moss, produced by the ensuing local variations of ecological conditions. In places where the moss cover has died and the moor has ceased to grow *depressions* (Schlenken) rich in algae and lichens or bare of vegetation are formed, while in places with particularly strong growth, so-called *hillocks* (Bulten) result. These dry out easily however and are colonized by heathers, leading to peat moder, or raw humus-like formations. *Moor eyes* (Kolke, Blänken) are pools in the high moor now filled with rainwater, usually rich in humus sols. Their banks are raised by further growth of moor peat and their beds show formation of *dy* (page 89). *Runnels* (Rüllen) are water paths by which the surplus moor water runs off the moor surface. These accumulate often also on the wet edge of high moors, the *lagg* (Swedish) or border swamp. In both, Rüllen and lagg, low moor-like peat formations are found.

Characteristics of the fresh moss peat layer: This is loose, yellowish coloured with the individual undecomposed moor plants easily recognizable (plate I). It contains 15-20 times its own weight of water, which can be squeezed out from it as in a sponge and is colourless. The mass shrinks little on drying, remains soft and becomes light yellow to pure white in colour. On re-wetting it takes up more than 10 times its own weight of water.

Characteristics of buried young moss peat (white peat): The moss is light brown, has a more compressed structure, and can be easily cut when dry *). Even then, it is still not hard, although no longer elastic and easily compressed. The peat shrinks little on drying but nevertheless reabsorbs water strongly. The various small moss plants are recognizable easily with a magnifying glass (plate I).

Characteristics of older moss peat (black peat): A peat layer of a red brown to blackish colour when wet, frequently buried under a 0.5 to 2 m. thick cover of young moss peat and which is either strongly decomposed (dygyttja-like) or consists only of compressed brown red coloured moss remains, little decomposed, but strongly impregnated by deep brown humus sols which can be easily shown in a thin section (plate I). With the naked eye, the moss remains are scarcely perceptible but those of cotton grass can be recognized distinctly. On drying the mass shrinks strongly (from 1/3 to 1/6 of its volume). It is deep dark brown to almost black, becomes as hard as rock and re-absorbs water with difficulty **). In the thin section, many black peats show a leafy structure (plate I).

Other peat forms in high moor regions: Differences in local conditions produce a strong admixture of other high moor plants, giving rise to local peat forms, which can also be found in buried moor profiles in the form of nests or thin layers. The most important are *Eriophorum* peat and *Scheuchzeria* peat. The *Eriophorum* peat consists predominantly of remains of the brown, tough, fibrous, leaf sheaths of *Eriophorum vaginatum* and is easily recognized by them. It is extraordinarily tough and difficult to decompose. On the other hand, the *Scheuchzeria* peat is easy to decompose (after draining, it forms better soils for cultivation, than the other kinds of high moor peat). It is composed mainly of the residues of *Scheuchzeria palustris* and has a similar external appearance to sedge peat but from which it is easily distinguished by the thin leaved, cutanous scales and by the numerous

---

*) This peat is extensively used technically and is recognized by insect collectors as a base for specimens.
**) Known as fuel peat.

tubular rhizomes, which, although glossy like reeds, are narrow and yellowish red with closely-spaced hairy nodes.

Condition after drainage : Due to its low rate of decomposition and generally unfavourable lowness in nutrients, strong acidity, coldness, dense structure properties Sphagnum peat produces a sufficiently fertile soil only very slowly and at great expense. The most unfavourable as parent material is black peat, exposed by peat cutting. With drainage and cultivation, the high moor settles down considerably, becomes less acidic, more animated and forms a loose top soil. The most frequent and favourable humus formation produced in this way is a peat moder (page 124).

Occurrence : In podsol regions, characterized by a cool and moist climate, parent rocks containing few nutrients and developing a strong raw humus formation. It is very widespread in North and North-east Europe, less important in Central Europe (here it is found partly in the podsolic brown earth region), practically non-existent in Southern Europe.

23. Tundra Moss
Tundra Peat Moor

General Specification : Peat moor appearing in the treeless cold steppe, generally strongly articulated, frequently in the form of numerous hillocks and ridges; its profile is characterized by the presence of a frozen layer and by the absence of buried layers of transition wood peat.

Characteristics :

Profile : Recent moss moors of the tundra arise primarily by the mossing over of the raw humus layers of tundra rankers. Old moss peat moors are often found on peat converted to land with mud peat and Carex peat layers. Only isolated buried layers of transition wood peat have been found and at the same time these occur only as fossilized formations. The frozen layer comes nearer the surface in the moss moor than in the nearby mineral soils due to the isolating moss cover, and in summer is found frequently at a depth of 30-40 cm.

Biology : It belongs to the biologically most inert soil formations of the world. To the unfavourable conditions of the Sphagnum moor of the podsol zone, such as lack of nutrients and bases, acidification, wetness, low aeration, are added here a long, extremely cold winter, the presence of a permanently frozen layer, lack of light due both to the polar night and in summer the low inclination of the sun's rays and the effect of extremely intense storms. The inclement environment, especially due to frost and wind, produces a severe destruction and dismembering of the moss peat cover and gives rise to the varied surface configuration.

Peat hillock formation : Recent moors generally have a strongly articulated surface but usually a relatively slight depth. Old peat moss moors form a landscape, specially in level places, of numerous closely spaced rows of hillocks and ridges of varying form and size (Palsmoor, peat hillock tundra). The hillocks (palsat) *) and ridges (pounut) are up to 3 m. and more high (hillocks of 7 m. have been recorded too) with a base of 2-25 m. The high forms are nearly always hillocks with circular bases. The narrow, deepened channels (rimpis) between the hillocks are usually strongly water-logged.

Vegetation : The peat forming vegetation to a great extent consists of sphagnum species (especially *Sphagnum fuscum*) although other moss genera may occur as peat-forming agents (*Dicranum, Polytrichum* species, etc.). In the moss cushions other tundra plants grow such as the crowberry (*Empetrum nigrum*), *Vaccinium uliginosum, Rubus chamaemorus,* the birches *Betula alba* and *Betula nana,* etc. The moss covers sometimes become overgrown with lichens, which often gives the surface of the hillocks a light to whitish hue.

Quality of the peat layer : The tundra moss peats generally show extraordinary compact growth and dense structure. The Dicranum peats form particularly dense, felted masses, which even when fresh can be cut easily. There are many transition forms permeated with dwarf shrubs, from the moss peats to the true raw humus formations which in the literature are sometimes described as «peats», but from which they must be carefully separated (cf. *tundra ranker,* No. 53).

Appendix to Section BD: Semi-Terrestrial Soil Formations on Old Peat Moors

24. Peat Anmoor

General Specification and Delimitation : Soil formation derived from partially drained peat layer with strongly fluctuating water level and anmoor-like humus form developed under the influence of a luxuriant new plant cover.

It differs from the *peat gyttja* (page 103) in that in contrast to the *peat anmoor,* the *peat gyttja* is formed exclusively *under water* and without any real addition of fresh land plant residues.

Characteristics :

Profile : *Peat anmoor* can be formed from very different kinds of peat. In all cases it shows a well humified, generally deep black to blackish brown

---

*) Finnish, singular Palsa.

coloured A horizon, above a little decomposed C_0 horizon *), which forms the parent material. Under this, various buried peat layers (D_0 horizons) *) can be found, which only, however, serve as sub-strata.

Humus Form: This is similar to the mineral *anmoor* (page 111) but is distinguished from it principally by the much lower mineral content frequently almost non-existent. The humus formation is not derived exclusively from the peat substance but as in the mineral anmoor, to an appreciable extent from stem, leaf and root residues of the newly developed, luxuriant vegetation cover. These residues serve as food for the soil microbes and the soil fauna producing a strong animation in the soil activity and a considerable loosening.

Plant Cover: Usually, the moors have an artificially lowered ground water level and a luxuriant grassland cover protected by human influence. *Peat anmoor* can also be formed from the vegetation of the firm wood fens.

Phenology: The top-soil is water-logged in spring and during long periods of rain, while in summer and autum it is free from ground water. When water-logged the humus is muddy and almost impassable, when dried-out earthy, crumbly and generally well aerated.

Biology: The yearly alternation of water-logging and drying out strongly influences the biology, composition of the soil fauna and of the micromorphology of the humus, which, in part, still shows a strong, gyttja-like character. During the wet periods, aquatic animals predominate, but in periods of drying out in which the soil becomes well aerated, easily warmed-up and loose, land animals are more important. Besides the formless, gyttja-like excreta remains, the droppings of land anthropoda are also found, in particular the casts of earthworms by which the soil is strongly colonized. From the inert peat humus, emerges an active humus formation with good decomposition and humification. Generally fertile grassland soils are produced, particularly if the anmoor is derived from low moor peats (fen peats), Sphagnum peats generally give rise to *dystrophic anmoor* characterized by a more browny colouring, lower decomposition and the presence of many recognisable plant remains in thin sections.

25. *Peat Moder Ranker*

Synonyms: Peat earth = includes as well *peat anmoor;* moder earth (RAMANN 1911) = also includes as well *peat anmoor* and moder formations on mineral soils; vegetable moder, vegetable mould soil.

General Specification and Delimitation: Loose soil formation on

---

*) The designations A_0, C_0, D_0 denote always that layers low in minerals, composed almost entirely of organic elements, are concerned. In all cases (also in the following new soil formations) information on the kinds of peat in the various horizons is important for characterizing the soil.

drained, dead peat moors in which under the influence of a richly devoloped land fauna extensive comminution of the peat residues and increasing enrichment of droppings and complexes of droppings of land anthropoda as well as earthworms and Enchytraeidi take place.

Thin peat layers on little weathered, sandy to silty mineral layers, permanently under the influence of the activity of earthworms develop into mineral rich mull-like moder. On loamy to clayey mineral layers and low moors rich in nutrients they often develop with the formation of clay humus complexes into even genuine mull (peat mull).

Characteristics:

Profile: The drained, loose moder horizon (A horizon) rich in animal droppings contrasts strongly with the immediately underlying undecomposed or partial gyttja-like predecomposed parent peat (C_0 horizon). As peat moder can be found on very different kinds of peat, the lower part of the profile may contain, according to the previous history of the location, a series of other buried peat layers which are not C_0 horizons (parent layers) but D_0 horizons (underground layers).

Humus Form: The transformation of the peats into moder occurs in principle in the sane way as that of the litter layer in woods, only in this case, far thicker moder layers are produced. In both cases it occurs through enrichment of excreta of a similar kind. The droppings are usually easily recognizable by their form of which small, short cylinders dominate strongly.

Biology: The transformation of the humus form to a true terrestrial form, dominated by land organism, is almost complete. The transition layers are richly colonized and normally show good decomposition and humification. Only moss moor peats may form relatively inert moder formations. In general the soil is considerably deacidified, with favourable water and air contents, loose with an easily warmed-up surface layer in summer. and it is not exposed to such strong cooling and to night frosts as the wet moor soils.

(16). Pitch Peat Anmoor
Pitch Peat Moor *)

General Specification and Delimitation: Peat moor strongly decomposed and humified in the top soil with low air content and tendency to water-logging and silting up, dominated by coprogenic elements which are moulded into a more or less homogeneous deep brown to blackish, pitchy mass and this breaks down superficially into small angular fragments on freezing-up or drying-out.

Most kinds of pitch peats are low in minerals, although mineral rich forms

---

*) The expression pitch peat was also used by AARNIO for peat formations rich in bitumen which should be designated bituminous peats.

do occur, in particular when transitions of peat layers of low thickness on mineral, primarily clay-rich strata are concerned. The soil, in this special case finally becomes a mineral *anmoor* (see pitch earth, page 111). The normal pitch peat has a certain external similarity to the alpine pitch rendsina (No. (37)). Especially with sediments of *pitch rendsina* which have been washed down to small depressions and share its lack of minerals and prevalence in coprogenic elements). The *pitch rendsina* however is a humus formation of completely different origin, different aeration and water conduction. Both soils have a strongly pronounced but completely different micromorphology and this allows the pitch peat to be easily distinguished also from other peat transformation forms.

Characteristics:

Profile: The normal profile consists of a strongly contrasting, blackish to dark brown A horizon, pasty when moist, with a slightly weathered transition horizon (A/C$_0$ horizon) and an undecomposed or very little decomposed parent peat layer (C$_0$ horizon). Under this, several more buried peat horizons (D$_0$ horizons) may follow. The A horizons occasionally attain a considerable thickness.

General Micromorphology: The pitch peat moor is essentially a strongly decomposed peat moor, i. e. the decomposition has proceeded excessivly (or has been brought to that step by human influence) so that the humus horizon consists practically only of peptized humic substances and no plant residues, i. e. it is composed almost entirely of binding substances with no structure supporting framework (fine skeleton). Therefore the soil formation becomes *pitch peat anmoor*, only when a foregoing peptization of the coprogenic masses has occurred. Then, the strongly swelling humus formation becomes remarkably dense in structure, impervicus to water with practically no porespace, and breaks down by loss of water and consequent large volume reduction into hard, sharp-edged, bony aggregates (plate 11). The survey of a thin section shows that the interior is composed of an almost homogeneous, deep brown mass with extremely dense structure in which the only variation of colour intensity is due to highly localized movements of substances. With transition forms, some plant remains, very small always, are embedded in the highly peptized mass.

Biology: Although no exact investigation has been made, a considerable reduction in the intensity of colonization by small animals can be assumed.

Phenology: The humus formation shows great differences in quality and behaviour during the course of the year, within a series of extremely low or very high rainfall years or even with different agricultural treatments. In general the *pitch peat anmoor* arises from an extensively decomposed peat moder. Due to the strong dispersion of the coprogenic masses a dense and impermeable structure is produced, which allows rain water to accumulate and gives rise to secondary water-logging. However, this occurs only during long periods of rain or after the snow has melted, while in dry summers the farreaching drying out and accompanying loosening of the soil can lead to the formation of aggregates.

Blowing Earth due to Bare Frost: Instead of the spring water-logging, after a winter with little snow and with strong bare frosts, on uncultivated soil another phenomenon may occur. The frozen surface layer, which has started the winter comparatively dry, frequently adquires during the winter characteristics akin to the arctic struture soils, i. e. it breaks up into polygonal fragments separated from each other by ice-filled fissures. The fragments are extremely small (only a few millimeters in diameter) so at first their appearance is not striking and only becomes distinct on examination with a magnifying glass or microscope using reflected light. In this condition the soil forms a coherent mass which breaks up in the spring, provided it is not strongly rewetted, into numerous loose aggregates which can be easily blown about by the wind. This blowing earth in spring which is a very striking phenomenon, wiping out cultivations, filling ditches, forming dunes and capable of doing a great deal of damage, is initially moist (blackening of house walls against which the wind blows) and dries out only gradually. Its formation occurs also in an exactly analogous way with strongly swelling mineral *anmoors* (pitch earth, *pitch anmoor*, No. (13)) particularly those with clay binding substances rich in colloidal silicic acid.

Development of Puffiness: Strong drying out can have a much more radical effect on the soils. This appears very strikingly with arable crops (especially market gardening) in hot summers with low rainfall, particularly after a series of dry years. The entire top soil breaks down into small, hard, completely dessicated, sharp-edged aggregates, which have practically lost their ability to reabsorb water. With the irreversible drying out of the binding substance, the soil loses its ability to recement the loose structural elements and with it the possibility to form crumbs. It becomes a pulverized mass, easily blown about by the wind and can cause extensive damage to the soil and crops. Such moors are designated as becoming puffy.

Puffiness occurs easily too with peats strongly impregnated by humus sols (black peats). Here too, with strong drying out there is seen the formation of numerous, small, dry fissures and the splitting up into small, sharp-edged aggregates, very difficult to re-moisten, almost incapable of swelling, which appear in thin sections as blackish brown to sepia brown coloured fragments (plate I).

26. Dystrophic Peat Ranker

Synonyms. Heath peat moor = for forms with heath vegetation.

General Specification: Dystrophic ranker characterized by raw humus formation on old high moor peats with lowered ground water level, under a cover of raw humus forming plants, especially under heath shrubs, knee pine or coniferous woods.

Characteristics:

Profile: Formation of raw humus horizons, occasionally thick, whose mass consists partly of old peat remains, but mainly of the residues of the raw plant cover with which it is permeated and overgrown. These A_0 horizons form a blackish to dark brown, dense, felted reticulum of easily recognisable stem, root and leaf remains (with coniferous woods also cones). They arise mostly on old high moors with lowered ground water level and dead moss peats.

Usually the mineral underground layer lies at such a depth, that it can only be reached by a peat borer and therefore serves only as a sub-stratum. The parent material forms the uppermost moss peat layer immediately under the A_0 horizon and is called the C_0 horizon. Following it are the buried peat layers, known as D_0 horizons or organic sub-strata. The underlying layers of the mineral sub-stratum are merely D horizons (designated as D_1, D_2 horizons).

Plant Cover: In North and North-east Europe, primarily heath or coniferous vegetation. With *peat rankers* in heath areas the raw humus forming heathers, *Calluna vulgaris, Erica tetralix, Andromeda polifolia, Empetrum nigrum,* etc., are the most important. With *peat rankers* in woods, Scoth pines, spruces, and partly beeches are the main agents. In the region of the Alps, *peat rankers* are very widespread under dense dwarf pine cover with *Rhodendrom ferugineum, Loiseleuria procumbens,* etc., and show especially thick raw humus covers.

Biology: The lowering of the ground water level and the consequent drying out of the moor surface causes the peat mosses to die. The formation of ranker begins under the heathers on the hillocks (page 119) and gradually spreads right over the whole moor. The resulting fresh humus layer is composed of crude-fibre rich, protein deficient plant residues containing substances impeding disintegration, but is more easily warmed-up and better aerated than the original moor. It shows low decomposition and incomplete humification and is low in nutrients. Although strongly acid, it is essentially less acid than the young high moors. In spite of feeble colonization by soil animals, the humus is characterized already by distinct land fauna.

27. *Peat Podsol*
(Frosterus 1912)

Synonyms: Peaty podsolic soil (J. WITYN 1911).

General Specification: Soil characterized by intense eluviation due to humic acids with the formation of a light grey to whitish impoverished horizon and a deep brown partly rust coloured enriched horizon and a lowered groundwater level, occurring generally on the tapering margins of old «dead» Sphagnum peat moors, rich in humus sols, generally with a plant cover of new-humus forming heather.

Characteristics:

Profile of iron-deficient varieties ((*17*) *Iron-deficient Peat Podsol*): Generally a superficial layer of raw humus (A_0 horizon), produced by raw-humus forming plants (*Calluna vulgaris, Erica tetralix,* etc.), is followed by a blackish peat layer (A_1 horizon). Their thickness varies considerably, but it is limited by the fact that for intense eluviation of the mineral soil, the humus horizon must be easily permeable to rain water. However, its thickness is usually greater than that of the average podsol, although raw humus layers only 5-10 cm. thin have been known to have a strong eluviation effect. There is a sharp boundary between the peat layer and the underlying, usually strongly percolated, bleached sand layer (A_2 or A_e horizon). Further division of the profile depends in the first place on ground water conditions and on the composition of the mineral parent material. For the formation of ungleyed enriched horizons, the normal ground-water level must always be below this. Very frequently an iron deficient, humus enriched B_h horizon is formed, of a blackish brown, coffee brown to light brown colour. It is either compacted (ortstein) or earthy (orterde) and corresponds exactly to the B_h horizon of *humus podsols.* Microscopically, its fabric consists of rounded, humus coated mineral grains (almost all quartz grains), which are bound to each other by their surface layers (plate II). The cavities between the grains are empty. The mineral parent material consists almost entirely of bare quartz sand, so that the humus coatings which surround the mineral grains of the ortstein as homogeneous coloured layers are extremely low in iron, which can be easily demonstrated by ignition of the humus substances before microscopic investigation. Owing to the lack of iron in the parent material, there is never the formation of a morphologically distinctly recognisable gley horizon under the ground-water level.

Profile of iron-humus podsol variety ((*18*). *Iron-humus Peat Podsol*): If the mineral parent material contains iron, then not only do the humus hulls of the ortstein (orterde) layer contain precipitated iron, but also the intense formation and deposition of eluvial masses rich in iron leads to the development of an iron-enriched layer (sesquioxide enriched layer) below the humus ortstein layer. This B_s horizon appears either as a brown seam or as a well-developed ochre to rust coloured layer. Further, below the ground-water level, the formation of a morphologically distinct gley horizon may occur.

Dynamic : Formation of considerable quantities of humus sols in the peat layer, leading to strong brown colouration and humus enrichment of the leachings. The humus sols are not only highly mobile themselves but also form a protective colloid for the mineral colloidal substances which become peptized and thus to a great extent eluviated.

Biology : Due to poverty of nutrients, strongly acid reaction, cold soil climate and the decomposition impeding substances in the humus, the soil is feebly colonized, inactive, with low decomposition and incomplete humification.

Occurrence : In old high moor regions of North and North-East Europe.

BD. Salt soils

Strongly salt enriched soils formed by ground-water with high content of water-soluble salts or soils derived immediately from them. The so-called *primary salt soils* are gley soils, mainly formed by gradual transformation of former subaqueous soils (gyttja formations of the steppe lakes into semi-terrestrial soils). *Secondary salt soils* are terrestrial soils of the most diverse kind (usually steppe and semi-desert soils) which have acquired their salt soil characteristics by secondary water-logging and salt enrichment. They retain their original name but with an adjective added, e. g. «saline chernozem», «solonized chestnut brown soil», etc. The following descriptions refer to the most important primary salt soils.

Key for the Determination of Types.

1. Soil rich in salts normally with striking efflorescences of salts on the surface in the dry part of the year or salt deposition within the soil near the surface. Moist or remoistened soil samples give secondary surface efflorescences on drying out.

XIII. Solonchak.

1*. Soil with no efflorescences or precipitations of salts in the dry part of the year. Moist or remoistened samples do not give efflorescences on drying.   2

2. Soil with whitish coloured bleached horizon under the surface layer or at least with a strong eluviation of colloidal material and the formation of eluvial and illuvial horizons.

XV. Solod.

2*. Soil with no bleached horizon, strongly swelling, pasty when wet, hardening like rock when dry, frequently showing a layer of columnar separation in the lower part of the humus horizon.

XIV. Solonetz.

Explanation of plate V

1. **Solonchak** with *Atropis distans* and strongly developed layer of salt enrichment (A/Sa) and superficial salt efflorescences (Sa). Summer aspect.
2. **Solonetz** with *Artemisia pauciflora* and well developed columnar horizon (A/B$_h$).

XIII. Solonchak
(Glinka, Russian folk name)

Synonyms: Szik soil (Hungarian peasant name) and zick soil (Burgenland, Austria): both names are used also for *solonetz*; white alkali soil (HILGARD) = for *solonchak* excepting *soda solonchak* *); «structureless» salt soils (because the horizon with «columnar structure» is missing; kebir (Kirghiz name) = loose *solonchak* similar to the salt powder soil; saliter, salniter = *solonchak* with accumulation of nitrates.

General Specification: Alkaline to strongly alkaline gley soils with strong concentration of water soluble salts in the upper soil layers, due to capillary rise and evaporation of the ground water, rich in salts.

Characteristics:

Profile: A horizons of greater or lesser humus content generally of a light grey, rarely dark grey colour, above usually typical gley horizons. The greatest proportion of deposited salt is found in the surface or in a precipitation horizon within the soil (Sa horizon). With complete drying out, salt deposits are found in all parts of the profile.

Humus Form: Gyttja (if not colonized by higher plants) to anmoor (if colonized by higher terrestrial plants) with increasing tendency to transformation into mull.

Dynamic: During wet periods solution, in dry periods capillary rise and precipitation of salts in the form of superficial efflorescences (white covering of crystal needles, threads, feathers, spikes and granules), interflorescences (precipitations held in capillaries) and efflorescences in cavities. Iron is present in the mobile ferrous form and is deposited primarily as rust flecks.

Biology: The soils are characterized by a very typical natural flora and fauna according to salt content and location. The soil life undergoes besides a periodic alternation of under-water and land «phases». Decomposition and formation of humus is good in general. The synthesis of clay humus

---

*) The present American nomenclature distinguishes: saline soils = salt soils not strongly alkaline (water soluble salts > 0,2 %) and alkaline soils = strongly alkaline salt soils.

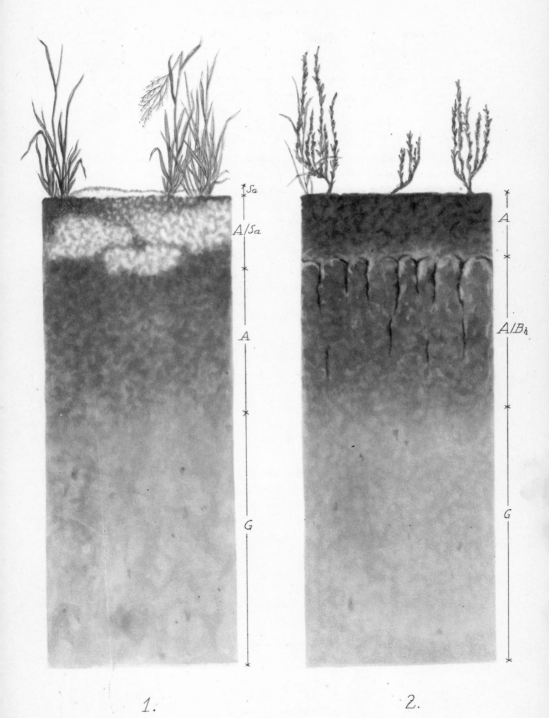

V

Sa
A/Sa
A

G

A
A/B_h

G

1.

2.

complexes is still inhibited in the gyttja and anmoor phases and increases only with advancing mull formation.

Phenology: In times of high ground water level (spring) almost all soils are covered with water and strongly water-logged. Soil surfaces not covered with water rapidly become green in the spring. In summer the vegetation turns yellow and withers, large areas are covered with white deposits of salt.

Nature of Salts: The main mass is formed of sodium sulphate, chloride and carbonate. Calcium sulphite is almost always present in greater or lesser quantities. In many cases magnesium and calcium sulphite and calcium chloride can be important.

Most Important Sub-types and Varieties: *28. Soda solonchak* (Hungarian soda szik) is a particularly extremely alkaline sub-type containing larger quantities of sodium carbonate, easily eluviated and eroded, with dark brown organic matter in solution. *29. Gipsum solonchak* contains predominantly calcium sulphate. *30. Calcium sodium solonchak* is rich in calcium salts. *31. Chalk solonchak* is characterized by a considerable quantity of calcium carbonate. *(19). Crypto-solonchak* (concealed solonchak) contains salt precipitates only in the interior of the soil at a certain distance from the surface, and is due to a deeper ground water level. *(20). Dry solonchak* *) shows a very low moisture content and strong impregnation of salt precipitates in all parts of the profile. *(21). Wet solonchak* **) rarely dries out completely and almost only superficial efflorescences are to be seen, frequently confined to prominent soil clods and plant remains.

Occurrence: *Dry solonchaks* rich in salts are frequently the final phases of development of semi-terrestrial soils of the dry steppe and desert. In the black earth zone (steppe zone) only young salt soils in the form of *solonchalks* generally appear. In humid regions salt soils are rare and only occur as young and unstable forms.

XIV. *Solonetz*

(Russian local name)

Synonyms: Clay szik soil (de SIGMOND), black alkali soil (HILGARD), structure salt soil, shokat (Kirghiz name).

General Specification and Delimitation: Slightly alkaline to neutral soil derived from solonchaks in which deep lowering of the ground water level has produced a considerable to complete washing out of the salts without,

---

*) Named by the Kirkhiz «sor».
**) Kirghiz name «chak». The designation «sas» (Turkestan, plural «sassy») refers to wet anmoor solonchak (Wiesenboden solonchak).

---

however, at the same time, removing the sodium ions adsorbed on the clay and humus substances.

34. Solonchak-solonetz designate transition formations to solonchak in which a few residues of soluble salts still remain in the top soil. These can even still produce surface efflorescences in dry periods. Especially to be distinguished are also: *32. Chalk-free solonetz* and *33. Calcareous solonetz*.

Characteristics:

Profile: The humus horizon is divided into an upper, loose part, the A horizon (occasionally divided into further sub-horizons) and a compact lower part which generally shows a typical columnar separation (columnar horizon, A/B_h horizon, in Russian literature designated as a B horizon, as its character is determined strongly by the enrichment of colloidal material from the upper A horizon). The gley horizon underlying the A/B horizon can already contain considerable quantities of washed-out salts (plate V).

Humus Form: Anmoor with tendency to mull formation.

Dynamic: The saturation of the colloids by sodium ions produces a very strong peptization of the clay and humus substances, and consequently easy setting up, low pore space, dense structure as well as strong erodability of the soil mass. Due to the dense structure, percolating moisture can only penetrate to a limited extent and this leads to the formation of the hardened, impervious columnar horizons. By changing the adsorbed ion from sodium to calcium, sodium carbonate is formed by the combination with carbonic acid.

Biology: In moist periods, the activity of aquatic organisms predominates; with increasing drying out, soil life is confined almost entirely to the fissures produced by shrinkage which are comparatively richly colonized because the strongly swelling soil mass only gives up water slowly and retains a certain moistness for a long time. Higher plants are severely restricted in growth by the dense soil structure.

Phenology: The soil in spring is a strongly dilated, thin, pasty mass, in which the upper soil water is stagnant due to the impermeable columnar layer. With increasing drying out, the soil hardens into a mass which is extremely difficult to work, with numerous fissures and when completely dried out, becomes like rock, especially in the columnar horizon.

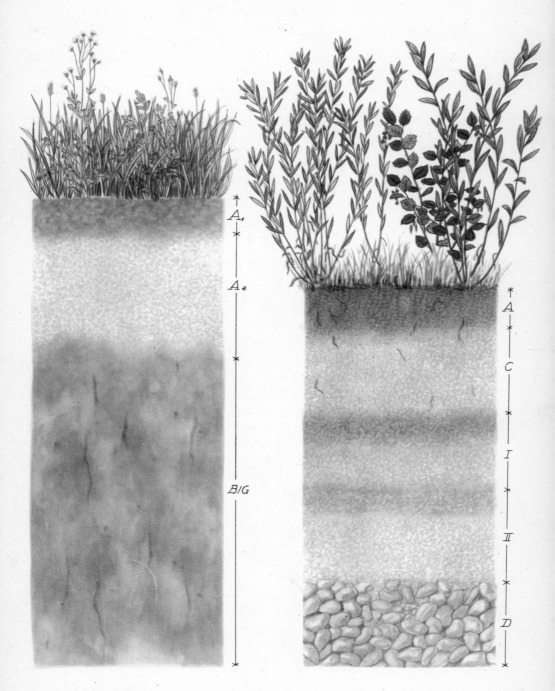

VI

1.

2.

XV. Solod
(Russian folk name)

Synonyms : Solodi, soloti, steppe bleached earth, salt earth podsol.

General Specification and Delimitation : Soil derived from solonetz in which, due to the easy eluviation of the sodium saturated colloidal material, enhanced by the protecting effect of considerable amounts of silica sols and the presence of a suitable skeletal framework in the soil structure (sufficient sand content), a gradual impoverishment of the upper soils in finely dispersed fractions and the formation of a bleached sand layer has occurred.

Solod soils are distinguished essentially from *podsols*, which also have a bleached sand layer, by the absence of raw humus layers (or dystrophic coarse moder layers), of strongly acid reaction and of the particular features of acid humic eluviation.

Characteristics :

Profile : In general an A_1 horizon low in humus is followed in the case of strongly solodized soils by a whitish bleached sand A_2 horizon (A_e horizon). This is followed by one or two B or B/G horizons, derived from gley horizons by enrichment of eluviated material and a certain oxydation (plate VI).

Humus Form : Humus deficient mull.

Dynamic : In addition to the above eluviation, there is increasing removal of the bases, which gradually leads to acidification (although only moderate) of the top soil. The weathering is accelerated, which is characterized by a higher breakdown of the silicates and the freeing of a considerable quantity of silica sols (cf. extraction with 5 % KOH as a help for the diagnosis of solodized soils, after K. GEDROITZ).

BE. Gley soils with Land Humus Formations
XVI. Gley
35. Moder Gley
Moder Gley Soil

General Specification : Soil water-logged up to the top soil, gleyed, but with no or only temporary water-logging in the humus layer which shows a mostly well humified mineral rich moder formation.

Characteristics :

Profile : A thin A horizon generally divided into a förna, F and H layer, primarily under deciduous, mixed or coniferous forests, whereas under a turf cover, a mineral rich humus horizon of more uniform composition is formed. The A horizon passes directly into a grey, bluey to greeny subsoil (G horizon).

Texture: Generally low clay content, predominately sandy to silty textures.

Biology: Proliferous plant growth, predominately in the form of deciduous, mixed or spruce forests with well developed herb layer and rich soil life, which occurs however mainly in the F and H horizons and does not reach far into the dense, gleyed, mineral soil. The soil fauna consists primarily of land animals. Earthworms, too, are quite frequent but owing to the low clay content a clay-humus complex formation generally does not occur. Moder gley soils under turf are found most frequently in alpine regions.

Humus Form: Predominately well humified mull-like moder (page 39). In alpine areas, kinds of dystrophic moder rich in minerals also occur.

Associated Soil Forms: Moder gley soils can be due either to a partial lowering of the ground-water in *anmoors* or to a temperary rise in ground-water level, sufficient to create gley horizons but not anmoor humus. According to each particular case they are found either in conjunction with *anmoors* or other soil formations (raw gley soils, brown warp soils, brown earths, etc.).

36. *Mull Gley*
Mull Gley Soil

Synonyms: Wiesenboden (this name also refers to anmoor warp soils, which is its main meaning).

General Specification: AG soils with mull humus formation, always moist, but never or only temporarily water-logged in the A horizon; usually derived from *anmoor*.

Characteristics:

Profile: When derived from *warp anmoor,* generally a deep A horizon rich in humus passes directly into a gley horizon more or less strongly permeated with precipitated ferric hydroxide. Those derived from hanging gley soils generally have shallow humus horizons, with the gley character of the upper part of the G horizon usually less pronounced.

Texture: Usually high in the fine fractions, heavy and clayey.

Biology: Usually a rich soil life of land animals, including a well developed earthworm fauna in the humus horizon. With warp soils generally luxuriant plant growth, therefore fertile grassland soils. The subsoil is badly aerated and cold.

Occurrence: In the regions of streams and rivers throughout Europe, particularly extensive in formerly swampy plains of Northern Europe by widely meandering rivers, therefore (considering the external similarity and neglecting the investigation of the profile) often confused with black earths (*chernosems*) (cf. also chernosem-like warp soil or *smonitsa*).

37. *Browned Gley*
Browned Gley Soil

General Specification : Soil formation with gleyed subsoil, but already with an embryonic or distinctly pronounced groundwater-free brown (B) horizon and groundwater-free humus horizon.

Characteristics :

Profile : The normal profile consists of an A horizon, a moderately thick (B) horizon (10-40 cm.) and a deep, grey, bluish-grey to greenish-grey gley horizon. The latter frequently consists of several sub-horizons and contains a greater or lesser quantity of rust flecks and channels.

Plant Cover : In the river flats of Central and Northern Europe in general, originally deciduous woods of peduncular oaks, elms, birches, hornbeams, alder buckthorn and hazel bushes. In the moistest parts willows and poplars frequently become important. Usually luxuriant secondary meadow cover.

Biology : Top soil well aerated and soil also moist, with rich production of plant remains for humus formation, well developed terrestrial soil life and good decomposition and humification. When, however, in development from raw gleys (*syrogleys*), a new formation of humus horizons has taken place, the soil generally shows only a slight depth of humus, due to its immaturity.

Humus Form : Generally mull-like moder or mull.

Occurrence : Particularly frequent in the river flats of central and northern Europe, excluding the extreme north. Brown gley soils further are frequently formed also from hanging gley soils of the brown earth and podsol zones.

BF. Ungleyed Warp soils with Land Humus Formations

Synonyms : Warp soils *) (WHITTLES 1928, from Lincolnshire), warpes, worps. Alluvial soils **). Aueboden, Auboden.

---

*) This term and the following have been used also for similar soils with gley formation and semi-terrestrial humus forms or with absence of humus horizons (s. *rambla, syrogley*).

**) The term alluvial soils is not very advantageous, since it indicates also the time of soil formation needed for paleopedological research (=recent, actual, holocene soils, in contrast to pleistocene and tertiary soils). But also if alluvial means the kind of deposition it refers only to the parent material; thus the river deposits are alluvial but not the soil formations on them.

1. **Borovina** (rendsina-like warp soil) below dry lawn on limestone gravel (C) above limestone sand (D) (Enns Valley, Styria).
2. **Smonitza** (chernosem-like warp soil) below buckwheat field on limestone gravel (Basin of Vienna).

Soils occurring in the flats of streams and rivers and derived from their sediments. They show no signs of water-logging in their profile but are generally moist and their water content, vegetation and biology are strongly influenced by their proximity to the rivers and by their water level. Most of them are flooded temporarily by high waters. The forms beyond the influence of high waters have the character of terrestrial soils to a high degree but are distinguished from them by their different origin which is shown in their biology as well as their water relations. These differences between warp and terrestrial soils appear as much more striking in Southern Europe than in Central or Northern Europe; there the difference is fundamental. Soils without the formation of a distincly distinguishable humus horizon have already been described previously (s. raw soils, page 106).

XVII. *Paternia*[*)]
Grey Warp Soil

General Specification and Delimitation: Young, chemically little weathered AC soil generally of a light grey colour with distinctly developed humus horizon on river sediment low in chalk. Light ochre-grey forms lead over to brown warp soils are called *slightly browned paternia*. Grey warp soils with gleying in the sub-soils are called «*gleyed*» *paternia*.

Characteristics:

Profile: Generally thin A horizon (often of only a few cm. but occasionally reaching up to 15 cm. or more) which passes gradually into the underlying C horizon without a sharp boundary. If the soil occurs near the course of the river, a stratified profile with several buried A and C horizons is often produced, due to repeated deposition (plate VI).

Humus Form: Under grassland generally humus deficient mull or mull-like moder; in very young woods on river flats often shallow fine moder formations.

Dynamic: Low chemical weathering. Highly permeable, tendency to water-logging and slight gleying only in silty soils.

Biology: Definitely more active and richer in species than the raw warp

---

[*)] Derived from river Paterna in the Alpujarras (Sierra Nevada), Spain.

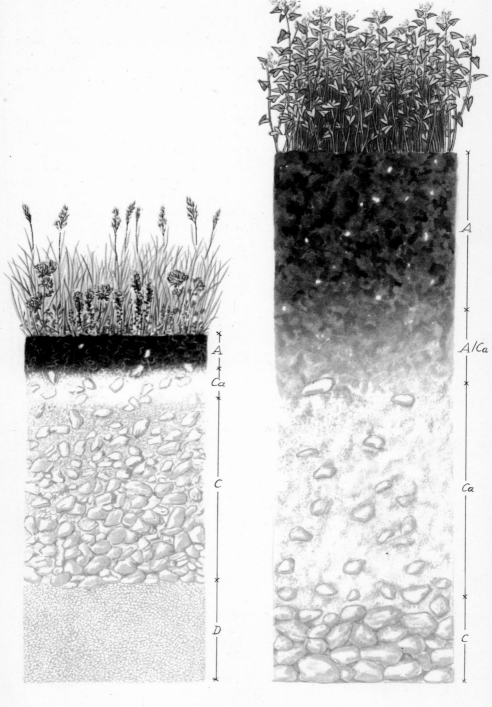

1.   2.

soil (*rambla,* type VI) from which it has been formed. Sufficiently silty or loamy soils are already colonized by earthworms.

Phenology: Frequently covered with water at high water level, at other times generally moist, only drying out in summer in locations where strong lowering of the ground water occurs.

Texture: Mostly pure to feebly loamy sand and silt soils.

XVIII. Borovina
(Polish folk name *))
Rendsina-like Warp Soil

General Specification and Delimitation: Young, chemically little weathered AC soils with distinct grey, to blackish humus horizon on calcareous river sediments.

Gleyed forms with slight gyttja-like humus formation lead over to calcareous anmoor warp soils, browned forms with slight chalk removal, to brown warp soils. Transition forms are recognized by adjective additions.

Characteristics:

Profile: With undisturbed development there is often a Ca horizon between the A and C horizons. As in the grey warp soil a stratified profile with several buried A horizons can be found occasionally.

Humus Form: Mull-like chalk moder to mull with low clay content.

Dynamic: Chemical weathering impeded by the high chalk content. Increasing removal of chalk from the surface layer and enrichment of $CaCo_3$ below the humus horizon.

Biology: Within the usually thin humus layer, rich soil life with good decomposition and humification during the wet part of the year. Frequently covered with water at high water. Otherwise very permeable and easily dried out. In summer often tending to extreme water shortage.

Texture: Almost pure to slightly loamy, sand and pebble soils.

XIX. Smonitza
(Serbian peasant name)
Chernosem-like Warp Soil

Synonyms: *Smolnitza* (Bulgarian peasant name) = also includes chalk deficient, relatively wet soils; steppenbodenartig veränderter anmooriger Aueboden (STREMME).

---

*) In addition to rendsinas in the region of river flats, the name has been used partly also for other rendsinas; these ought not to be designated as *borovinas* in future but exclusively as *rendsinas.*

1. **Allochthonous brown vega** (brown warp soil) below meadow with two buried profiles (I and II) with lightly anmoor-like humus formation. (Pulkau Valley, Lower Austria.)
2. **Braunlehm vega** (brown loam warp soil) in two layers. In irrigation channel (above right) stratified erosion sediments assorted by grainsize. Upon them lies a fragment of the heavily cemented surface crust. (Valley of Gallego, Zaragoza, Spain.)

General Specification and Delimitation: Mostly loamy AC soils, derived from calcareous anmoor by continual lowering of the groundwater, in which the effect of water-logging can no longer be seen.

The soil is very similar to the *chernosem*, but in general is easily recognized by its occurrence in river flats and by the many transitions on the one hand to anmoor warp soils and on the other hand to brown warp soils *).

Characteristics:

Profile: A horizons, occasionally of considerable thickness (up to 1/2 m. and more) pass without a sharp boundary into a whitish Ca horizon. The underlying C horizons (former G horizons) no longer show signs of gleying visible to the naked eye. Microscopically, the nature of this horizon is generally easily recognized by the various ferric hydroxide precipitates remaining from the preliminary stage of gleying, partly also the remains of aquatic organisms, especially diatomaceous shells.

Humus Form: Usually an excellent, well-crumbed mull, which scarcely permits the former anmoor character to be seen and is in no way inferior to the *chernosem* humus.

Dynamic: Chemical weathering obstructed by chalk and therefore with favourable parent material, great reserves of nutrients. No movement of colloidal substances, increasing leaching of the carbonates from the upper soil layers.

Biology: Very active fertile soil, rich in organisms, with good decomposition, humification and formation of clay-humus complexes.

Phenology: Moist in winter and spring, in summer occasionally drying out, leading to damage by drought, although not on the same scale as with the *chernosems*.

XX. *Vega*
(Huguet del Villar 1927)

Chemically strongly weathered soil in flats of streams and rivers of uniform ochre yellow, ochre brown to red colour.

---

*) The soil type already shows the characteristics of terrestrial soils to a high degree therefore for the safety of the identification reference is also made to it with *chernosem*.

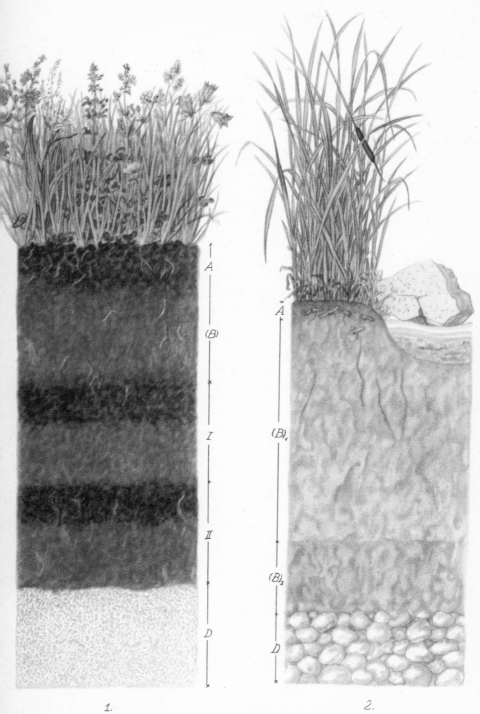

VIII

A

(B)

I

II

D

A

(B)₁

(B)₂

D

1.

2.

38. Brown Vega
Brown Warp Soil

Synonyms: Brauner Auenwaldboden (STREMME).

General Specification and Delimitation: Mature warp soil of brown to light ochre yellow colour with good weathering and oxidation which the characteristics of raw soils and ground water soils (grey raw colours or sporadic rust flecks and channels and bluish grey to greenish reduction colours) are repressed or only to be found deep underground or have disappeared completely.

Brown warp soils can either be *autochthonous*, having developed from the earlier named warp soil forms or can be *allochthonous*, derived from the sediment of eroded brown earths in river and stream valleys *).

Characteristics:

Profile: (22). *Autochthonous vegas* (brown warp soils) are easy to recognized since they contain, besides the necessary A and B horizons Ca, C or G horizons according to maturity and type of formation.

(23). *Allochthonous vegas* (brown warp soils) show a simple profile structure in general in the form of deep, uniformly brown layers of sediments, on which the A horizon, normally of low humus content, is formed. In the immediate neighbourhood of the river bed, a stratified profile of several buried A and (B) horizons is often to be found (analogous to the stratified grey warp soils).

Humus Form: Almost always mull, well-developed, although seldom very rich in humus.

Dynamic: Good chemical weathering and clay formation, generally with good aeration and favourable water relations. No movement of colloidal substances, strong leaching of the carbonates. In still existing, deep lying gley horizons, reduction and movement of iron in ferrous form.

Biology: Stable and balanced biology, with good decomposition and humification of the organisms remains, usually with good development of an earthworm fauna required for mull formation. The balanced water conduction generally allows already its extensive utilization as arable land.

Phenology: Most autochthonous brown warp soils are entirely beyond the reach of normal high waters, so that they are practically never flooded. The higher water capacity hinders strong drying out of the soil in summer, while the high permeability prevents water-logging of the upper soil horizons in wet periods.

---

*) Autochthonous brown warp soils can show extensive terrestrial soil characteristics, therefore for sureness of identification reference is also made to it with brown earths.

Texture: Owing to the intense chemical weathering and advanced clay formation, loamy texture is predominant.

39. Braunlehm Vega
Braunlehm Warp Soil

Synonyms: Gajnjatscha *) (Croat folk name = variety derived from the sediments of eroded *terra fusca*).

General Specification: Warp soil, usually with a vivid ochre yellow, ochre brown to reddish brown colour of striking intensity, with high erodability, dense structure and low water permeability, derived from erosion sediments of *terra fusca* (No. 74) or fossil *braunlehms* (type XXXIV).

Characteristics:

Profile: As the soil is always formed of deposits carried from mature soils of brow loam character, there is no C horizon. Sub-strata of the most varied kind serve only as D horizons. The A horizon is usually only of a very slight thickness with low humus content. The generally very deep (B) horizon shows the soil colour in pure form, while the A horizon is characterized by a more or less strong admixture of grey.

Structure: The soil is dense, generally strongly swelling, difficult to work, easily forming clods, on drying out hard, intersected with shrinkage fissures and frequently covered with surface crusts. Occasionally it breaks down into small, sharp edged aggregates.

Dynamic: The ferric hydroxide is peptized, protected by colloidal silicic acid, very mobile and separates out in the form of round concretions. In addition all the colloidal binding substances are capable of being easily peptized and are very mobile. The soil is generally de-calcified, slightly acid to acid.

Micromorphology: Although the soil structure is relatively young, owing to its highly active dynamics, it already shows secondary re-development of all the structural characteristics which can be determined in the original brow loam, undisturbed by erosion, from which the soils were formed. They are: uniform dispersion of the highly peptized ferric hydroxide which appears as an ochre yellow coloured ground mass in the thin section preparation (thus accounting for the strikingly vivid soil colour), numerous fluidal structures and doubly refracting streaks in the very mobile binding substances, formation of rounded, dark brown coloured concretions of ferric hydroxide, strong tendency to the formation of dense structures with low pore space.

Biology: The soil is far moister and more constant in its water relations than most European deposits of fossil *braunlehms,* beyond river valleys. This

---

*) Pronounced «gayniatsha».

is particularly noticeable in Southern Europe (Spain, Italy, Greece). Owing to the dense soil structure, the soil life is highly concentrated into the outermost surface layer (therefore also slight thickness of the humus horizon). Yet the humus form is almost always mull. Further, the dense sub-stratum generally prevents a deep root growth, which frequently can be noticeably troublesome, particularly in horticulture.

Texture : Starting from loamy sand, all kinds of textures are possible. The extreme heaviness of the soil, makes it always appear to have a finer texture than it really has. Therefore even forms with relatively high sand content have a far reaching clayey character due to their binding, plasticity and low water conduction.

Erosion forms : Braunlehm warp soils which still occur within the region of high waters are easily recognized as they show extraordinarily severe marks of erosion due to their unusually high erodability. Currents at high waters, not only cause deep channels and various other surface destructions, but also leave behind the most varied kinds of erosion sediments. The great difference of form arises because the whole of the soil structure is disintegrated by the running water into its individual constituent parts and these are laid down, sorted and divided according to particle size. According to the different water velocity, coarse constituents are deposited partly in the slowly flowing high waters and only the finest constituents in the residual pools. Thus a striking laminated fabric is often produced, in which the finest sediment, mostly concentrated on the surface, on drying out, breaks up into extremely hard «plates». Owing to the high mobility and washing out of the ferric hydroxide, these can also be completely free of iron and have a very light, occasionally almost white colour.

40.　Red Vega
Red Warp Soil

General Specification : River flat soil of striking red, yellowish red to brown red colour, derived from erosion sediments of *terra rossa*, fossilized red loams or red earths laid down by high waters.

Characteristics:

Profile of the Rotlehm Warp Soil ((24). *Rotlehm Vega*): This usually dense, easily silted-up variety of the red warp soil, derived from erosion sediments of fossil *rotlehm* (type XXXV) or loamy *terra rossa* (limestone rotlehm), has a thin A horizon, low in humus, over thick (B) horizons, similar to the *braunlehm vega,* and can be markedly similar to it in its characteristics.

Profile of Roterde Warp Soil ((25). *Roterde Vega*): This form derived from the erosion sediment of fossil *roterde* (type XXXVI) or of *earthy terra* *rossa* (limestone roterde) in contrast to the above, has a loose, crumbly, structure with many cavities and a much deeper A horizon richer in humus. Further the (B) horizon is not dense, but loose and permeable, making unimpeded deep root growth possible.

Dynamic: The dynamic of the *rotlehm vega* is similar to the *braunlehm vega*, except that it is richer in irreversible precipitations of ferric hydroxide, which always have a dazzling red colour (thin section examination with reflected light). Besides rounded concretions, the whole or a certain part of the structure is permeated by frequent flaky precipitates. These predominate strongly in earthy forms and produce besides the finely dispersed substances of aluminium hydroxide and clay (generally kaolinite) of low mobility, the loose structure of this variety. The soil is chalk free, acid to slightly acid, and further the red colour and other structural characteristics do not alter either with continuous percolation or even strong water-logging. Old fossil *rotlehm* sediments often show in thin section, a mosaic of hardened fabric fragments, embedded in a new ground mass.

Texture: The distinction between the *rotlehm* and *roterde* forms depends not on the fineness of the texture, but on the kind of structure and composition. The first is rich in silicic acid, plastic and easily peptized; the second, low in silicic acid, not, or only slightly, plastic, and can only be peptized to a low degree and further it contains free aluminium hydroxide. Both can therefore have the same particle size distribution.

Occurrence: *Red vegas* are very widespread in Southern Europe (especially in Greece and Spain).

C. Terrestrial or Land soils

Key for the Determination of Classes and Some Types.

1. Soils without macroscopically distinguishable humus horizons.

                                              CA. Terrestrial raw soils.

1*. Soils with macroscopically distinguishable humus horizons   2

2. Soils with distinct humus horizon, however, without B horizons, i. e. the humus horizon lies directly on the parent material or on a layer broken down only by mechanical weathering, not changed essentially by chemical weathering (AC soils)   3

2*. Soils with B horizons, i. e. with subsoil of brown, ochre yellow to red colour   5

3. Soils with generally uniform development on broad areas in the steppe regions or summer dry cultivated areas, occurring almost only on loose parent material.

                                              CD. Steppe soils.

3*. Soils occurring generally on hard parent rocks or outside summer dry areas on loose parent material   4

4. Soils calcareous or containing chalk humates, occurring on chalk, dolomite, gypsum or chalk silicate rocks.

                                            CC. Rendsina-like soils.

4*. Soils low in chalk and containing no chalk humates, occurring almost only on silicate and siliceous rocks, low in chalk, very rarely on chalk silicate rocks.

                                            CB. Ranker-like soils.

5. Soils with the appearance of gley soils, i. e. with light grey, dense structured horizons (frequently only in the top soil under the humus layer), but already distinguished from them by a strong alternation of wetting and drying in which the drying phase usually predominates. In general they show small concretions of ferric hydroxide in the top soil and strongly flecked to marbled zones in the usually brown subsoil.

                              CI. Pseudogley soils (see plate XXIV).

5*. Soils not having the appearance of gley soils   6

6. Strongly acid, nutrient deficient soils with acid, biologically inert humus formations, strong eluviation of colloidal material, formation of impoverished layers in the top soil and distinct illuvial layers in the top soil and distinct illuvial layers in the subsoil. Occurring generally in heath country or wooded areas with a cool and moist climate   11

6*. Soils without acid, biologically inert humus formations   7

7. Soils red to brown red coloured, not plastic even with high content, finely dispersed substances, when wet can be neither moulded nor kneaded.

Occurring only in remains or sediments of fossil soils   8
7*.   Soils either otherwise coloured, or with red to brown red colour, also
      with relatively low content of colloidal substances, always plastic   9
8.   Occurring only on limestone.

                                                    (49).   Allitic terra rossa.

8*.   Not confined to limestone.

                                                    XXXVI.   Lateritic roterde.

9.   Soils generally of striking red, brown red, or intense ochre yellow, or ochre
      to ochre brown colour; in wet regions of dense structure; on wetting,
      strongly swelling, becoming pasty on drying out becoming hard as
      rock. In extremely dry regions, shallow soils or the upper layers of deep
      soils often show secondary loosening and break-down into scabby, crumbly
      aggregates   10
9*.   Soils not of striking brown, brown ochre, light ochre to light brown
      colour, neutral to moderately acid, well crumbled, not tending to extreme
      silting up and erosion, showing no illuviation of colloidal substances or
      even an increase in heaviness in the subsoil.

                       CH.   Brown earths *)   (see plate XXI and XXII).

10.   Soils occurring on limestone, marls, dolomite or gypsum.

                                                    CE.   Terrae calxis.

10*. Soils occurring in the form of relict soils on siliceous or silicate rock or
      on deep deposits of sediments from fossile soil formations.

                                  CF.   Bolus-like silicate soils.

11.   With strongly developed bleached horizon in topsoil and typical, often to
      ortstein compacted illuvial horizons (B Horizon) in the subsoil.

                                                    XL.   Podsol.

11*. With enriched horizons, easily recognized by their greater heavines;
      however without pronounced bleached layer, but, at best, with bleached
      flecks or thin bleached sand seams or only numerous bleached sand
      granules in the humus horizon.

                                                    XXXIX.   Semi-podsol.

CA. Terrestrial Raw soils

Soils with low chemical weathering, usually scanty soil life, with no humus
horizon formation distinguishable to the eye.

Not all soils with humus horizons missing are, however, raw soils. Accumulations by erosion of maturer soil formations which may be easily recognized by their colour, rate of weathering, behaviour, etc., belong just as little
to them as soils which have had only a part of their profile truncated (including
the humus horizon).

―――――――
*) An exact distinction in transition formations between *braunerde* and *braunlehm* is only possible microscopically (see type XXXIV and plate XIX).

Determination of Types, Sub-types and Varieties.

1.   Very dry soils, occurring in regions of low vegetation with hot summer and extremely low rainfall.

                            XXII. Yerma (raw soil of the dry desert).   5

1*. Soils neither extremely dry nor occurring in a very low rainfall climate with hot summers   2

2.   Soils occurring relatively rarely as a young formation and then always in conjunction with mature soils.

                  XXIII. Syrosem (raw soil of the temperate zones).   10

2*. Soils occurring only in regions of low vegetation with extremely cold, frosty climate (cold deserts).

          XXI. Rawmark (arctic raw soil and high alpine raw soil).   3

3.   Either free from large stones or the rocks are embedded in fine soil and not precipitated in isolated parts of the soil.

                              (26) Common artic rawmark.

                              (29) Common alpine rawmark.

3*. Stones partially or almost completely segregated in particular parts of the soil   4

4.   Soils with a dense cover of stones, with little earth (stone armour) or at least covered with a simple stone layer.

                             (27). Arctic hamada rawmark.

                             (30). Alpine hamada rawmark.

4*. Individual stones on the soil surface arranged in the form of circles, ovals, networks or parallel dykes.

                                 (28). Structure rawmark.

5.   Soil loose not or only occasionally showing a thin, easily broken surface crust   6

5*. Topsoil hardened and usually, in addition, covered with a rock-like crust.   9

6.   Soil covered with a stone layer containing little earth or a single coating of stones.

                                45. Hamada yerma.

6*. Soils without a stony layer   7

7.   Soils sandy, of uniform composition and without a slightly solidified superficial «skin».

                                 46. Sand yerma.

7*. Soils powdery, frequently showing a thin, slightly solidified surface skin.   8

8.   Powdery soil mass, high in salts, generally with a few salt efflorescences on the surface.

                                 44. Salt dust yerma.

8*. Powdery soil mass containing no salt efflorescences visible to the naked eye.

                                  43. Dust yerma.

9.   Hardened topsoil, which usually becomes soft and breaks down on thorough wetting, the rock-like crust consist of gypsum (small fragments of it are soluble in boiling water).

                                 47. Gypsum crust yerma.

9*.   Hardened topsoil relatively water stable, the rock-like crust consists mainly of $CaCO_3$, effervesces strongly with HCl and is insoluble in boiling water.

48. Lime crust yerma.

10.   Embryonic formation of the temperate zone on loess.

(31) Loess syrosem (loess raw soil).

10*. Occurring on other parent materials   11

11.   Occurring on silicate rock low in chalk.

49. Silicate syrosem (silicate raw soil).

11*. Occurring on chalk or calcareous rocks.

50. Carbonate syrosem (carbonate raw soil).

Description of Terrestrial Raw Soils

A. Climax Raw Soils

XXI. *R a w m a r k*

(Swedish, råmark)

Raw Soil of the Cold Desert

41. Arctic Rawmark

Arctic Raw Soil

(26) Common Arctic Rawmark

Arctic Frost Earth

General Specification and Delimitation: Raw soil in the region of the melting soils of the arctic, appearing just beyond the tundra girdle as a climate form, but partly also reaching into the tundra zone with scanty chemical weathering, sparse soil life, low humification and generally with a continuously frozen sub-soil.

Characteristics:

Profile: The real soil formation starts with colonization by higher plants consisting of lichens, mosses, and low growing higher plants. There is never a closed plant cover. Under cushions of higher plants usually lies a distinctly formed (A) horizon and below it the C_1 horizon, free from ice in summer. This again lies on the permanently frozen subsoil, called *tjäle layer* (Swedish). This Gefrornis-Schicht (R. POHLE 1924) or *merslota* (Russian) is impermeable to water and when the snow melts produces water-logging in the C_1 horizon or in the whole of the thawing soil. Owing to the rawness of the soil and the low chemical weathering no gleying occurs. However, completely dry *rawmarks* with good permeability to water do occur. The depth of thawed soil reaches 25-80 in. and more. The cavities of the frozen layer are always filled with ice. The inclusions of pure ice are called *soil ice*

(Russian: podpochwenny liod). All horizons have almost the same colour owing to the low chemical weathering, grey colours predominating in general.

Environment Conditions: Generally strongly glaciated. The soil formation is confined, however, to areas free from glaciers which become free from snow in summer, thaw and are colonized by a scanty vegetation. The winter is characterized by perpetual night, unbroken frost and continuous snow cover. The short summers are cool, very cloudy and misty, with low rainfall, but also low evaporation and with strongly inclined and little effective sun rays.

Weathering: In contrast to the low chemical weathering, the physical weathering is important, although it is impeded by the long snow covering. The mechanical breakdown is primarily produced by frost cleavage.

Texture: On hard parent rock, predominately, coarse particles. At best the soils consist of a moist, gravelly, sandy grit, usually of a light or dark grey colour.

Phenology: Soil frozen in winter and continually covered with snow. Complete cessation of soil life and all soil forming processes. In spring it becomes free from snow, there is a thawing out of the topsoil (June-July), thorough wetting, water accumulation in flat locations, on slopes strong erosion, and a start of the vegetation. In late summer to early autumn, strongest alternation of freezing and thawing (regelation), the time of strongest weathering by frost rupture. In autumn (September) permanent freezing of the topsoil occurs, and therefore a volume increase which can produce blister-like formations of the surface and the appearance of cavities.

Nature of Erosion: Erosion is especially strong and is therefore a characteristic of the soil. In particular there is the intense earth flow (solifluction) on slopes produced by intense alternation of freezing and thawing.

Occurrence: Principally on islands in the Artic Sea, particularly the Russian, partly also in the region of the tundra zone on the European continent. Outside Europe predominating in the Arctic and Antarctic.

(27) Arctic Hamada Rawmark
Arctic Hamada Raw Soil

General Specification: Arctic frost earth with scanty humus formation, covered by a dense mantle or layer of stones separated by violent wind erosion.

Characteristics:

Profile: The «hamada» layer is almost free of finer fractions and varies in size from a simple stone layer to a thickness of several decimeters. Under it follows the C_1 horizon, which usually rests on a permanently frozen layer (tjäle, page 146). The sparse higher plants generally root in the frost earth or colonize small earth islands. The formation of a stone armour is a consequence of the violence of the arctic winds which can produce in exposed country a complete blowing-away of the uppermost soil layer. In particular, with frost soils on crystalline schists, an especially dense structured stone armour is produced, which can be partly recognized by the intricate arrangement according to the prevailing wind direction. The hamada protects the underlying frost earth from being blown away and forms a protection for the sparse soil life. Transformations to structure soils show earth islands with few stones («brodelherde», see No. (28)). The remaining characteristics are similar to the arctic frost earths already described.

(28) Structure Rawmark
Structure Soil (Meinardus 1912)

Synonyms: Stone polygon soil (J. S. HUXLEY and ODÉN, 1924), Brodelboden (K. GRIPP 1927), quarré soil, facette soil, polygon soil (HÖGBOM 1914); the last three descriptions also cover the *rutmark* or cellular soil as well (page 108); strip soil (GRIPP) = only for soils with striated structure form found on slopes; stone gardens (TARNUZZER), stone rings, stone nets, earth islets = these names refer only to the surface form and not the entire soil.

General Specification and Delimitation: Arctic soils characterized by a strong alternation of freezing and thawing, which on their surface show strikingly rounded areas of earth surrounded by stone dykes, or on slopes, the formation of striations of stone dykes and strips of earth.

Structure rawmarks are derived from gravelly frost earths and also from *hamada rawmarks*. The surface structures can be observed partly preserved in later phases of development or in transition formations in zones where arctic raw soil is no longer the climax form. The externally similar *rutmark* is described in Class B (page 108).

Characteristics:

Profile: The separation of the stones and the fine soil to form stone dykes occurs only in the upper part of the soil profile to a depth of a few decimeters (zone of regelation). Of importance for structure formation is a rich thorough wetting of the soils, which is always encouraged in loose soils by the presence of a frozen layer. The equivalent effect is produced by a hard rock subsoil. By the colonization of plants in favourable places, an (A) horizon is formed in the surface layer.

Surface Structures: If the topography is approximately level the surface forms are particularly striking and are often visible at a great distance occurring on broad areas and often show an astonishing regularity of form, almost as if it had been built artificially. On a level sub-stratum, the structures consist either of almost circular rings of stones or densely arranged criss-cross growth of a net of more or less polygonal shaped stone enclosures. On slopes, the rings of stones become oval in shape, with steeper slopes the dykes of the rings are opened out into striations of stones. The interior of the rings consists of a dense, fine, earthy material with few to no stones, and generally shows a slight arching. The rings of stones are formed by the continual alternation in volume of the fine soil due to freezing. As it contracts, the stones are isolated and, with subsequent expansion, these are pushed to the rim where they gradually accumulate to form walls. The diameter of the circles varies from a few decimeters to several meters.

Texture: While separation of stones and fine soil occurs in the upper soil layer, the sub-soil shows both components in a completely undisturbed state. In general, the fine soil is characterized by a higher content of finely dispersed constituents than the non-structure soils.

Biology: The first colonization by plants, mosses, lichens and also flowering plants (hence the designation «stone gardens») always follows the edges of the «tiles» and later on the stone walls also, but the dense arched centres of the tiles remain bare for a long time. The biological relations in the various parts of the soil differ considerably. The tiles are very wet, dense with low aeration, the stone rings are dry and well aerated. As a whole, however, decomposition and humification is slow and production of organic matter low.

Phenology: The soil is frozen for most of the year and under snow. In late spring after the melting of the snow cover, strong wetting with the formation of a thawing soil over the frozen layer occurs, but the soil temperature rises only very slightly above freezing point and this makes a rapid alternation of freezing and thawing possible.

Occurrence: The *structure rawmarks* occupy large areas, particularly in the Arctic on islands in the polar seas, partly also in the Alps (*alpine structure rawmark*), but only to a limited extent in isolated small localities. Here also the most perfect structure soils are found always on raw soils.

42.   *Alpine Rawmark*
High Alpine Raw Soil

Synonyms: Mountain desert soil (NEUSTRUYEV 1915), alpine carbonate raw soil = for formations on limestone or dolomite; alpine silicate raw soil = for formations on primitive rocks.

Explanation of plate IX

1. **Alpine Hamada Rawmark** (alpine hamada raw soil) below *Festuca duriuscula* on graphite sericite phyllite (Veleta, Sierra Nevada, 3740 m., Spain).
2. **Lime Crust Yerma** (lime crust desert soil) above loose marl. On the surface a lime crust fragment with endolitic lichens. On the left fissure filled up with eolic sediments with the formation of a surface rind. Scanty desert vegetation in fissures, in the picture *Anabaxis articulata* (Beach of San Juan, Alicante).

(29) Common Alpine Rawmark
Alpine Frost Eearth

General Specification: Shallow, localized raw soil with poor vegetation and humus formation and low earth content of the nival region of high mountains.

Characteristics:

Profile: The normal profile consists of an (A) horizon, a loose C_1 horizon generally grey-coloured and a hard parent rock (C_2 horizon). Soil frosts are frequent and lasting, but a true frozen layer (tjäle layer, page 146) is rare.

Weathering: Little chemical, but intense physical weathering by frost action and also by strong temperature fluctuations above freezing-point.

Texture: The soil shows nearly always coarse textures and consists in general of a stony gritty sand.

Biology: Low decomposition and humification, low production of organic matter which is mostly blown away by the violent wind. Therefore no humus horizon is found and there is rarely any humus accumulation. Colonization by plants takes place only in a few cushions of growth. These cushions of vegetation are usually extremely dense and often show intense root growth in a small area. This may simulate raw humus formation, but is predominately the accumulation of living plants and plant roots.

Phenology: The soil is frozen for the greater part of the year and is covered by an occasionally thick, snow layer. After the disappearance of the snow (in most places in July) usually a general thaw of the entire profile takes place. This produces strong temporary water-logging. When free from snow, the soil is subject to strong erosion by wind and flowing water.

(30) Alpine Hamada Rawmark
Alpine Hamada Raw Soil

General Specification: Alpine raw soils with scanty humus formation with a dense stone mantle or a single layer of separate stones (plate IX).

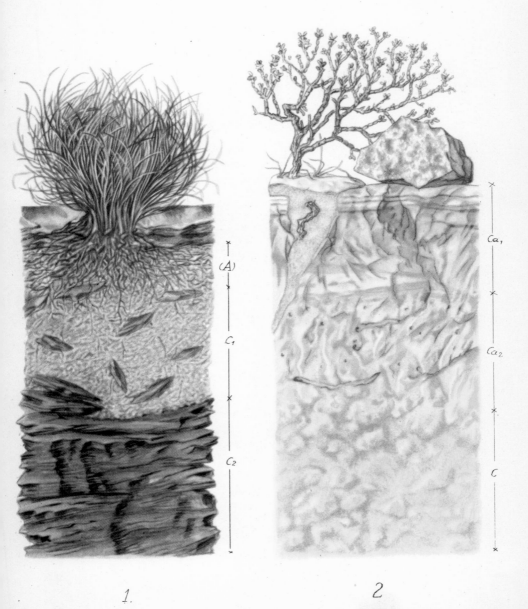

IX

1.

2.

Characteristics:

Profile: Normally the profile consists of a hamada layer (page 147), a loose C_1 horizon (generally grey) and a C_2 horizon of hard parent rock. The stone layer, formed by wind erosion contains extremely little earth. Often fine soil is not reached before a depth of 1/2-1 meter or more. With well fissured crystalline schists on large areas a pavement-like surface may be formed (Sierra Nevada). Pure tjäle layers are found only when the soil is permanently covered with snow. Near glaciers and in depressions, a generally rust-brown coloured crust, primarily of ferric hydroxide, can appear on the surfaces of the hamada stones (glacier crusts). These are essentially local formations of slight importance compared with the desert rinds (page 154).

Biology: The hamada of the nival raw soils always remains low in vegetation, while the stone layers of the sod and dwarf shrub regions are gradually colonized and under the closed plant cover the stones are slowly broken down by weathering. The cushions of plants have their roots in the fine soil under the stone layer or in the small islands of soil, protected by the vegetation, and in which a strongly through-rooted (A) horizon is formed. The extraordinarily dense growth of the cushions with accumulation of raw humus-like living masses cannot be observed with the same plant species in lower regions. Decomposition of the organism remains is slow, with low production of organic matter and low accumulation of humus.

XXII. *Yerma*[*)
Dry Desert Raw Soil

Synonyms: Desert soil.

43. *Dust Yerma*
Desert Dust Soil

General Specification and Delimitation: Powdery to almost completely loose soil, extremely low in humus, with scanty vegetation, not forming crumbs or aggregates, occurring in extremely dry, hot or hot-summer regions.

The dust soils are derived usually from deposits of fossil soils formed primarily under a wet tropical or sub-tropical climate in which large quantities of colloidal substances are preformed which could not be produced by direct weathering. *Braunlehms* and *rotlehms* are mainly concerned but the influence of the extreme dryness and heat can induce such strong alternation that the characteristic of a desert soil predominates (the presence of fossil and relict soils can also be detected on hard parent rock). Therefore desert dust soils are described in toto under raw soils. The strongest dust formation is always to

---

*) From Spanish, yermo = desert.

be observed in the surface layer and lower down the extreme looseness diminishes.

Characteristics:

Profile: The open soil surface is generally covered by a slightly hardened rind (dust skin), generally a few millimeters thick and of a dirty grey colour. The organic residues contained in it, which also influence the colour, are derived from its being colonized by algae, fungi and lichens. The rind is thus a particular kind of (A) horizon. It arises in the first place under the influence of a slight rainfall, which produces compaction of the structure, combined with silting-up and ensuing better glueing by recementation of the binding substances. The binding is also due partly to colonization by the previously mentioned organisms. The rind is easily pulverized between one's fingers and the powder produced is, externally, scarcely distinguishable from the remaining soil. Under the thin vegetation, which usually grows in this, fresh dust collects continuously, and generally, therefore, no surface rind is formed. In this case a more or less distinct, characteristically through-rooted (A) horizon with low humus formation is produced. The colour of the powder is generally light, even if it is formed from deposits of fossil *braunlehm* and *rotlehm*. The most frequent colours are white, light grey, yellowish grey, whitish ochre, reddish or pale violet. Occasionally strikingly red hues are seen.

Environmental Conditions: The pedological concept of «dry deserts» embraces extremely low rainfall areas in which desert raw soils (*yermas*) appear as the climax formation. The boundary of the semi-desert or dry steppe commences where humus horizons, although shallow and poor in humus, can be distinguished. The deserts have a very strong temperature variation between day and night in addition to the generally yearly temperature variation (cold winters and hot summers), as far as deserts outside the tropics are concerned.

Dynamic: The capillary rise of the ground and soil water exceeds by far the descent and, therefore, movement of material goes almost entirely from the deeper layers to the surface. The strong drying out, combined with the low strenght of the binding substances, owing to their impregnation with very fine salt deposits, produces a looser structure than would be expected with such high content of colloidal substances (see page 153).

Biology: Colonization by a specific, particularly drought resistant flora and fauna. The sparse soil life produces little organic matter. The decomposition (mainly by bacteria) is intense so long as the residues are sufficiently moist. With strong drying out mummification occurs. The production of organic matter, the humus formation and accumulation of humus is low.

Phenology: The soil is dry for most of the year, has a light colour, a certain content of salt in the surface layer and with destruction of the dust skin is strongly influenced by wind erosion. The little rain, which often falls in severe downpours, sometimes produces catastrophic flooding and severe soil erosion. The rapid run-off of the water and the intense evaporation, dry the soil out again very quickly. Strong soaking alters the soil considerably. With many dust soils formed from *braunlehm* or *rotlehm* sediments, the light colour of the soil disappears and is replaced by intense ochre yellow, ochre brown or brown red hues. The formerly pulverized soil becomes to a certain degree cohesive and plastic.

Occurrence : In a few dry areas in South Europe, in Spain, especially in the provinces of Almería and Zaragoza.

44. Salt Dust Yerma
Salt Dust Soil

General Specification : Powdery, loose soil, extremely low in humus, very dry, occurring in hot or hot-summer regions, with deposits of water soluble salts on the surface or within the soil visible to the naked eye.

Again, among the salt dust soils, a large number is found derived from deposits of fossil *braunlehm* and *rotlehm,* whose character has been very much altered by the extremely dry climate. What has been said already about the *dust yerma* applies to these too.

Characteristics :

Profile : The profile is only slightly differentiated and similar to the *dust yerma,* except for a gradual difference in water soluble salt content, and it generally shows a thin, very friable crust, which is absent under the loose tufts of higher plants. Here there is the beginning of an (A) horizon, with many roots in it. Humus formation is completely missing. The strongest soil pulverization is shown in the top soil, diminishing in the deeper soil layers.

Salt Precipitation : The salts precipitated in the pores, which can be seen by the naked eye, were brought to the upper soil layers by rising soil and ground water. Where the dissolved salt reaches the surface, visible white precipitations are formed. It never reaches the condition of a crust, owing to lack of water in desert soils; a crust is found only in salt pans over ground water soils. The most frequently occurring salts in dust soils are gypsum, anhydride and sodium chloride. More occasionally, $MgSO_4$ and Na_2SO_4 appear; and, rarer still, calcium and magnesium chloride, etc.

Microscopic Characteristics : The salt efflorescences on the soil surface soon lose their crystalline form and break down into a microscopic powder. The salts which do not reach the surface, due to rapid concentration and drying of the soil solution, are precipitated either in the soil cavities or in the pores of the cementing material (interflorescences). In this way the mechanical cohesion of the structure and the binding force of the cementing substances are strongly reduced. The structure is therefore easily destroyed and with the *dust yerma* (page 151) and *salt dust yerma* in particular, the top soil breaks down of its own accord. The interflorescences consist of very small salt microlites usually rounded in shape of about 0.5-2 μ in diameter. The greatest accumulation of microscopic salt fragments is also shown by the increased lightening in colour of the particular structural fragments. The resulting loose layers are composed of small, strongly broken up structural fragments rich in salts, isolated, generally bare mineral granules, fragments of detached binding substances strongly permeated and covered by precipitated salts, as well as white flaky precipitates.

Occurrence : In a few extremely dry regions of Southern Europe.

45. *Hamada Yerma*
Hamada Desert Soil

General Specification : Typical soil form of the stone deserts, extremely dry and deficient in humus and in vegetation, either covered with a single stone layer or with a stone coating.

Characteristics :

Profile : The stone layer (hamada), produced by strong erosion, covers either a gravel, gravelly-sandy soil or a dust soil, especially salt dust soil, which is protected from wind erosion. Under plant tufts the formation of an (A) horizon, without any appreciable humus formation, can take place.

Dynamic : Both in the loose soil under the stone layer and also in the stones of the hamada, when moistened by rain or dew, strong capillary action occurs. This sends the moisture to the surface and carries up the dissolved weathered material to be precipitated. Besides the salts, described earlier in the desert soils, in the case of a hamada layer movement and precipitation of colloidal material occurs, particularly of ferric and manganese hydroxides. This leads to the formation of a brown coloured crust on the surface of the stones of the hamada. Colloidal silicic acid acts as a protective colloid for the solution of ferric hydroxide, but partial movement of iron is possible without this. Physical weathering is important due to the strong temperature variation between night and day and the splitting effect of salts. Chemical weathering, intensified by the high temperature and the effect of dissolved salts, is more strongly expressed than with the raw soils of the cold deserts.

Characteristics of the Hamada : The hamada of the dry desert differs from that of the cold deserts (page 147) primarily by the formation of a deep brown, blackish, reddish brown, ochre or grey coloured rind on the surface of the stones (desert rinds, protective rinds, manteaux protecteurs;

with thin, shiny forms: desert varnish). Their principal constituents and colouring agents are ferric and manganese hydroxides. Their thickness varies from 0.2 to about 5.0 mm. On certain rocks, particularly soft stones, such as soft limestone, marl, gypsum, clay schist, etc., no rind is formed. The desert rinds are found, indicating their derivation, primarily on the upper surfaces of the stones, while their lower sides, projecting into the fine soil, show the usual marks of direct chemical weathering.

Occurrence : True *hamada yerma* with the above characteristics is very widespread in dry regions outside Europe and occurs in Europe only in particular transition forms.

46. Sand Yerma
Sand Desert Soil

Synonyms : Erg = arabic folk name of the Sahara (plur. areg).

General Specification : Loose, completely structureless, almost humus free raw soil of the sand desert, with extremely low colloid content, containing only the larger soil particles (sand and fine pebbles).

Characteristics :

Profile : The soil has practically no profile as even the rind layer of the dust soils is frequently missing. Under the very scanty vegetation indications of an A horizon can be determined.

Colour : In addition to the whitish, grey and intense ochre yellow hues, reddish yellow to dazzling red hues are found.

Microscopic Characteristics : The surface of the sand grains is usually roughed like frosted glass. In the depressions, cracks and corners of the surface remains of the hardened binding substances are always found. These deposits are generally of an intense red colour, seldom yellowish. The greater the number, size and thickness of these coverings, in general, the intenser the red colour of the sand as a whole, the more scanty and thin, the nearer the colour as a whole approaches a light reddish ochre or yellowish ochre. The deposits usually have a dense structure, sharp edged fractures and the typical waxy appearance of the ground mass of tropical *rotlehm*. Contained in it, is diffuse finely divided ferric hydroxide, and further, with reflected light, microscopic concretions can be seen, either in the deposits of the binding substances or loose, in the inter-granular spaces. They are either dazzling red coloured or blackish if rich in manganese. These deposits are distinguished from the ground mass and binding substance of the *rotlehms* as the colloidal silicic acid has become insoluble due to the strong heating and drying out. The deposits are therefore extraordinarily water stable and undergo no change on moistening or washing. Therefore there is not only a lack of binding material, but what little there is has been altered and irreversibly fixed.

The microscopic characteristics show that desert sands as well as most other desert soils are derived to a great extent from sediments of fossil soils (mainly *rotlehm* and *braunlehm*), in which wind erosion has produced a sorting out of the fine skeleton, the sandy to pebbly constituents.

Occurrence: *Sand yermas* are of little importance in the group of desert raw soils. In Europe they are almost of no importance except for small occurrences in the south-east.

47. *Gypsum Crust Yerma*
Gypsum Crust Soil (Blanckenhorn 1901 and Ramann 1918)

General Specification: Raw soil of dry hot summer regions, which show a slight hardening of the soil structure in the top soil and above it a compact, stony crust on the surface, in which the cement for the hardening and crust formation is gypsum or a mixture of gypsum and calcium carbonate with a preponderance of gypsum.

Characteristics:

Profile: The gypsum or Y horizons (after the Spanish yeso = gypsum) are divided into a compact gypsum crust (Y_1 horizon), which has a thickness of 2 to about 8 cm., and the underlying, porous, more or less spongy, hardened Y_2 horizon which goes without sharp boundary into the loose C horizon.

Nature of the Y_2 horizon: In contrast to the analogous Ca_2 horizon of the *lime crust yerma* (page 157), the Y_2 horizon is distinguished in particular as it «absorbs water like sugar» (GLINKA) and becomes soft and easily broken while the Ca_2 horizon is moderately water stable. On moistening soils derived from sediments of fossil *braunlehm,* the whitish colour disappears and changes generally into an intense deep ochre. With soils on hard gypsum rock which show a grey C_1 horizon, the whitish colour goes over to grey on wetting. Gypsum is precipitated in the Y_2 horizon, not only as a finely dispersed cement but also in the form of transparent, columnar crystals (prisms with slanting edges and swallow-tail twins) which can also serve as a diagnostic characteristic for the recognition of *gypsum crust yerma*. The same small crystals are also often found in the C_1 horizon.

Nature of the Gypsum Crust: This can be scratched by a finger nail and, if it consists of pure gypsum, will not effervesce with dilute HCl (whereas a calcium crust always does). Gypsum crusts can generally be distinguished from calcium ones, by a peculiar, dull whitish, almost always a bluish hue and by a dull, marzipan-like, rough surface. As with longer percolation, the gypsum crust goes partly into solution, so that by re-crystallization conversion to a coarse crystalline structure can occur by the formation of colourless crystalline aggregates. Also, the development of sintered, nodular surface formations with coarse crystalline interiors can be typical for certain gypsum crusts.

Occurrence : In particular dry areas in Southern Europe. Particularly beautiful *gypsum crust yermas* are found, near *salt dust yermas* rich in gypsum, in Spain in the province of Zaragoza. *Gypsum crust yerma* is found in dryer habitats than *lime crust yerma*. However, the areas of occurrence of both soils are outside the extreme desert region.

48. Lime Crust Yerma
Chalk Crust Soil (Blanckenhorn 1901 and Ramann 1918)

Synonyms : Nari (local designation in the province of Jerusalem).

General Specification : Raw soil of dry hot-summer regions whose top soil has a spongy but moderately coherently solidified structure with a compact, rock-like surface crust above it, the cement for the solidification and crust formation being calcium carbonate.

Characteristics :

Profile : The normal profile consists of a lime crust (Ca_1 horizon), which in Southern Europe attains a thickness of 5-50 cms. (the Nari in the environs of Jerusalem reaches up to 2 meters in thickness), a spongy, solidified Ca_2 horizon, which goes over gradually into the C horizon underneath (perhaps a C_1 and C_2 horizon) (plate IX).

Nature of the Ca_2 horizon : The porous masses which effervesce strongly with HCl have a higher compressive strength than the corresponding Y_2 horizon of the gypsum crust soils, although they can still be crushed between one's fingers. They have a considerable water stability. This caracteristic as well as the protective effect of the lime crust (Ca_1 horizon) allows the local inhabitants of true lime crust areas to build earth homes and other earth buildings.

Nature of the Lime Crust : This is extraordinarily hard, can only be broken with a hammer, dense, marly, never coarsely crystalline, generally cream coloured, occasionally reddish with dirty grey flecks and spots on the surface. This is usually colonized by endolithic lichens whose thin fruiting bodies can be seen with a magnifying glass, and further, its algae layer can be detected by the green colouration of the scratches produced on the surface rind by a hammer or a knife. In a transverse section the lime crusts occasionally show a slight banding.

Dynamic : The lime is dissolved as calcium bicarbonate by the soil water rich in carbonic acid and is precipitated as calcium carbonate in various parts of the upper soil layers, according to the intensity of carbon dioxide delivery, evaporation and concentration of the soil solution rising by capillary action. The moisture relations are sufficient to bring the soil solution to the surface, where the hard lime crust is gradually formed. Its formation is shown pre-eminently by small surface hills, where, due to the higher evaporation, the capillary pull is strongest. For the solution and transloc-ation of the large quantities of lime, far greater quantities of water are necessary than are found in extreme desert soils. The greater amount of rain also leads to the washing out of the water soluble alkali salts, only traces of which are still to be found in the lime crust and to a greater extent also the calcium sulphate. The rising soil solution carries up colloidal silicic acid which, partly due to the strong heating, is irreversibly precipitated and, therefore, is frequently found as an additional constituent of the lime crust. The strong wind erosion and simultaneous occurrence of loose dust and sand soils produce a frequent covering of the lime crusts with wind-borne sediments.

Occurrence: The *lime crust yerma,* although the product of an extremely dry habitat, is a distinct Mediterranean formation and is frequent in Mediterranean countries but, of course, mainly in regions outside Europe. In Spain they are particularly frequent in the province of Almería.

B. Non-climax Raw soils

XXIII. S y r o s e m
Raw Soil of the Temperate Zones

Synonyms: Skeletal soil, lithosol = designation only applicable for a very stony raw soil; regosol = only for a very sandy raw soil.

Young embryonic soil formation which still has no humus horizon visible to the naked eye. Mature soils, strongly differentiated from their parent material, which have only lost their humus horizon by translocation or surface erosion, do not count as raw soils. Their relation to particular other soil types is generally easy to identify by the characteristics of the existing non-humus horizons.

49. Silicate Syrosem
Silicate Raw Soil (Pallmann)

General Specification: Very young, chemically little weathered soil, loosened predominately by physical weathering, extremely low in humus and without visible humus horizon, on silicate rocks with low lime content.

Characteristics:

Profile: The soil has neither a humus horizon nor any other horizon characteristic of more mature soils. The upper soil layer, more strongly through-rooted and more colonized by organisms, forms the (A) horizon. The underlying raw layer is designated as C horizon. With hard parent rocks a mechanically loosened (generally grey) C_1 horizon and a compact, more or less untouched C_2 horizon is distinguished.

Humus Form: Raw soil humus (syrosem humus, page 35).

Dynamic: The physical weathering far exceeds the chemical weathering. Movements of material in the soil profile are very slight or non-existent.

Biology: Biologically inert, due to feeble colonization by organisms, or considerably less productive than more mature soil formation on the same parent material.

Texture: Principally sand, shingle, grit, pebble and gravel soil with low colloid content.

50. Carbonate Syrosem
Carbonate Raw Soil (Pallmann)

Synonyms: Chalk raw soil; white earth (DOKUCHAEV 1899); white rendsina (MIKLASZEWSKI) = white earthy masses forming raw soils on chalk, on marl, dolomite, chalk sandstone, gypsum, etc.

General Specification: Very young raw soil, extremely low in humus, characterized generally by a dry summer (on the surface partly also hot summer) soil climate on calcareous parent rocks.

Characteristics:

Profile: The normal profile consists of an (A) horizon and C horizon (with hard parent rocks, C_1 and C_2 horizons). Occasionally more or less distinct Ca horizons can already be formed.

Humus Form: Raw soil humus (syrosem humus, page 35).

Dynamic: Predominately physical, however, partly also chemical weathering which is restricted to a partial solution of the lime. In this way the soil frequently has an overwhelming lime content compared with other constituents (white rendsina). Part of the dissolved lime is washed down into the deeper soil layers and can produce there already visible enrichment. In the loose top soil gypsum is weathered to a great extent to calcium carbonate.

Biology: The white rendsinas, especially in warm southern countries, show a particular biology due to their dryness (high permeability of the chalk) and strong surface heating in summer. So long as there is some moisture in the organism residues they are rapidly decomposed. For vine growing *) these soils are regarded as hot, decomposing manure rapidly,

---

*) As chalk soils, very widespread in France, particularly favourable for red wine production.

and induce rapid decay of the stakes (for the grapes). But if the organism residues dry out rapidly and completely, decomposition ceases and the residues are mummified. In Karst country, occasionally in cemeteries on these soils, not only are the corpses mummified but the coffins are almost completely preserved, which in soils with normal biology would always be strongly decomposed and desintegrated. In the northern *carbonate syrosems,* this biology is considerably less developed in appearance, but it is still almost always distinguishable from the silicate raw soils by a tendency to more rapid decomposition and to a much dryer soil climate, especially in summer.

Texture : Almost always coarse textures only. Also the white earthy varieties are principally sandy to marly sand soils.

(31)   Loess Syrosem
Loess Raw Soil

General Specification : Fertile raw soil on loess rich in nutrients, easily worked, with good water conduction, however, without any humus horizon visible to the naked eye.

Characteristics:

Profile : The normal profile contains an (A) horizon with stronger through-rooting (in cultivated soils this is combined with the loose top layer) and a C horizon. Occasionally there is already an indication of a characteristic whitish chalk enriched Ca horizon. The soil is light ochre to almost pea yellow and in colour scarcely distinguishable from the parent material.

Chemical Properties : All horizons are rich in lime and effervesce strongly with dilute HCl. The still little decomposed soil generally holds a good reserve of nutrients.

Texture : Predominately fine sand and silt, while coarse sand and raw clay are very unimportant.

Physical Properties : Forms crumbs easily, with excellent water and air economy, high water permeability (in dry regions tending to summer drought) and is easily worked.

Nature of Parent Material : Very uniformly decomposed sediment with a mealy feel, light ochre colouring, unlayered, slightly compacted but crumbling between one's fingers, often rising up with vertical walls. Rounded to oval cavities are frequently filled with white lime concretions (loess kindl, puppies). Numerous fine, vertical channels (former plant root channels) are filled with stalky, calcite crystals arranged in parallel rows one on top of the other.

Dynamic : In contrast to mature soil formations the raw soil shows low chemical weathering and hig lime content. The lime begins to be dissolved, to move and to enrich the deeper parts of the soil profile.

Biology : Due to the favourable physical and chemical conditions, it is generally easily colonized by organisms. Therefore the *loess syrosem* remains as a raw soil only in dry regions, while in humid regions it is comparatively rapidly weathered and made loamy. It is to be found primarily on old cultivated land or in dry woods with traditional removal of the forest litter where there has been insufficient humus accumulation for the formation of a humus horizon. Also included here are areas where the soil layers have been removed by wind or water erosion. Although the fertility of *loess syrosems* exceeds that of all other raw soils and also many mature soils on other parent rocks, it is, however, always less productive and biologically less active than the other more mature soil formations on loess, such as *loess chernosem* and *loess braunerde*.

Humus Form : Raw soils humus (syrosem humus, page 35).

Microscopic Characteristics : In thin sections, loess has a fine porous fabric. This arises partly because the inter-granular pores are not completely filled up. The bulky ordered mineral grains are only. bound to each other in some places by bridges of mortar-like binding substances *). Besides the inter-granular spaces produced in this way, many larger cavities arise where the mineral grains are spaced so far apart that they are not bridged over with mortar. The mortar bridges are of a light ochre colour and consist of fine mineral fragments with a small amount of clay which are interspersed with numerous small (1-2 μ) calcite microlites. In places in the thin section, where there is an accumulation of these microlites, bright flecks with whitish interference colours appear under crossed nicols. The numerous, vertical former plant root channels are almost always filled with stalky, small calcite crystals which are arranged like a string of pearls along the axis of the cavity (generally in three concentric layers). These crystal tubes have a diameter of about 0.5 mm. The separate small crystals are about 150 μ long and 50 μ wide.

Erosion Forms : The stable structure enables loess not only to remain with vertical walls, but also artificial caves such as earth sheds, dwellings, wine cellars, etc., to last for a long time. Owing to the high water permeability, slowly flowing water is completely absorbed and uniformly distributed without signs of erosion. When, however, the water velocity is increased, or there is a constant or periodic stream of water and a stronger mechanical action is exerted on the structure, its rapid destruction and removal occur. The erosion only reaches as far as the mechanical force

---

*) Intertextic fabric.

is sufficiently strong and a sharp boundary is formed with the non-eroded sediment (formation of deep gullies with steep walls). The mechanical force need not be due solely to water. On tracks which lead over areas of loess it is often already the continued effect of the carriage wheels, horses hooves and people walking. With the strong pulverization there is a continual destruction with freeing of structural constituents which are blown away by the wind. In this way the waggon tracks are rapidly deepened to form the numerous ravines of loess areas.

The strong eroding power of constant or periodic flowing of water often produces drying up above ground of the water streams, similar to the phenomena of the Karst.

Occurrence : Predominately in the steppes and cultivated steppe regions. Frequent in North-East Austria, in Czechoslovakia (Hanna), Silesia, Roumania, Hungary and South Russia.

CB. Ranker-like soils

XXIV. Ranker [6]

Synonyms: Tasca (Aragon folk name for a *ranker*, which can be rolled up like a carpet; occurring on solid parent rock).

General Specification: Soil formation, low in lime, whose humus horizon lies immediately on the parent material which consists usually of lime deficient siliceous or silicate rocks (AC soils on parent material low in lime).

Key for the Determination of Sub-types and Varieties.

1.   Occurring only in the tundra region.

                                                          53. Tundra ranker.

1*.   Not only occurring in the tundra … … … … … … … … … … … … …   2

2.   Only occurring in high mountains … … … … … … … … … … … …   3

2*.   Not only occurring in high mountains … … … … … … … … … … …   5

3.   Soil always loose, rich in minerals, crumbling easily, earthy when moist, showing no horizon forming accumulations of raw plant remains or matted peat-like plant roots.

                                      (32) Alpine mull-like ranker.

3*.   Uppermost soil layer not earthy, but consisting predominately of raw plant remains or matted plant roots … … … … … … … … … … … … … …   4

4.   Soil very shallow, usually only a few cms. deep, consisting essentially of a very dense root mat of peaty appearance.

                                         54. Eilag ranker.

4*.   Soil occurs in the dwarf shrub region on southern high mountains, generally deep, consisting of an upper 5-25 cm. thick horizon, with a similar appearance to raw humus (tangel layer) and a lower 20-60 cm. thick, blackish, mineral rich, earthy horizon (mull-like layer).

                                         55. Tangel ranker.

5.   Humus horizon lying directly on the hard parent rock without the connecting link of a loose, humus deficient mineral layer … … … … … … … …   6

5*.   With a loose humus deficient mineral horizon between the humus horizon and parent rock … … … … … … … … … … … … … … … … … … …   8

6.   Soil formation very young, soil layer very thin, generally blackish coloured, without aggregate formation, consisting only of incoherent constituents, i. e. comminuted, bitten through plant remains, droppings of small animals and unweathered mineral fragments.

                                         51. Protoranker.

6*. Advanced soil formation, generally with distinct formation of aggregates.   7
7.   Humus browned by free ferric hydroxide, humus form mostly mull.

> 59. *Brow ranker.* (Forms without C$_1$ horizon
> and without thin seam-like (B) horizon.)

7*. Not browned by free ferric hydroxide, humus form mull containing clay, plant remains completely decomposed and humified, humus substances contained as finely divided, colouring material in the clay fraction.

> 56. *Mull ranker.*

8.   Humus browned by free ferric hydroxide, often on its lower edge with brown humus deficient mineral seam or with a kind of thin (B) horizon.

> 59. *Brown ranker.*

8*. Humus not browned by free ferric hydroxide, between the humus horizon and parent rock, a usually grey coloured humus deficient mineral horizon.   9

9.   Soil with raw humus cover or very acid coarse moder. The humus free mineral layer is extensively bleached due to strong eluviation of all products of chemical weathering. Occurring in *podsol* regions and in association with *podsols.*

> 58. *Podsol ranker.*

9*. Humus free mineral layer not bleached by eluviation of the finely dispersed products of chemical weathering   10

10. Humus free mineral horizon (C$_1$ horizon) lying under the humus horizon, generally grey coloured, is very loose and shows little chemical weathering.

> 57. *Grey ranker.*

10*. The grey coloured, humus free mineral horizon (C$_1$ horizon) is very dense, easily silted up, on drying considerably coherent, shows advanced chemical weathering, however, with almost no formation free ferric hydroxide.

> (33) *Gant ranker* (ganter).

51. *Protoranker* (n.f.)

General Specification: Young ranker formation which is composed entirely of loose, incoherent constituents, i. e. droppings of animals comminuted, bitten through plant residues, and little weathered mineral fragments.

Characteristics:

Profile: Very thin humus horizon, generally only a few centimeters thick, loose and usually of blackish colour. This lies directly on a nearly unweathered lime deficient, mostly hard silicate or siliceous rock (C horizon).

Plant Cover: Mosses, fruticose lichens, cushion plants, thin grass or herbaceous lawn.

Microscopic Characteristics: The humus shows no sign of aggregate formation. In it are contained very small, generally well humified droppings of low mineral content, mainly in the form of short cylinders, derived primarily from mites and collembolae.

Humus Form : Silicate moder (page 37).

Occurrence : Embryonic soil formation, frequent in wooded regions and mountains, in dry areas rare. In dry regions, shallow, humus deficient, mull-like rankers appear instead.

52. Dystrophic Ranker (n.f.)

Synonyms : A_0 silicate raw soil (PALLMANN 1933) = for forms developed generally under moss and lichen covers, consisting simply of raw humus layers; A_0/A_1 silicate raw soil (PALLMANN 1933) = for forms under very mossy dwarf shrub covers consisting of a raw humus layer and a thin blackish H layer.

General Specification and Delimitation : Nutrient deficient, strongly acid, inactive soil whose usually felted humus horizons consist primarily of little decomposed plant remains and which lie with a sharp boundary directly on the hard or loose, little weathered parent material.

Characteristics:

Profile : Very young soils with strong dystrophy usually with A_0 horizons of low mineral content. Frequently at the boundary to the parent material a generally blackish coloured transition horizon (A_1 horizon) is formed whose development is due to enrichment by small animal droppings. With mechanically loosened parent rock or with a considerable supply of windborne mineral fragments a more or less stony admixture of mineral substances may be seen. The A_0 horizon is usually thick and the A_1 horizon thin. *Dystrophic grey ranker* also shows the formation of a mechanically loosened C_1 horizon above the hard C_2 horizon.

Plant Cover : In coniferous woods of podsol regions, particularly on boulder strew, acid eruptive rocks and crystalline schists, this soil form is frequently combined with strong mossing over (by *Hylocomium splendens*, *Hylocomium triquetrum*, *Hypnum crista castrensis*, etc.) which is gradually colonized and overgrown by bilberries and cranberries, etc. In addition, *dystrophic ranker* may arise in coniferous woods with almost no herb cover. Especially deep formations can be found under white pine woods on granite gneiss in the Guadarrama mountains. In heath areas of central and Northern Europe they appear on hard parent rock, frequently in association with a cover of *Calluna vulgaris*, *Erica tetralix*, *Vaccinium vitis idea*, etc.

Biology : The soil life compounds in all its facets to a pronounced land humus form. Although the growth of the plant cover, which for the habitat is highly specific, especially in the shade of the woods, must be described in many cases as unusually prolific, the soil life, due to the strong

---

acidity, nutrient deficiency, cool soil climate and the presence of decomposition impeding substances, in view of the large quantity of plant remains is insufficiently developed. Decomposition and humification is therefore slow and incomplete.

Humus Form: Raw humus or dystrophic coarse moder. Deep, dystrophic forest ranker has usually dark brown raw humus formation, always well moistened, usually with peaty appearance and dense structure which lies on a blackish, mineral rich moder.

Occurrence: In the *podsol* and podsolic brown earth regions, i. e. in cool and humid air and soil climate, frequently to be found on hard (particularly nutrient deficient and acid) parent rock which is little weathered (rocky or boulder strewn areas) and shows no development of deeper mineral horizons, but already the formation of raw humus. *Dystrophic rankers* are the initial formation in the development sequence to the primary *podsols* (type XL), which develop via *dystrophic grey ranker* (No. 52) and *podsol ranker* (No. 58) directly to the *podsol* climax and not via brown earths.

Principal Parent Rocks: Acid, base and nutrient deficient, hard rocks, such as bare quartz sand, sandstone, quartzite, siliceous schists, acid igneous rocks, crystalline schists, etc.

53. Tundra Ranker

General Specification and Delimitation: Soil without water-logging or peat formation, but with a very inactive land humus formation of matted, little decomposed plant remains, occurring in the dry tundra.

Owing to the peaty appearance of the raw humus cover, the *tundra ranker* is easily confused with pure peat formations (cf. *tundra peat moor, tundra moss*, page 121), but from which it must always be carefully separated. There are various transition formations from the *tundra ranker*, which is to be found in true form especially on the rock hills (fjälls), to the true *tundra moss*. On old peat moors of the tundra, soil forms with raw humus formation can occur frequently, corresponding to the *peat ranker* (page 126).

Characteristics:

Profile: Matted, brown, mineral deficient A_0 horizons, of variable

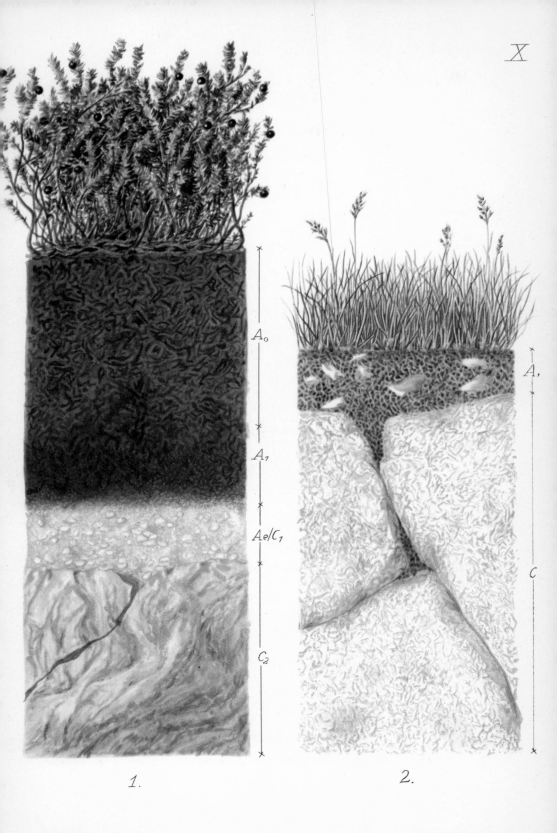

X

A_0

A_1

Ae/C_1

C_2

A_1

C

1.

2.

thickness, go over into more or less mineral rich, blackish A_1 horizons, which either lie directly on the C horizon consisting of hard rock or a purely mechanically broken down and to a very small extent chemically weathered, loose, transition horizon, the C_1 horizon (then the hard parent rock is called the C_2 horizon). Frequently signs of a distinct bleaching can be seen in the mineral layer. Usually these layers are only a few centimeters thick and are called A_e horizons or A_e/C_1 horizon (with less bleaching). Illuvial horizons are never formed, however, owing to the low content of chemical weathering products and the comparatively low bleaching at most iron and humus flecks arise on the surfaces or in fissures of the parent rock. The *ranker* of the rock tundra generally has no permanently frozen (tjäle) layer. Also in looser parent material the frozen layer is generally found only at a greater depth.

Plant Cover : Plants producing large quantities of residues, most of them rich in raw fibre, low in protein and containing decomposition impeding substances are very important. The plant cover most frequently found is of crowberries (*Empetrum nigrum*) or *Loiseleuria procumbens* with the lichens *Cladonia rangiferina, Cetraria nivalis,* as well as *Stereocaulis paschale, Festuca ovina,* etc.

Humus Form : Raw humus and dystrophic coarse moder, in the A_1 horizon occasionally mull-like moder with relatively good humification.

Dynamic : Low chemical weathering, tendency to strong acidification. Due to strong development of humus sols, distinct eluviation can already be detected.

Phenology : The soil is frozen and covered with snow for the greater part of the year. It is found in habitats where the snow melts early and the thaw water can run off. The soil is then only temporarily wet, although it never dries out completely in midsummer.

Biology : Low decomposition and humification, except for the A_1 horizon of some *tundra rankers* which can be very rich in the most varied forms of blackish droppings of small animals. Many habitats are so rich in lemming's droppings that the soil surface is extensively covered with them and the kind of humus formation is strongly influenced towards better decomposition and humification. In general, the life of plant microorganisms is hampered considerably while soil micro-fauna is only restricted by the low availability of nutrients (failing the pre-decomposition of the plant remains by bacteria, which many of the small animals require). In *tundra rankers*, the soil life always has a land humus character and is thereby clearly distinguished from the life of the *tundra anmoors* (page 113) and the *tundra mosses* (page 121).

1. **Mull like ranker** below *Festuca varia* on chlorite schist (Wöllaner Nock, Carintia, ca 2000 m, Austria).
2. **Grey ranker** below spruce forest on sericite phyllite (Rottenmann, Styria, ca 750 m. Austria).

54.   Eilag Ranker *)

Synonyms: Eilag soil (SACHAROV 1906), peaty mountain soil (GLINKA) **), root ranker.

General Specification: Non-dystrophic shallow *ranker* formation, characterized by a dense mat of roots and root remains, generally containing numerous blackish, small animal droppins, occurring in locations strongly exposed to strong winds within the alpine grass heath or cushion turf grass region of high mountains.

Characteristic:

Profile: The usually very shallow profile consists either of a uniformly composed A horizon with peaty appearance or of a brownish A_1 horizon extraordinarily rich in roots, usually always containing droppings of small animals and also small rock fragments, and a blackish A_2 horizon. The entire soil layer is mostly only a few centimeters thick and lies in general, directly on the surface of the rocky parent material (C horizon). Occasionally much thicker, partly cushion shaped humus formations can be found.

Habitat: The plant cover consists primarily of grasses or alpine Carex species. The locations are strongly exposed to the force of the wind so that the snow covering is generally small, the melting of the snow takes place relatively early, the snow water flows rapidly away and the very shallow soil, with no underground moisture at its disposal dries out easily. The soil is found not only on mountain peaks (i. e. those not reaching into the nival region) but also in other places strongly exposed to winds. It is possible on relatively steep sub-strata for *eilag rankers* to expand, i. e. spread out on the nearly vertical rock surfaces.

Humus Form: The strongly matted humus formation not only has a similar appearance to peat but can also be cut like peat. By its biology, however, it is a pronounced land humus formation, not only showing no water-logging but almost a xeromorphic character. It is distinguished from a raw humus rich in root content, because it is not a dystrophic, humus sol

---

*) Pronounced «A-lag».
**) Considering the constant confusion with moor peats which the description «peaty» here and in other humus formations (see dry peat) has led to, it is advantageous to avoid its use completely.

1.

2.

forming, strongly acid humus formation but moderately acid to almost neutral, producing no eluviation action. The root mat contains numerous, generally well humified, blackish droppings of small animals. At the same time, a considerable quantity of mineral powder and small rock fragments can generally be found, brought by winds and bound by the roots. In this way, the mineral parent material consists to a great extent of allothigenous windborne sediments. Part of this sediment as well as a large part of the small animal droppings are loosely contained in the root mat and can be isolated easily by shaking. The droppings are well preserved in shape and can frequently have a considerable mineral content. The humus formation is therefore either a moder, rich in roots, or a mull-like moder.

Occurrence : The soil appears not only in the *ranker* climax region (Sierra de Guadarrama, Caucasus) where it can occupy larger areas, but it occurs locally in suitable habitats within the *alpine sod braunerde* and *sod podsol* regions.

(32) Alpine Mull-like Ranker

Synonyms : Humus silicate soil (JENNY 1926) definition given by PALL-MANN 1933) = for «climax formations of the alpine region in equilibrium with their enviroment»; mountain wiesenboden (BOGUSLOWSKI, NEUSTRU-YEV 1915) = is only a synonym for forms without gleying or anmoor-like humus formations (i. e. not for the so-called marshy mountain wiesenboden of NEUSTRUYEV), also for forms without brown (B) horizons.

General Specification : Mineral rich, often considerably deep AC soil on lime deficient silicate rocks of the alpine grass heath region, partly also in the cushion heath region of many high mountains.

Characteristic:

Profile : The thickness of the humus horizons varies very considerably from a few centimeters to 1/2 meter and more. Frequently a more strongly through-rooted A_1 horizon may be determined. Transition A/C horizons to the C horizons can also be distinguished.

Colour : Grey, browny grey, dark grey to blackish, according to humus or mineral content.

Structure : Always loose, crumbling easily, when wet earthy, on drying out easily blown about by the wind, however, rarely very powdery.

Microscopic characteristics : Practically always distinct aggregate formation although usually of low cohesion. When dry they are brittle and break easily. They consist almost entirely of the droppings of small animals or fragments of them. Their mineral content is high, but the mineral material consists mainly of little-weathered mineral powder which in general can be easily isolated micro-mechanically and separated from the organic constituents. Undecomposed plant splinters are rare.

Humus Form: Mull-like moder. Well developed soils have a strong mull appearance, but microscopic investigation always allows the pronounced mull-like moder character to be distinctly recognized.

Texture: Generally pronounced sandy textures. The humic binding substances occasionally exhibit a certain loamyness when wet which is not due, however, to the presence of mineral clay.

Dynamic: Low chemical weathering, low clay formation, considerable acidification, little translocation of substances.

Biology: Relatively good decomposition and humification. The soil life corresponds to a distinct land humus formation in spite of a temporarily water-logged phase when the snow melts. Deep forms are successfully used as cultivated soils (vegetable gardens of alpine tourist houses, field near Albergue Universitario at 2,500 meters in the Sierra Nevada).

Occurrence: Frequent in the Caucasus, Central Alps, Sierra de Guadarrama (already from 2,000 meters), Sierra de Gata (Extrem.) and Sierra Nevada.

55. *Tangel Ranker* (n.f.)

General Specification: Humus rich, generally deep AC soil of the alpine dwarf shrub region which is formed, like the *tangel rendsina* (page 182), under the influence of humus plants yielding large quantities of plant residues and which is characterized by an upper humus horizon, externally similar to raw humus, but not dystrophic, and a lower mull-like humus layer.

Characteristic:

Profile: The humus horizon is divided into a litter layer (A_{00} horizon) which is rich in undecomposed plant remains, mineral deficient, deep brown tangel layer (A_0 horizon) and a blackish mull-like layer (A_1 horizon). All the sub-horizons blend into one another without sharp boundary. The entire humus layer generally attains a considerable thickness for alpine soils (from

A_{00}

A_0

A_e

A_e/C_1

A_1

C_1

C_2

C_2

1.

2.

20-60 cms.), in which the litter layer occupies 2-3 cms., the tangel layer about 5-25 cms., the A_1 horizon passes gradually into a C_1 horizon, only loosened mechanically and underneath into the hard parent material (C_2 horizon).

Structure : The tangel layer consists of bulky ordered plant remains and is more or less strongly permeated with plant rootlets and animal droppings. The A_1 horizon is always moist, earthy and crumbly.

Plant Cover : Primarily under the broom *Sarathamnus purgans*, which grows in a similar way to the dwarf pine, further under *Juniperus communis*, *subsp. nana*.

Humus Form : Tangel humus (page 36). The tangel layer is similar to that of the *tangel rendsina*. Also, it is distinguished from raw humus by its intense life, its richness in animal droppings, its failure to form humus sols, with corresponding podsolizing effect and by its occurrence above a well-developed, occasionally very thick layer of well humified mull-like moder into which it gradually passes. Most A_0 horizons show a distinct tendency to transform into mull-like moder on their lower side.

Biology : The bulky, rich in cavities, always moist tangel layer shows a rich soil life, particularly under *Sarathamnus purgans*. Towards the A₁ horizon increase in decomposition and humification.

Dynamic : Low chemical weathering, moderate acidification.

Occurrence : In particular on the eastern side of the Sierra de Guadarrama at a height of about 1,800-2,000 m., in the lower part mainly under *Sarathamnus purgans*, in the upper part of the dwarf shrub girdle more under *Juniperus*. In the absence of a forest girdle, a *brown tangel ranker* occurs already at a height of 1,500 meters, which is a transition formation to *Centro-European braunerde*.

56. *Mull Ranker* (n.f.)

General Specification : AC soil on lime deficient silicate rock with mull formation.

Characteristic :

Profile : A horizon generally shallow excepting on permeable parent material in the areas of steppe black earths, where the soil is designated *para-chernosem* (type XXXI). In the most frequently occurring form of the *grey mull ranker* (cf. *grey ranker*, No. 57, and *gant ranker*, No. (33)), the A horizon passes gradually into a usually grey coloured C_1 horizon, in the case of the *brown mull ranker* (*brown ranker*), often into a thin, seamy, brown-coloured (B) horizon.

Humus Form : Mull (page 41).

Reaction : Never strongly acid. Usually nearly neutral.

Texture : Mostly loamy to clayey textures. When moist, plastic.

Smell : Clayey to earthy.

Principal Parent Rocks : Clay schist, easily weathered basic igneous rocks.

Occurrence : In Central and Northern Europe rate, frequent in steppes and dry forest regions.

57. *Grey Ranker* (n.f.)

Synonyms : A/C$_1$ ranker.

General Specification : Soil on lime deficient silicate rocks showing a generally grey-coloured, loose layer between the humus horizon and the parent rock, which is formed by mechanical weathering, and is characterized by low chemical weathering and low precipitation of free ferric hydroxide.

Profile : The A horizon of variable thickness is followed by the characteristic loose C$_1$ horizon, usually grey, in some cases whitish coloured which gradually goes into the hard parent material (C$_2$ horizon).

Dynamic : Primarily mechanical, little chemical weathering and no distinct marks of translocation of material. The soil shows good water conduction and aeration and therefore the grey C$_1$ horizon is never a gley horizon.

Behaviour on Ignition : Free iron compounds are missing or only present in small quantities with primary rocks including those in the ferrous form. The C$_1$ horizon therefore gives in general no, or only slight, red-colouring on ignition, while earth from gley horizons reddens strongly on ignition.

Humus Form : Generally mull-like moder. In dry regions mull appears prominently.

Texture : Mainly sandy to silty textures. In dry regions with low chemical weathering, unbrowned soils also with loamy and clayey textures occur frequently (mainly on clayey parent rocks).

Principal Parent Rocks : In Central Europe in general, the formation of brown earths on lime deficient silicate rocks is so rapid that *grey rankers* are rarely found and only occur on difficult to weather, iron deficient, parent rocks. The principal parent rocks are sericite phyllite, muscovite schist, quartzite, iron deficient sandstone, etc. On sericite phyllite (graphite phyllite) besides brown earths, silty *grey rankers* are almost always seen, which are often under cultivation and then their ash-grey to intense dove-grey colour in the midst of the brown earths is very striking even at a distance. In Southern Europe *grey rankers* are frequently found on other parent rocks.

(33)   Gant Ranker
Ganter *)

Synonyms : Grey goose or wild goose (local name of the Bohemian Central Mountains).

General Specification : Particular form of the *grey ranker* having a C_1 horizon with high content of finely dispersed substances, low oxidation but not gleying, dense structure and low permeability to water, on easily weathered quartz-deficient and relatively iron-deficient parent rocks, particularly phonolite.

A related form occurs in the south of Spain (particularly in the Alpujarras, the south slopes of the Sierra Nevada), the *launa ranker,* which is described in the appendix (page 173).

Characteristics :

Profile : The soil generally has a humus deficient A horizon of slight thickness (2-5 cm.) which passes into a light grey, dense C_1 horizon, occasionally of considerable thickness. The parent rock (C_2 horizon) consists, usually of light grey to whitish phonolite. With arable cropping, the humus horizon is completely obliterated, uncultivated fields are striking due to their peculiar light grey colour.

Structure : The soil, particularly the C_1 horizon is low in cavities and forms when moist, a peculiar grey to whitish mud and becomes on drying out, a hard mass, difficult to work. As the soil is extremely low in quartz, the essential fine skeleton for a normal, biologically favourable structure is missing. Cultivated soils are easily silted-up and tend strongly to form crusts.

Dynamic : In spite of advanced chemical weathering, ferric hydroxide is only precipitated in small quantities. This is due partly to the dense, badly aerated structure (low oxidation) and partly to the iron being contained in the parent material in the form of hornblende stalks relatively difficult to weather. There are no apparent movements of substances in the structure, the accidification of the soil is low.

Behaviour to Water : As the soil has a low water conduction it shows either a rapid run off or local accumulations of water on the soil surface in the form of small pools, while most of the interior of the soil contains little water. Due to the strong erodability of the soil mass it is easily silted up.

Humus Form : Shallow humus-deficient mull.

---

*) Ganter = gander.

Biology: Life in the soil interior is impeded by the dense structure. Under grassland, the soil becomes in relatively good condition for cultivation. Owing to its proportionately deep soil profiles it often becomes used as arable soil. The dense, unstable structure of the soil, its low aeration, its unbalanced water economy, the difficulty of working it, as well as a certain general rawness and non-uniform development justifies the name «wild goose» soil.

Occurrence: Is known particularly by its occurrence in the Bohemian Central Mountains.

[2] *Launa Ranker*

General Specification: *Grey ranker,* similar to ganter, formed on feebly metamorphized phyllite or clay schist, of East Andalusia, with dense, easily silted up C_1 horizons.

Characteristics:

Profile: The humus horizon is generally better developed than that of the *gant ranker* of the Bohemian Central Mountains. Its thickness varies between 5-10 cms. The C_1 horizon can attain much greater thicknesses. The hard parent rock (C_2 horizon) is relatively soft and undergoes a strong leafy breakdown, however, without any browning due to the precipitation of free ferric hydroxide.

Nature of the C_1 horizon (Launa): The material of the C_1 horizon has considerable importance as it is used for packing the flat roofs of the houses particularly in the mountains of East Andalusia in the Alpujarras, the Sierra Contraviesa, as well as several areas in the province of Almería. The mass, called Launa, feels like talc, is light grey, silver grey (when sparkling strongly), to intense violet grey in colour and is obtained directly from the profile by digging. It is spread out on the flat roof surfaces and forms of its own accord after the first fall of rain (probably due to rearrangement of the leafy clay particles), a surface skin completely impermeable to water. The dried out mass is usually hard, so that the coating, in spite of strong mechanical strain (the inhabitants spend a great part of the time on their roofs), shows relatively little wear. The active constituents of the launa are micaceous clay minerals.

The launa layer in an undisturbed soil profile has a dense structure and on removal of the plant and humus cover it may be easily eroded. In summer, on drying out, it becomes very hard, making re-colonization of the eroded surfaces extremely difficult.

Dynamic: Essentially, softening and extensive mechanical break down of the soft parent rock, low chemical weathering with very slow precipitation of free ferric hydroxide. Soil development is therefore strongly retarded, so that in the brown earth region, *launa braunerde* is rarely found, generally launa raw soils and *launa ranker* predominate. Even on the difficult to weather, strongly metamorphized graphite sericite phyllites of the Alpujarras which are frequently found in the vicinity of launa soils, brown earth formation appears much earlier. It is worth noting further, that the *launa braunerde* is always characterized by the presence of a thick, dense C_1 horizon, under the usually shallow (B) horizon.

Humus Form: Usually, moderately raw mull-like moder containing numerous undecomposed plant remains.

Biology: The soil always exhibits a certain characteristic rawness, decomposition and humification is distinctly impeded, and the launa layer appears to contain scarcely any life at all.

58. *Podsol Ranker* (n.f.)

General Specification: Nutrient deficient, strongly acid, *dystrophic grey ranker*, whose light grey to whitish C_1 horizons are at the same time strongly bleached eluvial horizons (A_e horizons).

Characteristics:

Profile: This is the same as the upper part of a *podsol*, finishing at the A_e horizon, which lies directly on the hard parent rock, i. e. there are no B horizons. The A_0 horizon, usually formed by raw humus covers (in the case of mineral rich, dystrophic, coarse moder, A_1 horizon), is followed by a light grey, violet grey, to whitish bleached horizon, eluvial horizon or A_e/C_1 horizon (or A_2/C_1 horizon), and then by the C_2 horizon. Beginnings of B horizons are shown in the fissures of the unweathered parent rock (often deep down and can only be observed in quarries) consisting of incoherent flecks of blackish humus or rust brown iron precipitates; horizon formation does not occur.

In addition to pure raw humus covers and pronounced dystrophic coarse moder formations, transition forms can arise with the following profile structure: A_0 horizon (raw humus layer), A_1 horizon (coarse moder layer), A_e/C_1 horizon (bleached sand layer) and C horizon (hard parent rock).

Plant Cover: Generally raw humus plants, such as *Calluna vulgaris*, *Erica* species, *Empetrum nigrum*, etc., also coniferous wood covers.

Dynamic: Strong acidification, strong eluviation of chemical weathered products, protected by acid humus sols, which are lost in the parent rock or completely washed away.

Texture: Almost only loose sands with low colloid content.

Biology: Luxuriant development of a highly specific plant cover, in inert humus and mineral layers, partly sparse soil life due to lack of nutrients, strong acidity, cool soil climate and presence of decomposition impeding substances. Slow and incomplete decomposition and humification.

Humus Form: Raw hums or dystrophic coarse moder.

Principal Parent Rocks: Primarily, nutrient deficient, acid, difficult to weather kinds of rock such as quartzite, siliceous sandstone, siliceous schists, acid igneous rocks and crystalline schists.

Occurrence: Appearing in small localized areas, un-productive heath or coniferous wood soils or high mountain soils of the podsol zone, characterized by cold and humid air and soil climate.

59. *Brown Ranker* (n.f.)

General Specification: A soil form with stronger chemical weathering, with distinct formation of free ferric hydroxide and also with extensive browning of the humus, frequently underneath the humus horizon already showing a brown humus deficient seam, indicating a transition form from *ranker* to *braunerde*.

Variability and Delimitation: The *brown ranker* has an extraordinary variety of forms and characteristic varieties occur both in dry and wet regions. In the brown earth region ((35) *Central European brown ranker*), it is a short lived and therefore correspondingly rarely found transition formation to *Central European braunerde* which never forms a climax. In dry regions ((36) *brown xeroranker*), it is a relatively frequent transition form to *meridional braunerde* (No. 81). The *brown ranker* in dry regions is very similar to the *para-serosem* (type XXXII). Therefore, the distinction between the two forms is not easy. In general one can say that a *brown xeroranker* is a soil of limited extent on predominately hard parent rocks, while the *brown para-serosem* is a pronounced soil of the dry steppes on predominately loose or slightly hardened sedimentary parent rocks.

The variation of the *brown rankers* with humus form will be occasionally referred to under the paragraph humus form.

Characteristics:

Profile: The essential feature of the profile is the absence of true, well-developed (B) horizon and that the future (B) horizon is only indicated by a seam-like or striated formation. Its mode of description is similar to that of the *braunerde*: A horizon, (B) horizon, and C horizon. The A horizon is usually distinctly browned by ferric hydroxide, the lower humus and higher ferric hydroxide contents can give rise to doubts as to whether it is not alreay a brown earth. The soil, with strong browning is a *ranker* in every case, where the A horizon reaches to the C horizon. With many forms the seamy (B) horizon is missing, with others it appears as the only distinctive characteristic when the browning in the (usually humus rich) A horizon is little marked. Above hard parent rock (C_2 horizon) usually a mechanically loosed, in general, grey coloured C_1 horizon is seen.

Humus Form: Most *brown rankers*, the *Central European* as well as the *xerorankers* of Southern Europe, show mull formation. However, the soil may occur in conjunction with other humus forms. The form with tangel humus (*brown tangel ranker*) often shows a particularly deep development of humus, principally A_1 horizons. If this still shows no recognisable signs of browning, the seamy (B) horizon is always well developed (Sierra de Guadarrama, Sierra Nevada). Further, this is shown frequently in corresponding transitions from alpine silicate soil to the *alpine sod braunerde* or to the *Central European braunerde* of the forest region (Sierra de Guadarrama) with mull-like moder. In the extreme north, at the boundary of the tundra, transitions from *tundra ranker* to *northern semi-podsol* are found.

Dynamic: There are distinct signs of chemical weathering, particularly in the formation of clay and the precipitation of free ferric hydroxide. In general, low acidification, as well as no movements of substances.

CC. Rendsina-like soils

Key for the Determination of Types and Sub-types.

1. Soil resulting on «pure» or marly limestone, marble, marl, dolomite, magnesite or gypsum (eurendsinas) 2

1*. Soil resulting on calcareous silicate rock or on parent material which though calcareous consists mainly of quartz grains.

XXVII. Pararendsina.

2. Occurring in humid regions 3

2*. Occurring only in dry regions, very high in lime, ash-grey in colour, mainly loose and strongly powdery.

61. Xerorendsina.

3. Only occurring in the alpine region of high mountains 8

3*. Not only occurring in high mountains 4

4. With 8-30 cm. thick, mineral deficient, upper soil layer (tangel layer) of raw humus-like appearance, consisting to a great extent of little decomposed, mostly needle to stalk shaped plant remains.

(39). Tangel rendsina.

4*. Upper soil layer without raw humus-like appearance 5

5. The mineral rich humus layer is browned by free ferric hydroxide or on

its lower edge, a humus deficient brown seam or thin (B) horizon may be seen.

                                                (42) Brown rendsina.

5*.   Humus layer not really browned by ferric hydroxide or with a visible brown seam …   6

6.   Soil formation very young and generally only a few centimeters deep, usually blackish coloured without aggregate formation, consisting principally of incoherent constituents, e. g. bitten-through plant remains, droppings of small animals and calcite or dolomite powder.

                                             (36) Protorendsina.

6*.   Soil formation advanced, with definite development of mineral rich aggregates, usually visible to the naked eye … … … … … … … … … … … …   7

7.   Humus usually with moder smell, loose, low in, or free from, clay; aggregates small and generally of low cohesion.

                                         (40) Mull-like rendsina.

7*.   Humus with moderate to high clay content, mostly plastic, generally with continuous spongy fabric, plant remains completely humified, humus highly dispersed and contained in the clay as a finely divided colouring material (formation of clay humus complexes).

                                         (41) Mull rendsina.

8.   Soil occurring, like the plant cover, in isolated cushions of the upper alpine region, with a raw humus like outer layer and well humified, light grey to almost black nuclear layer.

                                   (38) Alpine cushion rendsina.

8*.   Soil not occurring in cushion form … … … … … … … … … … … …   9

9.   Soil usually light grey in colour, loose and without aggregate formation, rich in minerals, consisting to a great extent of chalk sand.

                                 [3]   Alpine protorendsina.

9*.   Soil when wet, almost black in colour, dense, pitchy, very low in minerals, consisting practically of very fine, strongly humified coprogenic elements.

                                   (37)   Alpine pitch rendsina.

XXV. *Rendsina (Eurendsina)* [7]

Synonyms: Rendsina (Polish peasant name, SIBIRTZEFF 1896), humus carbonate soil *), chalk humus soil, fleinserde; chrap (Russian local name) = = for very stony rendsinas; alvar = rendsina of the Baltic sea islands Gotland and Moon and the Baltic states; gadja or gaza (Caucasian local name, GEDEVANISCHWILLI 1930) = particularly for rendsinas on gypsum; gashi = = humus rich gypsum rendsinas of the North Caucasus; humus sulphate soils (AKIMTZEFF 1931) = rendsina on gypsum.

General Specification and Delimitation: According to humus

---

*) In the nomenclature of PALLMANN, the humus carbonate soil is not synonymous with *rendsina* but includes essentially the *protorendsina* and the *mull-like rendsina; rendsina* is identified with *mull rendsina* only (cf. LEUENBURGER 1950).

content blackish, dark grey to light grey coloured soil, usually calcareous to extremely calcareous, characterized by the formation of chalk humates and humus horizons which are formed directly on the limestone, marble [8]), dolomite, chalk marl or gypsum parent rock.

The designation *rendsina* is for AC soils only and not for *braunerde*, *braunlehm* or *rotlehm* on limestone.

Characteristics:

Profile: Most *rendsina* profiles divide into A, Ca and C horizons. With very young *rendsinas* on hard rock the Ca horizon is missing. The *rendsina* has an extreme diversity of form and each variety has a very different profile structure, particularly in the differentiation of the A horizon. Young *rendsinas* have a very shallow profile, usually containing very many stones. But, mature rendsinas (*mull rendsinas*) also seldom attain a soil depth greater than about 50 cm. They usually have also a certain stone content in the A horizon, which increases strongly with depth.

Humus Form: The humus formation is very variable. Mature, biologically often highly active *rendsinas* show mull formation. Other humus forms are: chalk moder, mull-like chalk moder, mineral deficient fine moder and tangel humus. Very wet locations also show transitions to anmoor.

Dynamic: Chemical weathering is strongly impeded by the high chalk content, to which the fixing of the humic substances of the animal droppings in the form of calcium humate is also due. In the humid zone, continuous leaching of chalk, in dry areas, partly capillary rise of chalk and water-soluble salts. Otherwise no movements of substances in the soil profile.

Occurrence: Due to the strongly retarded chemical weathering, especially in the formation of clay and free ferric hydroxide, soil development on limestone remains a long time in the *rendsina* phase. *Rendsinas* therefore occur more widely than *rankers* (which have a similar profile structure) and initial development stages even in the *podsol* region have relatively long lives and are therefore more frequently found. In spite of their external similarity, *rendsinas* in humid and arid areas differ essentially in their dynamic, biology and micromorphology.

60. Humid Rendsinas
(36) Protorendsina (n.f.)

Synonyms: Urfleinserde.

General Specification: Very shallow embryonic soil formation which consists entirely of loose constituents, e. g. bitten through plant remains, blackish, humus rich droppings composed of chalk humate, and unweathered mineral fragments (mostly calcite or dolomite).

1. **Alpine pitch rendzina** below moist *Firmetum* on limestone (Hochkönig, Salzburg, 2300 m., Austria).
2. **Grey alpine cushion rendzina** below *Silene acaulis* on limestone (Dachstein, Styria, 2800 m.).
3. **Black alpine cushion rendzina** below *Saxifraga Rudolfiana* on limestone (Hochkönig, Salzburg, 2700 m.).

Characteristics:

Profile: A horizon of uniform composition a few centimeters thick, usually lying directly on hard rock.

Plant Cover: Generally cushion-shaped or trellis-like growing rock plants.

Dynamic: Low chemical weathering, no movement of substances. Due to the high content of powdered calcite (effervescing strongly with HCl) no acidification. Chalk when dissolved undergoes strong leaching so that no secondary precipitation of calcium carbonate is seen in the structure.

Phenology: In winter moist, part of the time completely frozen; in summer, drying out easily, then completely loose to powdery, easily blown about by wind causing damage to the plant cover.

Humus Form: Mostly humus rich and calcareous rendsina moder (page 40).

Biology: Principally colonized by drought resistant horn mites. Deficient in Collembolae and other hygrophilous arthropoda. Relatively good good decomposition and humification in the coprogenic fraction of the humus formation.

Microscopic Characteristics: The plant remains are split into small pieces and exhibit numerous feeding marks. The droppings are throughout very small (ca. 50-100 μ long) and consist of well humified mineral deficient small cylinders which, in general, are well preserved. The mineral fragments are always found outside the droppings and consist usually of rounded calcite or dolomite granules.

Texture: Only coarse or fine sands.

Occurrence: Principally in the wooded regions of Central and Northern Europe, while it is rare in typical form in Southern Europe.

[3] *Alpine Protorendsina* (n.f.)

General Specification: Light grey calcite (dolomite) sand soil with mull-like appearance of the alpine region of high limestone mountains, generally silted up, frequently occurring washed down between rock débris.

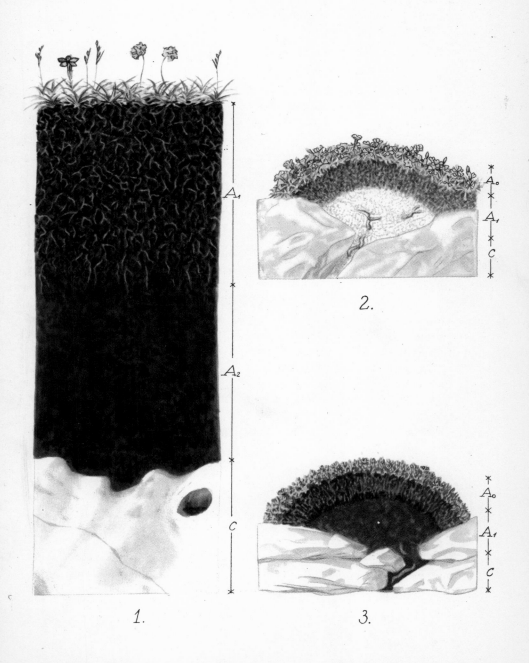

XIII.

A_1

A_2

C

1.

A_0

A_1

C

2.

A_0

A_1

C

3.

Characteristics:

Profile: The soil is easily eroded and with the sparse plant covering is exposed to strong puddling, particularly when the snow melts. Its depth therefore varies enormously, even that of the usually uniformly composed A horizon (from a few cms. to 2 dm. and more). This goes usually into a sandy-stony C_1 horizon, which, in turn, lies on the hard parent rock (C_2 horizon).

Phenology: The soil is frozen in winter and with the melting of the snow, owing to the extremely large quantity of water released, it becomes strongly water-logged, and on steep slopes with little vegetation strongly eroded, repeatedly rearranged, rapidly producing an extremely dense, puddled structure on drying out. During a long spell of fine weather in summer the soil is completely dried out and in places bare of vegetation, strongly blown about by the wind. With rain, the soil rapidly absorbs water and becomes, with too much moisture, an easily flowing sandy mud.

Microscopic Characteristics: The humus has a mull-like appearance to the naked eye, but it is not a mull-like moder as it consists almost entirely of very small mineral deficient droppings which are arranged loosely in the spaces between the granules of the mineral sand. Practically no aggregates are formed. It exhibits therefore, the typical structure of a *protorendsina*.

Dynamic: Low chemical weathering, due to the high chalk content, reaction always alkaline. Dissolved chalk undergoes strong leaching, so that even in mid-summer no precipitation due to capillary action occurs.

Humus Form: Mineral rich, rendsina moder.

Occurrence: Very widespread in the Limestone Alps.

(37) Alpine Pitch Rendsina (n.f.)

General Specification: A striking deep black, almost always moist but never water-logged, very mineral deficient *rendsina* with pitchy appearance, occurring in the alpine grass heath region of chalk high mountains.

Characteristics:

Profile: The soil is divided into an essentially loose A_1 horizon, 8-20 cm. thick, intersected by a dense root mat and a dense, deep black A_2 horizon, 10-15 cm. thick. The A_1 horizon is of a somewhat browny colour, due to the large number of roots present. The A_2 horizon generally lies directly on the hard parent rock. If this is laid bare, various small troughs (karren) due to strong solution weathering may be determined on its surface. Small stones in the soil show lixiviated edges and corners, and therefore rounded forms predominate. Rupture planes of the moist soil mass are dull and

Explanation of plate XIV

1. **Tangelrendsina** below *Pinus montana* and *Rhododendron hirsutum* on dolomite (Dachsteingebiet, Styria, 1700 m.).
2. **Brown rendsina** below *Quercus Ilex* and *Juniperus oxycedrus* on dolomitic limestone (Guadalix, Prov. Madrid, 850 m.).

---

lustreless, while the washed soil surfaces in places bare of vegetation give a pitchy or shoe polish lustre.

Microscopic Characteristics : The soil has an extremely low mineral content, so that in many places mineral fragments are completely missing. The humus in the A_2 horizon is composed exclusively of coprogenic elements, while in the A_1 horizon fresh plant roots are the only other constituents. Macroscopically the humus gives the impression of a highly dispersed mass, but on microscopic investigation, it consists of well formed cylindrical droppings of almost the same size, which are fastened together like semi-soft groats and in this way enclose a system of finely pored cavities. The soil mass shows a great uniformity in its inner construction and an extraordinarily characteristic fabric formation to which reference has already been made (page 40).

Water Relations : The humus takes up water rapidly, swells considerably and forms on drying out numerous macroscopic and microscopic fissures. In nature it rarely dries out, so that even in an extremely dry summer, in which all other soils in the neighbourhood are completely dessicated, the *pitch rendsinas* are still moist. On the other hand, it never suffers waterlogging.

Dynamic : Strong solution weathering and strong leaching which lead to the disappearance of all mineral substances (consisting of calcite) strong lixiviation of the stones remaining in the soil and produce the trough-shaped formation on the surface of the hard rock sub-stratum.

Biology : Good decomposition and humification but no possibility of forming clay-humus complexes. The soil life is concentrated principally in the loose A_1 horizon and is characterized by the prevalence of a Collembolae fauna.

Humus Form : Alpine pitch moder (page 40).

Principal Parent Rocks : Highly soluble limestone, deficient in residues forming impurities.

Occurrence : Frequently a climax soil formation of the grass heath region of the *Limestone Alps* (between ca. 2,000-2,600 m.). At the boundary with the *tangel rendsina*, transition formations are found.

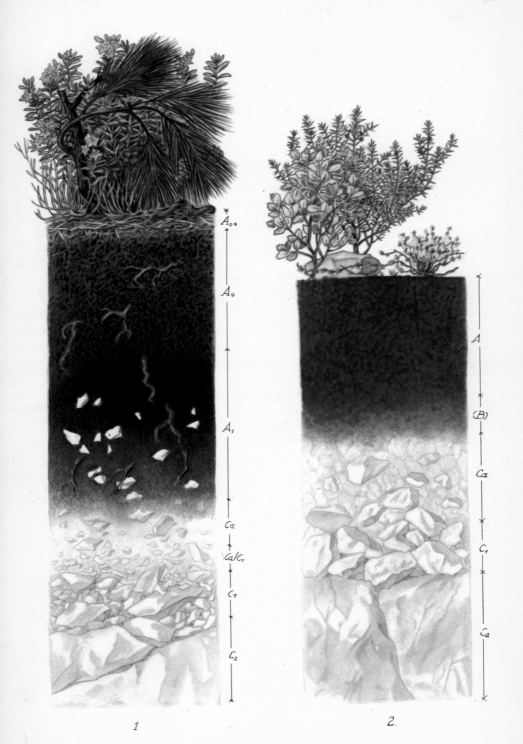

XIV

1.

2.

(38) Alpine Cushion Rendsina (n.f.)

General Specification: Very shallow *rendsina* occurring in the upper alpine region of chalk high countains under cushion plants, characterized by the formation of a dense, little humified, raw humus-like upper humus horizon and a well humified lower humus horizon rich in coprogenic elements.

Characteristics:

Profile: The soil has a cushion-like form as the plant cover. The brown exterior layer is formed by densely interwoven, living and dead plant stems and browned yet little decomposed leaf residues (A_0 horizon). It is very deficient in animal droppings, humus substances and mineral fragments and attains a thickness of 3-7 cm. The nucleus of the cushions (A_1 horizon) is filled up with well humified earth, which is either rich in minerals, sandy, and of a grey to light grey colour ([4]. *grey cushion rendsina*) or it can be blackish to deep black with little or no mineral content ([5]. *black cushions rendsina*).

Microscopic Characteristics: The A_1 horizon of the grey variety is rather like the *alpine protorendsina* (page 178) in structure and composition, while that of the black variety has a very similar composition to the A_2 horizon of a *pitch rendsina* (page 180). From many transitions between these two forms it is easy to recognise the genetic relationship between the two, the light grey form being the initial phase, the deep black mineral deficient the end phase.

Dynamic: From the *grey* to the *black cushion rendsinas* there is an increasing intensity of solution weathering and leaching, combined with decreasing alkalinity of reaction and chalk content. No precipitation of recrystallized chalk fragments in the structure.

Occurrence: Very widespread in the cushion grass region of the Limestone Alps (in ca. 2,400-3,300 m.).

(39) Tangel Rendsina (n.f.)

General Specification: *Rendsina* formed under luxuriantly growing humus plants yielding large quantities of plant residues, whose thick humus horizons are characterized by an A_0 layer of little decomposed needle- to stalk-shaped elements and an A_1 horizon consisting of a humus-rich mull or mull-like rendsina moder.

Characteristics:

Profile: Under the förna (A_{00} horizon) is seen a tangel layer (A_0 horizon) consisting of little decomposed plant remains and partly of deposits of animal droppings; it attains a thickness of from 8-40 cm. and passes

1. **Mull-like rendsina** below forest of *Pinus nigra austriaca* with *Sesleria varia* on dolomite (Mödling, Southern Wienerwald).
2. **Mull rendsina** below meadow on marl (Southern Wienerwald).

---

gradually into the underlying mineral rich well humified A_1 horizon. This is from 5-30 cm. thick and in locations within the forest phase consists frequently of a well developed mull. Under certain conditions the thickness of both horizons can considerably exceed the values given above. Attached to the A_1 horizon is usually a strongly developed Ca horizon (perhaps above an A/Ca horizon), which is formed above the hard parent rock (C horizon).

Humus Form: Tangel humus (page 36).

Plant Cover: So-called tangel plants (page 36).

Dynamic: Strong removal of chalk and enrichment of calcium carbonate in the lower part of the soil profile, considerable acidification in the A_0 horizon, no formation of humus sols, no movement of finely dispersed substances, no podsolization.

Biology: The tangel layer usually shelters a rich soil fauna, while the A_1 horizon is, in general, rich in earthworms, including both the mull-like varieties and those with mull formation. Due to the upward movement of the earthworms to the soil surface, the tangel layer, through which they pass, is also always permeated by calcareous worm casts, which inhibit strong acidification and create better conditions for decomposition in the upper soil horizons. In high lying locations, particularly facing north, the intensity of life is reduced, the tangel layer approaches more the character of the raw humus form ([7] *dystrophic tangel rendsina*). Yet even here no eluviation or podsolization occurs.

Phenology: Above the tree line the soil is frozen in winter and only thaws with the melting of the snow cover, which lies deeper in the dwarf shrub region and remains somewhat longer than in bare places. In the late spring the soil is thoroughly soaked and it retains a certain moisture content even in mid-summer.

Occurrence: Widespread in the dwarf shrub region of the Limestone Alps (between ca. 1,800-2,100 m.), further occurring frequently in Erica-rich relict pine woods (*Pinus nigra austriaca*) of the East Alps (from 800 m.) and in Erica-rich spruce woods with considerable humus horizons.

(40)   Mull-like Rendsina (n.f.)

General Specification: Mineral rich rendsina with mull-like appearance, however deficient in clay, in fine structure moder-like, characterized by

XV

A_{00}

A

Ca

C_1

C_2

A_1

A_2

A/Ca

Ca

Ca/C

C

1.

2.

the formation of loose, almost completely coprogenic aggregates, which show an intimate association of mineral and organic constituentes, but no development of clay-humus complexes.

Characteristics:

Profile: The thickness of the generally dark grey coloured humus horizons (A horizons) varies from a few centimeters (under pioneer turf) up to 25 cm. (under forests) or more. In forests it is normally differentiated into a more or less distinct förna, F horizon, with semi-decomposed, but still recognizable plant remains and thick H horizon. The A horizon passes gradually through an A/Ca horizon into a Ca horizon, which is usually easily recognizable in deeper profiles, but in embryonic soil formations very reduced or completely missing. The transition from the Ca horizon to the parent rock (C horizon) is equally gradual. Often the Ca horizon coincides with a gravelly to gravelly-gritty C_1 horizon and then it will be called the Ca/C_1 horizon and the hard parent rock the C_2 horizon.

Texture: Sandy, few or no clay constituents.

Humus Form: Mull-like rendsina moder (page 40). The humus frequently has a strong resemblance to a mull, so that the mull-like moder character usually only becomes distinct by microscopic investigation (especially in a thin section preparation). Simple diagnostic signs are: pronounced sandy condition when dry, easy break down of the aggregates (crumbling easily), absence of clayey or earthy smell, not infrequently typical (similar to the silicate moder smell) moder smell, low plasticity.

Microscopic Characteristics: See page 40.

Dynamic: Increasing solution weathering and removal of dissolved chalk, no acidification due to the continual presence of rich reserves of chalk minerals; clay formation impeded, almost no precipitation of free ferric hydroxide, high permeability of soil and sub-stratum and absence of ground water.

Plant Cover: On rocky heath pioneer turf and shrubs, closed pasture vegetation, forests, principally mixed and coniferous forests. Particularly well developed profiles are shown under the East Austrian black pine forests (Pinus *nigra*).

Biology: Good decomposition and humification, rich soil life which with forest rendsinas reaches deep into the mineral soil and as the soil is rarely frozen, the activity of the bulk of the soil fauna is scarcely interrupted by winter. Strong appearance of *Julidi, Glomeridi, Engerlings, ants* (rocky heaths), insect larvae, already partly earthworms (particularly in forest *rendsinas*), but no formation of clay-humus complexes by their activity.

Phenology: *Rendsinas* in rocky heaths and tree-less regions undergo a strong alternate freezing and thawing in winter, while in summer drying out occurs early. Forest *rendsinas* in general do not freeze up with sufficient snow and also in summer show a balanced moisture content. As the soil has a high permeability, it is never water-logged.

Principal Parent Rocks: Clay deficient limestone, siliceous limestone, dolomite. On marly limestone and marl rocks mull formation appears quite rapidly, so that *mull-like rendsinas* are rare on them and only found as very shallow, embryonic formations.

Occurrence: The most frequently occurring forms of *rendsina* in Central and Northern Europe.

Spruce Wood Phase: Under spruce forests with few shrubs, a phase is frequently formed, whose H horizons are not only distinguished from the other forms by their brownish colour, but also by slight acidification, low preservation of the shape of animal droppings and a tendency to form a coherent structure, in which the humus substances derived from the droppings are acting as binding substances. The binding is decidedly stronger than in normal aggregates of the *mull-like rendsinas.*

(41) Mull Rendsina (n.f.)

Synonyms: Mullfleinserde.

General Specification: Especially active and fertile *rendsina* with moderate to high clay content, excellent crumb structure and mull formation.

Characteristics:

Profile: The light grey, dark grey to blackish humus horizon (A horizon) is about 15-35 cm. thick and passes gradually through an A/Ca horizon into a generally well developed Ca horizon (occasionally up to 1/2 m.). Between this and the hard parent rock (C_2 horizon) there can be either a C_1 horizon of rock débris primarily loosened mechanically or one which contains, in addition to the débris, abundant secondary precipitates of calcium carbonate (Ca/C_1 horizon). With forest soils (primarily deciduous forests) there is low accumulation of litter (generally only of the previous year) and the almost complete absence of an F horizon is characteristic. The *mull rendsina* is generally considerably less stony, than the other sub-types. Occasionally on hard parent rock (e. g. marl schists) almost completely stone-free humus horizons occur.

Texture: Sandy-loamy, loamy to clayey.

Humus Form: Generally excellently developed mull (page 41), in no way inferior to that of the *chernosem* (type XXX).

Macroscopic Characteristics of the Humus Layer : The humus has a good crumb structure, in which the individual aggregates are generally rounded in shape and are glued to each other at their points of contact. In this way a structure very rich in cavities is produced (spongy fabric), a characteristic which is shared by most other mull soils, in particular by the *chernosem.* Here, as in the others, the rounded to bulbous or kidney-shaped aggregates must be regarded as typical and the rare sharp-edged aggregates occurring with extremely low clay content are only characteristic of transition forms to limestone braunlehm (*terra fusca,* No. 74). The soil, when moist, is highly plastic (easily moulded by kneading) and usually has a distinct clayey, or with especially active forms, a typical earthy smell.

Microscopic Characteristics : Investigation even with a binocular microscope (magnification 8-16 times) already shows distinctly, in neadly every case, that the soil aggregate complex consists of bulbous to kidney-shaped earth-worm excreta. Further, where the contours are very indistinct, the coprogenic origin of the individual aggregates can be unequivocally determined by splitting with a needle, further, in a thin section preparation by the various typical form remains, such as kneaded or compressed structures, crescent-shaped cavities (which occur frequently in the dropping complex) saucer-shaped depressions and by the frequently mosaic composition of parts of different colouring and different humus and iron contents (droppings of material from different parts of the profile). The thin section further clearly shows the typical spongy fabric (which does not occur in other *rendsinas*), the absence of any undecomposed plant remains and the resulting presence of highly dispersed humus substances in the clay fraction of the soil.

Dynamic : Strong solution weathering and removal of the calcium carbonate from the upper soil layers, strong chalk enrichment in the subsoil. Increasing clay content due to the release of clay constituents as the parent rock is weathered, but formation of new clay and precipitation of brown iron are still low.

Water Relations : The soil has a much higher water capacity than the other mineral-rich *rendsinas;* therefore it is characterized by balanced water relations, a higher, more lasting moistness with high air content and a reduced risk of complete drying out.

Principal Parent Rocks : Highly soluble, principally marly limestones, marls and marl schists.

Preferred Location : Everywhere in which the accumulation of clayey solution remains is favoured and with it the development of *mull rendsinas* may be considerably accelerated and facilitated. Primarily steps in slopes, relief depressions, level bases of slopes and lower parts of slopes.

Biology : Rapid and complete decomposition of organism remains, excellent humification and clay-humus complex formation, rich soil life with the activity of the mull-forming earthworms particularly prominent.

Occurrence : Fertile forest and meadow soils, principally of the hill phase of Central Europe. In mountainous country they are restricted to comparatively small areas and show very unequal development (strong alternation in depth of humus and soil). They are therefore only exceptionally cultivated.

(42) Brown Rendsina

Synonyms : Degraded humus carbonate soil (LAATSCH 1938).

General Specification : Rendsina with advanced chalk removal and brown iron precipitation, which is characterized either by a striking browning of the always mineral-rich humus horizons or by the formation of a brown seam on their lower edge or by both.

Characteristics :

Profile : The A horizon, with humus deficiency always grey brown in colour, dark grey in soils rich in humus, is frequently followed by a more strongly browned but still humus-containing A/(B) horizon or by humus deficient brown or ochre brown seamy (B) horizon coloured entirely by free ferric hydroxide. In the lower part of the profile there is usually a strongly developed Ca horizon, which goes through a strongly gravelly Ca/C_1 horizon, still containing a large quantity of calcium carbonate due to secondary precipitation, eventually developing gradually into the unweathered parent rock. Forest profiles are characterized generally by a thin förna, containing almost only the previous year's litter, and by a little developed or completely missing F horizon.

The profile structure of the soil has a great similarity to that of the *degraded chernosem* (No. 71) with which it has many other characteristics in common.

Dynamic : Strong solution weathering, and strong removal of the already extensively used up chalk, generally no longer effervescing with dilute HCl in the A horizon. Increasing clay enrichment, also due to the formation of clay by chemical weathering, and precipitation of free ferric hydroxide.

Humus Form : In most cases mull (page 41).

Texture : Loamy textures predominate. With transitions to *terra fusca*, highly dispersed clays are not infrequent.

Structure :In general, similar to that of the *mull rendsina* (page 185). consisting of rounded to bulbous elements compounded into a spongy fabric, whose formation is due in the first place to the activity of earthworms.

Transition formations to *terra fusca*, with easily puddled, highly swelling clays, break down on drying into sharp-edged aggregates (separations).

Water Relations : High water capacity, with spongy fabric good water conduction with good aeration, absence of excessive moisture contents, excluding transition formations to *terra fusca* in which due to the soil mass becoming easily puddled its permeability to water may be sharply reduced.

Biology : Generally good decomposition and humification, which, in spite of the intensity of the soil life and the thickness of the living humus layer, is inferior to that of the *mull rendsina*. As with the *mull rendsinas* the activity of earthworms is very important.

Occurrence : Chiefly forest and meadow soils of central Europe in comparatively small areas. As with the *mull rendsina*, there is usually a very irregular formation (strong alternation in the depth of the humus and soil layers).

61. *Xerorendsina*

Synonyms : Popylucha or Popelucha (Russian folk name in Saratow, DIMO 1904) = ashy rendsina; rendsina cinérea (Spanish), dry rendsina.

General Specification and Delimitation : *Rendsina* ash grey in colour, usually very loose, when dry in general very powdery, with extremely high chalk content often also of water-soluble salts, particularly gypsum; ocurring in dry regions.

The soil is very similar to the *serosem* (type XXVII) in profile structure, micromorphology, dynamic and biology. One calls a soil on solid parent rock with strongly varying structure and composition, occurring in primarily mountainous places, a *xerorendsina*. A soil of the dry steppe with distinct mull formation and distribution over wide areas, on predominately loose parent material ought to be called a *serosem*.

Characteristics :

Profile : Whitish ash grey to dark ash grey, shallow, loose A horizon, always effervescing strongly with HCl and varying from about 30 to 10 cm. in depth. This passes through a mostly well developed, easily hardened, whitish-grey to almost white Ca horizon on to hard parent rock. The upper part of the A horizon is frequently somewhat lighter with a lower humus content (A_1 horizon), followed by a somewhat darker layer of a brownish hue (A_2 horizon), subsequently by a layer again lower in humus, lighter and whitish grey (A/Ca horizon). The surface of soils on gypsum rock or marls containing gypsum, frequently show whitish flecked efflorescences of gypsum.

Dynamic : Strong mechanical weathering owing to the considerable temperature variation, scant weathering by solution and little eluviation owing

Explanation of plate XVI

1. **Xerorendsina** below xerophitic flora of rock steppe, in the picture *Lavendula latifolia* and *Brachypodium ramosum* on marl rich in gypsum (Sierra de la Muela, Prov. Zaragoza, Spain).

2. **Serosem** on marl containing gypsum below scanty vegetation of the dry steppe, in the picture *Herniaria fructicosa* and *Ononis tridentata* (Vallecas, near Madrid).

---

to the low rainfall. Fragments of limestone show a distinctly lower mechanical hardness and roughened finely-corroded surfaces. As the chalk cementing material in the fine rock débris is partially dissolved and re-precipitated in the finest micro-crystals, the rock structure breaks down into individual grains. Such separated particles are also brought in large quantities to the A_1 horizon by wind. In soils with sufficient clay content, on drying out sometimes a distinct permeation of the structure with minute calcite crystals occurs, carried up to the surface in the soil solution by capillary action. These chalk precipitates do not have a hardening effect, as with the *chalk crust yerma* (page 156), but a strong loosening effect, as in the *dust yerma* (page 151). A similar effect can be produced by deposits of gypsum. The formation of clay and the liberation of free ferric hydroxide, due to chemical weathering, is strongly impeded by the high chalk content. The rain water and subsequent percolation water which the soil temporarily obtains are sufficient to produce a solution and a washing down of a certain quantity of chalk and the formation of a chalk enriched horizon under the humus horizon. It is also formed by stronger weathering of the rock, which can be observed in the Ca horizon where the moisture conditions are relatively the best.

Plant Cover: Open, in summer completely dried out plant cover of the dry rock steppe, showing considerable bare soil. The tendency of many plants to woodiness and the development of thorny branches is typical.

Humus Form: On loamy soils frequently a dry, humus deficient mull ((44). *Mull xerorendsina*) also mineral-rich mull-like rendsina moder ((43). *Mull-like xerorendsina*) with very low aggregation.

Phenology: The soil is heated up extremely in summer with extraordinarily high surface temperature variation, particularly with stony forms of hard limestone. After rain, owing to its high permeability, there is no stagnation or lasting moistness. Non-loamy forms dry out strikingly quickly.

Biology: In spite of the dryness, good decomposition and humification, the soil is however, very low in humus due to the slight production of organic parent material by the scant plant cover. Loamy soils contain also a particular earthworm fauna. Due to their activity, the surface is often covered by heaps of cylindrically shaped, rather small (3-5 mm. long) earthworm casts.

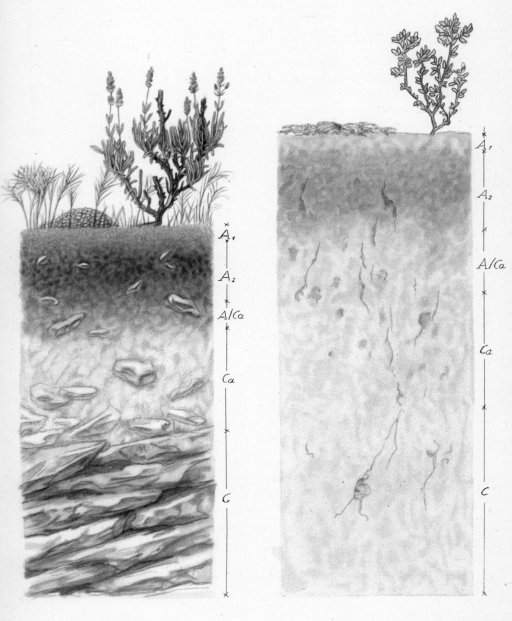

XVI

1

2

Occurrence: In karst areas in the mountains of dry regions in Southern Europe on limestone, marl, gypsum and gypsum-rich marls, very widespread. The soil forms no coherent surfaces but varies strongly with rocky floors, fields of boulders and bare débris and also shows very unusual development in depth, stoniness, humus content and humus depth.

XXVI. *Pararendsina*

Synonyms: Mixed rendsina (MIECZYNSKI).

General Specification and Delimitation: *Rendsina* with a predominantly siliceous and silicate micro-skeleton, developed on basic rocks which with weathering form much calcium carbonate, or on calcareous silicate and silica rocks.

The *mull-pararendsina* can be very similar to a shallow *chernosem,* so that in steppe regions they are very difficult to distinguish. One calls a *pararendsina* a shallower, less uniform soil occurring in small isolated areas on hard parent rock with the above characteristics and a *chernosem* a soil formation uniform over wide areas on loess or similar sediments containing chalk. Soils within this category occurring outside the steppe region are always called *pararendsinas*.

Characteristics:

Profile: A horizons of very variable depth which usually pass through a Ca horizon into the mechanically loosened C_1 horizon and finally followed by the hard parent rock (C_2 horizon). With loose parent material there is no division of the C horizon into sub-horizons. A horizons with high humus content have a dark grey to blackish colour. With areas low in humus the colour and type of the micro-skeleton (sand or silt fraction) are very important and exert a considerable influence on its appearance and characteristics. Therefore its colour can vary from light grey, yellowish grey, reddish grey to green grey (chloritic chalk-silicate schists). Calcareous silicate shifting sands (lower Austria, West-Slovakia) produce grey incoherent humus horizons in which, even in advanced stages of development, no binding material is present. High terraces and boulder layers of «nagelfluh» in the alpine foothills form initially, AC soils with a very prominent micro-skeleton of rounded silicate rocks and chalk sandstone. These give rise generally to loose A horizons with humus substance composed of chalk humates and a mineral fraction of predominately quartz sand.

Humus Form: Most frequently, mull and mull-like moder. In humid regions generally the mull formation occurs more quickly than with most eurendsinas due to the usually rapid breakdown of the rock. Correspondingly the *protorendsina* phase is proportionately rare. On the other hand, in *podsol* regions, especially on certain rocks (e. g. calcareous mica schists, in the region of the *alpine sod podsols* of the East Alps), it sometimes happens that the *pararendsina* appears only as a short-lived initail soil formation in the form of a *protorendsina,* which rapidly becomes decalcified and is changed into a chalk deficient silicate soil sequence (*ranker, alpine sod braunerde, alpine sod podsol*).

Texture : Mostly sandy to sandy-loamy textures.

Dynamic : The washing out of the $CaCO_3$ in general takes place easily, and, owing to the lower chalk reserves, the process is brought to an end more rapidly than in the eurendsinas. Accordingly, the *rendsina* phase has, in general, a much shorter life in the *pararendsina* sequence than in the eurendsina. In the podsolic region, as the silicate rich micro-skeleton of the soil structure is easily eluviated, it is followed very soon by podsolic soils or *podsols,* which again emphasizes strongly the special position of the *pararendsinas.*

Parent Rocks : In arid regions (South-east Spain, Canary Islands) basic igneous rocks which, on weathering, form large quantities of free $CaCO_3$, such as basalt, basanite, tephrite, etc. *). The other most frequently occurring parent rocks are: chalk sand-stone, calcareous sands, conglomerate and breccia with calcareous cementation, calcareous mica-schists, calcareous phyllite, calcareous silicate schists.

Occurrence : Limited to comparatively small areas and occurring only on particular parent rocks in both humid and arid regions of Central and Southern Europe.

CD. Steppe soils

AC soils primarily derived from loose parent material or on easily weathered hard to semi-hard parent rock easily transformed into deep loose layers, generally with uniform development on broad, level rolling to low hilly areas in steppes, desert steppes or cultivated regions with dry summers.

General Classification : The steppe soils described in soil science literature belong exclusively to the group of soil formations resulting on calcareous sediments. The chalk content is also essential here for the formation of typical AC soils, because it impedes the chemical weathering and retards further development to braunerde-like A (B) C soils. The typical climate of the steppe, dry summer and soil frost in winter, retards the washing out of the chalk and therefore the effect of the chalk is maintained. In contrast to this, parent materials low in chalk either show from the beginning a more or less strongly progressive browning and weathering (deposits of fossil soil

---

*) In Extremadura (Almendralejo) even on gneis rich in plagioclases.

formations of *braunlehm* or *braunerde* character) or they gradually take on to an increasing degree the character of a *meridional braunerde* (at the edge of the steppe, even *Central European braunerde*) [9]). The distinction and separation of steppe soils into those on parent material with high chalk content and those on parent material with chalk deficiency is of great importance, as it is not only reflected in their different morphological and chemical characteristics and in another development, but also (particularly the AC soils) in their area of occurrence.

Ranker-like soils on chalk deficient parent material, with deep chernosem-like humus horizons are to be distinguished from the calcareous *chernosem* and are called, according to my nomenclature *para-chernosems*. Analogous formations to the calcareous *serosems* lead to the designation for the chalk deficient varieties of *para-serosem*. Chalk deficient chernosem-like soils with A(B)/C profile (i. e. with partially browned parent material and browned humus formation) receive the name *brown para-chernosem*. Also the *para-serosem* is not a climax and can often be transformed into a very dry variety of *meridional braunerde*. The transition form, I have designated *brown para-serosem*.

Classification of Calcareous Steppe Soils : The classification and geographical delimitation of calcareous steppe soils has often proved troublesome in the past because they all more or less correspond to the *chernosem* ground-type (type XXX) and are only distinguished chiefly by humus content and colouring, depth of soil and degree of eluviation. Thus it is for example easy to find in strongly eroded *chernosem* regions a shallow humus deficient, highly calcareous steppe soil which in construction and appearance is very similar to a *serosem* but which is nothing else than the initial phase of a black earth or a truncated *chernosem*. In spite of this there exist fundamental differences between the two formations, which are, however, to a great extent unsuitable for general, easy practical diagnosis. But there is one characteristic easily used for diagnosis which must be considered first: the primitive steppe soils (*serosem, burosem,* brown desert steppe soil) are easy to recognize in that they occur only as climax formations i. e. maturer, deeper, more strongly leached formations richer in humus are not found in their region of occurrence. Closely related to it is the characteristic form of the plant cover for each type as well as its uniformity and permanence for the primitive soils of the desert steppe. Extremely characteristic also is their biology *) but their diagnostic evaluation is on the one hand only available to the specialists and, on the other, is still little worked out.

---

*) A *serosem* is distinguished for example from an embryonic soil in the *chernosem* zone, from the beginning, by a particular biology corresponding to the conditions of life in the desert steppe.

Key for the Determination of Types.

1. Soil formed from calcareous to highly calcareous parent material   2
1*. Soil formed from chalk deficient to chalk free parent material   6
2. Humus horizon extensively decalcified with seam or narrow band-like (B) horizon on its lower edge, coloured brown by precipitations of ferric hydroxide.

71. Degraded chernosem.

2*. Soil neither with brown seam or band-like (B) horizon   3
3. Soil occurring only in the desert steppe, always very humus deficient and with low depth of humus, very dry, with open xerophytic plant cover only cultivable under irrigation   5
3*. Soil usually with a deep, dark-coloured humus horizon, cultivable without irrigation, with closed natural turf cover or used as arable soil   4
4. Humus when moist, blackish to dark grey.

XXX. Chernosem.

4*. Humus when moist, chestnut brown.

XXIX. Kastannosem (chestnut-coloured soil).

5. Humus horizon light grey, often scarcely distinguishable from the mineral soil.

XXVII. Serosem.

5*. Humus horizon grey brown.

XXVIII. Burosem (brown soil of the desert steppe).

6. Soil occurring only in the desert steppe, always very humus deficient and with low depth of humus, very dry, with an open, sparse xerophytic plant cover.

XXXII. Para-serosem.

6*. Soil not occurring only in the desert steppe, generally with deep humus horizon under a closed, natural turf cover or used as arable soils.

XXXI. Para-serosem.

XXVII. Serosem

(Neustrujeff 1900)

Synonyms: Sierosem, sierosiom *) = grey earth; grey desert steppe soil, grey soil of the semi-desert (STEBUTT), grey desert soil; bielosem = = white earth (DOKUTSHAEFF 1893), refers equally to marl raw soil.

General Specification: Light grey coloured, very humus deficient but extremely calcareous AC soil, with very little leaching, shallow humus horizon, sparse, open, xerophytic plant cover and scanty soil life, occurring exclusively as climax formation in the desert steppe.

---

*) Written this way to correspond with the Russian pronunciation.

Characteristics:

Profile: Common to all varieties is a shallow humus horizon of 5 to about 20 cm. in depth, contrasting little with the subsoil followed by a usually cemented, crusty Ca horizon, which gradually passes into the generally looser C horizon. In the surfaces of the A horizon a lighter coloured bright grey A_1 horizon is seen which is either powdery to dusty or in many loamy forms, has a dense, partly leafy structure. Its formation is due to a large supply of wind-borne calcareous sediments, which either remains loose or becomes puddled by rainwater. Under the A_1 horizon is seen a usually somewhat darker and richer in humus, slightly brownish coloured A_2 horizon which again is followed by a light grey A/Ca horizon (see the very similar *xerorendsina*, plate XVI). On highly calcareous parent material, the Ca horizon often differs very little from the C horizon. With stronger colonization by soil animals, the humus and chalk enriched horizons have a more or less distincly spongy fabric. The «krotowinas» (page 201), so typical of *chernosem* profiles, are missing.

Principal Parent Materials: Loess, loess-like sediments, marl and marl sand.

Dynamic: Strong physical, low chemical weathering, impeded by the high chalk content and the extremely dry soil climate, little leaching, therefore also usually low chalk enrichment. In summer capillary rise to the soil surface.

Chemical Characteristics: High chalk content already in the surface layer. Due to the slight leaching occasionally only slight differences in chalk content together with slight differences in the general, composition of substances in the various horizons. The *common serosem* is deficient in salts to almost completely free from water-soluble salts. The reaction is always alkaline. A neutral or slightly acid reaction is possible only on serosem-like soils on very chalk deficient parent material (see *para-serosem*, page 205).

Plant Cover: Open, very sparse, strongly xerophytic vegetation consisting of very woody shrubs of the desert steppe.

Common Species: *Artemisia tridentata, Anabaxis aphylla, Ceratocarpus arenarius, Alhagi camelorum, Rosa berberifolia*, etc.

Humus Form: On loamy soils not infrequently mull, otherwise usually mineral rich, mostly extremely calcareous, mull-like chalk moder.

Humus Content: 1-2 %. An important characteristic compared with other steppe soils.

Biology: In spite of dryness and low colonization, mostly good decomposition and humification of the few organism remains, sparse production of organic matter, low accumulation of humus. On loamy *serosems* characterized by mull formation, colonization by earthworms can often be observed, usually recognisable externally by the presence of heaps of worm casts. The *serosem* can only be used for agricultural purposes if irrigated. It is often difficult to work owing to the cemented subsoil.

Association with other Soil Types: Especially in very undulating country, occasionally a rapid alternation of raw soils, *common serosems, saline serosems* (see below) and salt soils (almost only *solonchaks,* which form in the relief depressions) is found. Of the salt soils the common one is the so-called *grey solonchak,* while the *black solonchaks,* which preponderate in the *chernosem* zone, are absent.

Uniformity of the Serosem Steppe: On broad generally level areas it shows, with only very slight variations, the uniform profile of the *common* or *saline serosem,* or on more undulating surfaces, an almost equally uniform alternation of the above mentioned types, where one or the other of the types may be left out (occurrence of type complexes which is referred to particularly in Russian literature).

Variability: The *serosem* shows some variations. These must therefore be distinguished from the common, normal (simplest) ground type (62. *Common serosem*) and given particular names. The following are the most important varieties (besides the chalk deficient *para-serosem,* see page 205).

63.   Solonchak-Serosem: As the ground-water of the desert steppe is frequently rich in water-soluble salts, salty *serosems* are very wide-spread. They are distinguished from *common solonchaks* in that they are never derived from soils formed under the influence of ground-water, therefore they never show marks of gleying or former gleying but exhibit besides their particular characteristic the normal *serosem* profile. They are characterized generally by a distinct enrichment of water-soluble salts, which may become apparent in efflorescences on the soil surface. The A_1 horizon, in the same way as the *salt dust yerma* (page   ), and *dust yerma* is generally loose, powdery and crumble into powder at slight presure. Besides the Ca horizons not infrequently gypsum enriched horizons are formed too.

64.   Solonetz-Serosem: Due to their association with *solonchaks, common serosems* occasionally become covered with powder rich in sodium salts, whose salt content is sufficient for the formation of sodium-rich absorbing complexes. With sufficient clay content, a solonetz-like variety is formed without the preliminary solonchak-like phase. They are characterized therefore without the preliminary solontshak-like phase. They are characterized therefore by the soil containing an adsorption complex rich in Na- ions and a profile showing a dense A_2 horizon with slight tendency to columnar formation. There are various transition forms both between the solonetz-variety and the *common serosem* and between the *solonchak-serosem* and the typical form.

Occurrence: As the greater part of the Russian *serosem* steppe occurs in the Turkestan region, the grey desert steppe soils, which appear in broad areas on other continents, are of little importance in Europe. It occurs in limited areas in South Russia, Roumania and Spain.

XXVIII. Burosem
Brown desert Steppe soil

Synonyms: Brown soil (DOKUTSCHAJEFF 1989), brown soil of the semi-desert (STEBUTT), light brown steppe soil = mostly for transition formations to *serosem*.

General Specification: Calcareous, climax forming AC soil of the desert steppe with lightbrown coloured top-soil due to the low humus content, ocurring under an open, xerophytic plant cover and in respect of humus content, humus depth and intensity of soil life being superior to the *serosem* but inferior to the chestnut soil.

Characteristics:

Profile: The soil is quite variable which is strongly reflected in the profile. All varieties have in common a humus horizon from 20 to 50 cm. in depth, which is divided into a light, more grey coloured, nearly always loose A_2 horizon and a very much lighter A/Ca horizon of a brownish light grey colour. The formation of the loose A_1 horizon is strongly influenced by the supply of wind-borne sediments. Joined to the humus-layer is a more or less cemented Ca horizon, which gradually passes into the usually calcareous parent rock.

Soil Colour: The brown colour is of a much lighter hue than in chestnut soils. Il the colouring is conditioned almost entirely by humus, it shows a typical grey shading in the same way as in the chestnut soils. In soils which already show a certain amount of free ferric hydroxide in the parent material its influence on the brown coloration is stronger than with humus-rich *chernosems*.

Dynamic: Moderate rate of washing out of the chalk, somewhat stronger chalk enrichment in the subsoil than in the *serosem*. The chemical weathering is impeded by the chalk content. No movement of substances occurs besides that of calcium or magnesium carbonate in normal brow steppe soils.

Chemical Characteristics: Still effervescing with HCl in the surface layer, though frequently only feebly. Reaction generally slightly alkaline. Slightly acid soils with similar profile structure are derived from parent material low in chalk (see *brown para-chernosem*). Besides the always distinct enrichment of chalk in the Ca horizon, and differences in humus content, in normal soils almost no variation in chemical composition is found in the various horizons.

Humus Content: On the average 2-3 %.

Principal Parent Rocks: Loess, loose marl and marly sands.

Plant Cover: Generally characteristic open plant cover of the dry-steppe, leaving however distinctly less bare areas. Predominately xerophytic shrubs. Typical species are *Artemisia incana, A. austriaca, A. sieberi.*

Humus Form: Always mull.

Biology: Good decomposition and humification, although low production of organic parent material. Almost always colonized by earth-worms. The soil, due to the economic weathering and low rate of leaching, is rich in nutrients and normally has a porous, stable structure which, on irrigation, forms a luxuriant habitat for cultivated plants. The chalk enriched horizon is usually not reached during cultivation.

Association with other Soil Types: In strongly undulating country brown soils can occur frequently with pure salt soils which are formed in the depressions. These are generally solonchaks, and they often exert a great influence on the neighbouring brown soils.

Variability: The brown soil occurs not only in its normal form (65. *Common burosem*) but with several variations, which differ from it in certain characteristics. The most important are the following (besides the externally similar *brown para-serosem,* see page 206).

66. Solonchak-burosem: Due to the saline ground-waters in the region of true solonchaks, the normal brown soil easily becomes enriched with salts by capilliary action. These solonchak-like varieties are usually less saline than the corresponding *serosem* forms. In addition to the chalk-horizons, here there arises occasionally a gypsum-enriched horizon but occurring at a greater depth than in the *serosem.*

67. Solonetz-like burosem: This can either be derived by the leaching of the *solonchak-burosem* or more frequently formed, when dry, salty powder is blown over from neighbouring saline soils. After rain, the saline ground-water penetrates into the soil and causes the formation of Na-clays. Solonized forms show a dense structure in the A_2 horizon and feeble, cylindrical-shaped separation on drying.

Occurrence: The principal region is in South Russia, in the Volga basin of Astrakhan and in the province of Uralsk where *solonetz-burosems* occur widely, further in the centre of Dobrudsha and in South Bessarabia. Most of the forms, described in other European areas, are doubtful [10]. By their external profile structure certain *degraded chernosems* with humus-horizon coloured brown by free ferric hydroxide may be easily mistaken for *burosems.* They lie however on the humid side and not on the dry side of the *chernosem* belts.

XXIX. *Kastanosem* *)
Chestnut Coloured Soil

Synonyms : Chestnut-brown soil, chestnut soil, dark brown soil (MAR-BUT).

General Specification : Dry in summer, climax forming steppe soil, similiar to the chernosem but distinguished from it essentially by its chestnut colour, the much lower value of its maximum atainable humus content and maximum depth of soil, the lower intensity of soil life and the more strongly xerophytic character of the plant cover.

Characteristics:

Profile : The depth of the humus horizon varies from about 30-60 cm. reaching on an average about 50 cm. It consists mostly of a lighter, greyish coloured, loose A_1 horizon, occasionally showing slight leafy separation in the upper part, and a chestnut-brown A_2 horizon, which in common (normal) soil forms is rich in cavities and has a spongy fabric. This passes gradually through a light brownish grey transition horizon (A/Ca) into a whitish, when dry more or less crusted, cemented Ca horizon and finally into the loose parent material.

Principal Parent Rocks : Loess and loess-like calcareous sediments.

Soil Colours : When moist, the colour is that of a ripe chestnut and when dry a light chestnut brown with a slightly grey hue.

Influence of Texture : Sandy soils have a light brown ground hue, the Ca horizon is usually less distinctly developed.

Dynamic : Besides increasing leaching of the calcium and magnesium carbonates there is no real movement of substances in normal soils. The formation of the frequently lighter A_1 horizon of lower humus content is generally strongly influenced by wind-borne sediments.

Chemical Characteristics : The soil usually no longer effervesces in the surface layer, but only at a depth of about 30-40 cm. The only exception to this are formations on highly calcareous parent material. The reaction is slightly alkaline, in the top-soil almost neutral.

Humus Content : Maximum about 5 %, average 3-4 %.

Humus Form : Mull.

Natural Plant Cover : Generally a closed short-grass steppe cover. The wetter it is the more grasses there are, the drier, the more Artemisia species. Typical grasses are : *Festuca sulcata, Koeleria gracilis, Bromus inermis,* various *Stipa* species.

---

*) After the Russian kashtannosiom.

1. **Chernozem** on loess (Haugsdorf Lower Austria).
2. **Degraded chernozem** on loess (Mistelbach, Lower Austria).

Phenology: The soil is superficially frozen in winter, in spring moist, while in summer the upper parts generally dry out extensively.

Biology: Excellent decomposition and humification, already rich accumulation of plant remains for the formation of humus, always colonized by earth-worm fauna which strongly influences the humus formation. The soil life reaches its maximum intensity in the spring, while in summer it assumes a more xerophytic character. As the soils are excellently suited for farming, almost all areas are under cultivation and show a considerable and enduring fertility, which does not, however, reach that of the deep humus rich *chernosems*. In contrast to the brown soils, they can be worked without irrigation, but in dry summers there is nearly always considerable drought damage.

Variability: While solonchak-like (saline) chestnut soils are of little importance, solonetz-like varieties occur very frequently and often are found over greater areas than the normal forms.

69. Solonetz-Kastanosem: This is easily recognized, as the A_2 horizon has a dense structure which on drying-out is intersected by parched, vertical fissures causing the horizon to break up into compact, 4-6 cm. wide, cylindrical separations. The solonetz-like forms are more easily puddled, more cloddy, with inferior crumb structure and aeration and therefore are biologically less active than the normal form (*common kastannosem*).

Occurrence: The main areas are in south Russia, south of a line through Rostov, Saratov, Orsk; in the Crimea peninsular, in Roumania, partly in Hungary.

XXX. *Chernosem*

Synonyms: Chernosiom *) (Russian folk name, AFONIN, 1771 [14]). Steppe black earth, black earth.

70. *Typical Chernosem*

General Specification and Delimitation: Generally deep, usually moderately calcareous AC soil of the grass steppe, with a colour varying from brownish-grey, dark-grey to blackish (when moist, deep black) according to humus content.

---

*) Written this way to correspond with the Russian pronunciation.

XVII

1.   2.

The soil is similar to the chernosem-like warp soil (*Smonitza*); this however is derived from *calcareous anmoor*, and generally occurs in conjunction with it especially in the former ground-water region of rivers, lakes and marshes (page 163).

Characteristics:

Profile : The normal profile is differentiated into A, Ca and C horizons, in which the fully developed A horizon attains a depth, rarely reached in other mineral soils (up to 1 m. and more). Occasionally profiles are covered in many places by humus rich wind-borne sediments, so that a (not completely autochthonous) humus formation of more than 1 1/2 m. can be found. The humus horizon is divided usually into three sub-horizons, the A_1, A_2 and A/Ca horizons. The A_1 horizon has the darkest colour and normally no longer effervesces with hydrochloric acid (excluding young *chernosem* on very calcareous parent material). The A_2 horizon (pseudomycelium-layer) generally contains efflorescences of very fine needles and filaments which often resemble a mould formation (hence the name pseudomycelium). The soil itself does not effervesce with HCl in this horizon. In the A/Ca horizon the soil is light grey in colour with a much higher lime content (distinct effervescence with lime). Here the Cl does not produce needle or filament efflorescences, but mealy or crusted forms which are composed of precipitates of very fine, rounded crystal elements about 1 μ in size (hence the name, microlith-layer). Occasionally white deposits are found in cavities, with circular cross section, up to the size of an eye, and in this case the Russian designation «bjeloglaska» (white-eye layer) is used. The thickness of the Ca horizon depends on the chalk content and on the degree of eluviation and therefore varies considerably.

Grass Förna : Virgin, undisturbed *chernosems* often have a fine, soft, carpet-like blanket of half-comminuted plan remains on their surface. Close under it a thin, richly colonized, loose mineral layer is found, intersected by numerous plant roots.

Principal Parent Rocks : Firstly, loess, secondly, loose loess-like sediments. With sandy sediments sufficient content of marl must always be present. On all easily weathered rocks which can be transformed into calcareous loose layers, chernosem formation is possible if not in optimum form.

Formation of Krotowinas : Krotowinas (Russian) are the holes and channels of soil vertebrates of the steppe (*Spermophylus, Spalax, Aretomyx,* etc.), filled with earth. Although only apparent when filled with earth from other horizons and therefore of a different colour, they are found so frequently in chernosem profiles that they can be counted as a typical chernosem characteristic. In chestnut coloured soils and allied black earths, they are rare, and in soils of the desert steppe, almost completely missing. The krotowinas formed in the A horizon are visible if filled with whitish earth from the Ca or C horizons and those in the subsoil (excluding the upper part of the C horizon) if filled with the blackish earth of the humus horizon. They are circular or oval in cross-section. This is irregular due to the mixing activity of earthworms, which also bring about the disappearance of the krotowinas. The earth content may be either homogeneous (simple krotowinas) or consist of a cylindrical wall, cointaining other particles (compound krotowinas). Occasionally they consist of several concentric or excentric cylinders of different soil material (layered krotowinas).

Humus Form: Excellent mull.

Humus Content: Values vary between 4-16 %. The so-called *deep* or *fat chernosem* has a humus content of 10-13 % or higher to a depth of one meter or more, the *common* or *average* (to a depth of about 70 cm.) of 6-10 % while the *southern chernosem* similar to the chestnut coloured soil 4-6 % (figures after GLINKA 1914).

Structure: Usually typical spongy fabric, due to the activiy of earthworms. With cultivation, a very stable crumb structure. Only on sandy soils, with intensive and one-sided cropping, does the crumb structure deteriorate, but can be restored by several years of green fodder plants.

Dynamic: The chemical weathering is slowed down by the incompletely removed chalk and the dry summer, cold winter climate. The breakdown of the minerals therefore occurs economically so that the soil always contains a large reserve of nutrients, and only relatively slight leaching of nutrients takes place. Moderate and slow leaching of the carbonates, no translocation of humus or mineral colloidal substances.

Chemical Characteristics: The soil is saturated with Ca ions, the reaction of the topsoil is neutral to slightly acid. Except for the content of carbonate and humus, there is no difference in the material composition of the various horizons.

Characteristic Minerals: Due to the slow chemical weathering, as with the previous steppe soils, the most easily weathered minerals are only slightly attacked, so that even green biotites which are not baueritisized (browned) or only transformed into chlorite, may be found.

Water Relations: In virgen *chernosem* high water capacity, moderate capilliary action, good aeration with moderate soaking. In soils which have been damaged by intensive one-sided cropping (the A_1 horizon having become powdery, dense and lighter in colour), capilliary action is considerably increased but water conduction and aeration reduced.

Biology: Intense, deep-reaching soil life with excellent decomposition, humification and formation of clay-humus complexes under the action of a richly developed, particularly active earthworm fauna. In most chernosem structures the earthworm casts are so well preserved that on examination with a microscope in reflected light, it is easy to see that practically the whole of the crumbs, including part of the Ca horizon, are composed of the excreta of worms of various sizes. The increased activity of soil-burrowing rodents is also essential for the biology of the *chernosem*.

Plant Cover: Grass steppe with *Festuca*, *Stipa* and *Koeleria* species (*Festuca ovina*, *Stipa pennata*, *Stipa capillata*, *Stipa laessiagiana*, *Koeleria gracilis*, *Koeleria cristata*, etc.). In moister parts of the grass landscape, on river banks and in depressions, clumps of trees.

Phenology: Soil generally frozen to a considerable depth in winter with a snow covering which rarely melts. In spring, strong surface waterlogging due to damming up of the snow waters, whose percolation is impeded by the frozen soil. The resulting anmoor-like puddling and impassability is called, in Russia, «rasputitza». Spring is characterized by luxuriant vegetation development and rich soil life. There follows, in summer, a gradual drying out which after many years can be severe enough to cause drought damage.

Occurrence: On the Russian great plain, south of the line Kiev-Tula-Kazan, in Roumania, Bulgaria, Syrmia, Banat, Hungary, Austria, in the Moravian Hanna, in the Magdeburger Börde and other small regions in Central and Southern Europe.

71. *Degraded Chernosem* *)
(Korschinsky 1886)

Synonyms: Suglinok (Russian folkname), forest-suglinok, degraded steppe black earth [12]), browned steppe black earth, grud (Russian folkname, KRUEDENER 1927).

General Specification: Steppe black earth on loess and loess like calcareous sediments, browned by precipitates of ferric hydroxide due to intensified chemical weathering with the stronger chalk removal and increasing acidity, whose profile frequently shows the beginnings of the formation of a seamy braunerde-like (B) horizon.

Characteristics:

Profile: The normal profile consists of an A horizon which does not reach the depth of the *common chernosem*, followed by a brown seam or thin brown (B) horizon (about 10-15 cm. thick). Both horizons are free from chalk. These are followed by a more or less strongly developed Ca horizon, according to the chalk content of the parent material, which passes gradually

---

*) Transition forms closely related to the *degraded chernosem*, occurring in northern Russia called grey forest soils. I have not included it in the following descriptions as I have had no opportunity to study them myself.

into the C horizon. This profile formation appears, however, only with a sufficiently high humus content. In humus-deficient soils the browning due to ferric hydroxide is seen even in the A horizon. As there is insufficient humus to mask it, the soil has a brown colour right to the surface. The boundaries of the various horizons are never sharp but the horizons blend into one another.

Humus Form: A good relatively deep mull.

Dynamic: Increasing chemical weathering, more intense leaching of the carbonate, however, but no other translocation of substances.

Biology: Good decomposition, humification and formation of clay-humus complexes. The intensity of soil life lies between that of a black earth and that of an *eutrophic braunerde*.

Phenology: The condition of the soil varies very little from spring to summer. Further the danger of damage by drought in cultivated soils is considerably less.

Occurrence: On the northern edge of the Russian chernosem belt, as well as on the humid side of the chernosem zone in Roumania, Bulgaria, Hungary, Austria, Czechoslovakia, the Magdeburg plain and other limited regions in Central Europe.

XXXI. *Para-chernosem*

General Specification: Chernosem-like and at the same time ranker-like soil in steppe regions on loose, very chalk deficient to chalk free sediments.

Characteristics:

Profile: The humus horizons can attain depths commensurate with those of the *chernosem*. They go straight into a loose C horizon without pseudomycelium layers and Ca horizons. With low humus content there is usually a slight browning of the A horizon due to ferric hydroxide precipitations. This browning is also frequently observed in the C horizon *) and this often permits the *para-chernosem* to be recognised at first sight. On parent materials with iron minerals only weathered with difficulty (mostly sandy sediments) in the steppe climate the formation of ferric hydroxide is strongly repressed, so that *para-chernosem* can be formed almost without traces of browning.

Humus Form: Mull.

Water Relations: No water-logging, no gley formation, no anmoor-like humus forms.

---

*) Original colour of the parent material.

Dynamic : Rather slow chemical weathering, due entirely to the soil climate as the inhibiting effect of chalk is absent. There is no translocation of humus or mineral colloidal substances.

Biology : In general similar to the soil life of the *chernosem*, although slightly less intense, with good decomposition, humification and mull formation. It produces cultivated soils of high and lasting fertility.

Delimitation from Chernosem : Chernosem-like formations on chalk free parent rocks have been included in *chernosems* by many authors. Their separation is important, however, as the calcareous nature of the true *chernosem* not only exerts a far-reaching influence on the biology, the intensity and the depth of humus formations, but also on the dynamic of the soil.

Delimitation from Degraded Chernosem : This is a soil formed on calcareous parent material, the *para-chernosem* is not. The *degraded chernosem* when well-developed has a brown seam, which arises from the processes of soil formation; the *para-chernosem* shows at best a certain original browning inherent in the parent material.

Delimitation from Braunerde : The *para-chernosem* is distinguished from the *braunerde* by its deep, chernosem-like humus formation corresponding to the biology and less intensive chemical weathering of the steppe.

Occurrence : Especially characteristic of the drier parts of the steppe, excluding the zone of the brown soil of the desert steppe. Differentiation as with the calcareous steppe soils (i. e. a division of the sub-types corresponding to chestnut coloured and brown soils) is hardly possible here.

XXXII. *Para-serosem*

General Specification : Light grey to brownish grey coloured, very humus deficient, chalk deficient AC soil of the desert steppe with very shallow humus horizons on predominately loose, chalk deficient sediments, with sparse, open, xerophytic plant cover and sparse soil life.

Characteristics:

Profile : This soil is very similar to the *serosem* (page 194) but shows no Ca horizon and also no precipitates of chalk in other parts of the profile. The humus horizon forms only little contrast with the loose C horizon and usually is less than 10 cm. thick.

Humus Form : Generally clay deficient mull.

Reaction : Neutral to slightly acid.

Biology : Mostly rapid and complete decomposition and humification of the organism remains. Due to the very scanty plant cover, little accumulation of organic parent material, low development of soil life.

Principal Parent Rocks : As the *para-serosem* itself is, even in the semi-desert, rarely a climax, and on easily weathered parent material, in spite of slow development, can be transformed nearly always into humus deficient *meridional braunerde,* it is found in uniform larger areas almost only on iron deficient parent material difficult to weather.

Dynamic : No translocation of substances, low chemical weathering which, however, is much more strongly impeded although not as low as in the calcareus *serosem.* Lack of rain with high temperatures impedes chemical weathering much less than at lower temperature, so that it is more intense in the semi-desert with hot summers than in the dry regions with cool summers. Therefore, chalk deficient parent materials tend much more to form AC climax formations in dry high mountains (Sierra de Guadarrama, Sierra Nevada) and in low rainfall, sub-arctic areas, than in the semi-deserts. In the latter, a very low degree of moistness in conjunction with the high summer temperatures is sufficient to produce qualitatively distinct effects (as shown by the microscope), of course, limited to small areas and therefore quantitatively too little to produce apparent effects seen by the naked eyes.

Browning : On easily weathered parent material with many iron-containing minerals, AC soils are transformed gradually into *meridional braunerde.* Besides the normal form (*72. Common para-serosem*), occur relatively frequently transition formations (*73. Brown para-serosem*) between the two development phases, which can be easily confused with the brown soils of the desert steppe (type XXIII). Their brownish colour is, however, derived primarily from the increased content of free ferric hydroxide and in the brown semi-desert soils, the colour is decided by the colouring of the humus substances. The former are chalk deficient to chalk free, the latter calcareous. The *meridional braunerde* differs from the *brown para-serosem* in that browning of the latter occurs only in the topsoil, i. e. only in the region of the humus horizons or in the form of a brown seam under them, while the former always has well developed (B) and (B)/C horizons. The browning of the *para-serosem* is not a degradation as it appears in moister and therefore always more favourable habitats (hence the designation *brown* and not degraded *para-serosem*).

Occurrence : Frequently in smaller areas of the dry steppe, rarely in large uniform expanses.

CE. Terrae Calxis

Included in this group will be *braunlehms, rotlehms,* and *roterdes* derived from calcareous rocks, whose interrelationship will be shown by the type designation «Terra» [14] (*terra fusca, terra gialla, terra rossa* *). This refers

---

*) Cf. also the related iron deficient weisslehms (terra bianca) and buntlehms (terra colorada).

to very mature, extensively weathered, usually completely chalk-free soils with ochre yellow, ochre brown to red coloured (B) horizons (or B horizons) which contain iron in the form of ferric hydroxide with varying water content, either peptized and diffusely dispersed in the soil mass or secondarily precipitated from this dispersion into concretions and crusty deposits or flaky, crumbly elements which permeate the entire structure like a framework. They are partly very dense, highly plastic, bolus-like, of shining waxy appearance, partly rough, scabby-crumbly to completely unplastic.

Key for the Determination of Sub-types and Varieties.

1.   Soil red to brown-red in colour   4

1*.   Soil ochre-yellow, ochre, ochre brown to red brown in colour   2

2.   Soil with light grey or whitish bleached layer below the humus horizon.

(46). Bleached terra fusca.

2*.   Soil without bleached layer   3

3.   Soil with intense colour, generally strikingly dense and heavy, more or less bolus-like. Primarily occurring in humid regions (plate XVIII).

(45). Typical terra fusca.

3*.   Definitely with loose crumb structure, at least in the upper layer (not only forming angular aggregates on drying out), usually of a dull brown colour. Occurring in southern dry regions.

(47). Earthy terra fusca.

4.   Soil when moist only slightly plastic or non-plastic, i. e. it can scarcely be kneaded or formed.

(49). Allitic terra rossa.

4*.   Soil when moist, plastic to highly plastic, in most cases also very adhesive.

(48). Siallitic terra rossa.

74. *Terra fusca (n. f.)*

Synonyms : Limestone braunlehm; terra gialla = for intense ochre-yellow coloured forms of the Mediterranean sea region.

General Specification : Usually humus-deficient loamy soils with ochre yellow, brown to reddish brown colour on limestone rocks which contain ferric hydroxide in the form of limonite. This is either strongly peptized in the ground mass or appears partly in the form of rounded, smooth concretions, with sharp contours in the cross section which usually have a dark brown colour on microscopic examination, besides precipitates in the form of fine crumbs (as with the *earthy terra fusca*).

Explanation of plate XVIII

1. **Typical terra fusca** (limestone brown loam) below beech forest on limestone (Southern Wienerwald).
2. **Siallitic terra rossa** (limestone-red loam) below xerophytic top flora in the picture *Ptilotrichum spinosum* and *Festuca Hystrix* on limestone. Summer aspect (Prov. Valencia, Spain).

---

(45)   Typical Terra fusca (n. f.)

Synonyms: Humid limestone braunlehm, loamy terra fusca.

General Specification: Dense, bolus-like soil, striking deep ochre-yellow, ochre-brown or reddish brown in colour, chalk free, humus deficient, with limonitic ferric-hydroxide mainly peptized in the soil mass, occurring on limestone in regions of high rainfall.

Characteristics:

Profile: The depth of profile varies greatly. On the high and middle parts of the slopes it is usually low (about 20-30 cm.) on the lower slopes, on slope steps, on the level slope bases, and in relief depressions it is often considerably deep (about 70-150 cm.). The humus deficient A horizon is generally very shallow, about 2-5 cm. and rarely exceeding 10 cm., and is a dirty ochre-grey or grey-brown in colour. It is dense and consists usually of puddled worm casts of low humus content. Occasionally, too, on drying, it breaks up into sharp edged aggregates. Under cultivation and in vineyards the A horizon is scarcely perceptible due to its lack of humus and mixing with the upper part of the (B) horizon.

It is in the (B) horizon that the braunlehm properties and bolus-like character appear most markedly. The colour is extremely intense, the soil mass extraordinarily dense when moist, with practically no cavities, impermeable, sticky, difficult to work and with few roots. When dry, it is hard, sometimes like rock and is split up by more or less numerous fissures, and by digging it breaks up into large angular fragments and small sharp edged aggregates. The thickness of the (B) horizon varies from 15-20 cm. in shallow soils and frequently in deep soils buried profiles can be determined (usually with indefinite A horizons).

In moist cases the soil which is easily eroded and therefore liable to repeated displacement lies directly on the unweathered C horizon. But profiles also occur which show a series of transition horizons to the C horizon. As such there may arise a (B)/Ca horizon if the otherwise chalk free (B) horizon is calcareous in its lower edge. Usually this shows well delimitated (very noticeable in a thin section preparation) chalk filling of the pores in the otherwise brown, non-calcareous soil mass. Secondly, a Ca horizon if it is so calcareous

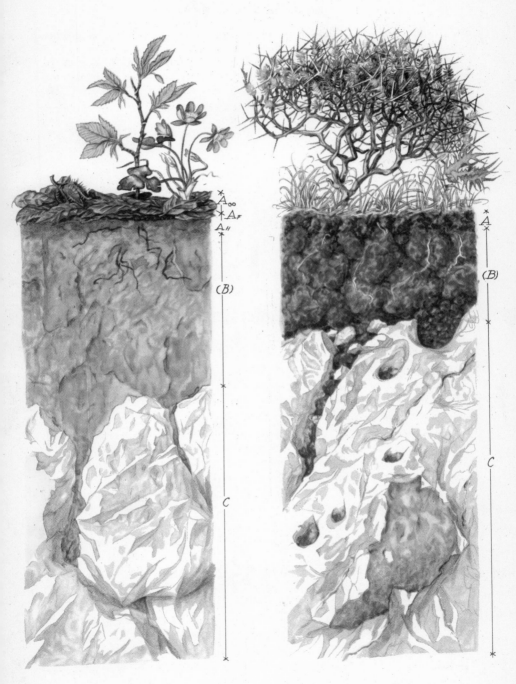

XVIII

*A*₀₀
*A*ꜰ
*A*ᴠ

(*B*)

C

A

(*B*)

C

1.   2.

that the whole soil mass is permeated by whitish powdered chalk, and the pores filled with deposits of precipitated chalk. This makes the structure much looser and more earthy. Thirdly, a Ca/C horizon, if there is distinct chalk enrichment in the upper, extensively loosened and mechanically broken down part of the C horizon. Further, the underlying C horizon can divide into a loose and strongly attacked C_1 horizon and an unweathered, hard C_2 horizon. In soils where Ca horizons are missing usually washed down (B) material may be seen in the fissures and joints of the parent rock.

Humus Form: Mull with transitions to mull-like moder. In deciduous and coniferous woods, under the litter layer, there is a thin moder F horizon which lies with a sharp boundary on the dense, loamy H horizon (mull horizon).

Micromorphology: In thin sections, the dense, uniform soil mass appears light ochre to egg yellow in colour owing to the finely divided hydroxide in it. The high mobility of the ground mass produces various fluidal formations which are particularly striking under crossed nicols, when they appear as doubly refracting streaks (produced by alignment of the particles). They appear in filled up cracks and earthworm channels and as deposits on mineral grains or walls of cavities. The fillings of cavities of circular cross section often give rise to black interference bands. The ferric hydroxide concretions are almost always rounded, smooth, in cross section circular, and generall of a dark brown colour. In addition to iron concretions those of manganese are found frequently, which appear deep black in direct light. Flocculated iron precipitates, typical of the *braunerde* and *earthy terra fusca* are here absent or of very little importance. Transition forms can show partly the characteristics of *earthy terra fusca* or of *terra rossa* (among others red concretions).

Texture: On «pure» limestone, dolomite and gypsum rocks, whose insoluble residue consists entirely of fine colloidal material, loamy to clayey soils are formed. An increased sand content corresponds, in general, to an increased content of sandy constituents in the parent rocks.

Nature of the Clay Substances: The bolus-like character is seen already by eye in many limestone braunlehms, by its peculiar waxy appearance which on microscopic examination with incident light (about 70 times) appears very strongly. This is shown also by soils which contain kaolinitic or halloysitic clays, primarily produced by the colloidal silicic acid which permeates the soil mass. The mixture is easily peptized, swells strongly and shrinks correspondingly on drying.

Chemical Properties: The soil is strongly decalcified. Deposits of chalk present in cavities are due to secondary supplies (deposits of calcareous sediments on slopes, enrichment by capillary rise, etc.). It is slightly acid to acid in reaction. Alkaline pH values are due to chalk nests in the structure.

Dynamic : The soil is the product of intense chemical weathering so minerals other than quartz and muscovite are rarely found in the micro-skeleton. Further secondarily deposited calcite is rapidly dissolved and gradually washed into the subsoil. The dense soil structure, difficult for percolating water to penetrate, has numerous signs of the migration of sub-stances produced by diffusion but shows no real eluviation.

Water Relations : Although the soil is rarely completely dry, the interior of the soil is usually low in water and the water content in general is very unbalanced. As rain-water has difficulty in penetrating into the soil, it runs easily off slight slopes and collects in hollows, producing temporary water-logging. Here the upper soil layers swell up so that the interior of the soil obtains little of the rain-water and the water supply is insufficient even in hollows.

Biology : Compared with the humid *rendsinas* the *terra fusca* shows a striking reduction in biological activity and intensity of humus formation. *Rendsinas* are very active, usually rich in humus, densely colonized and develop relatively deep humus horizons. In the very humus deficient, shallow, heavy dense *terra fusca* the soil life does not reach far into the soil. In deciduous forests, the F horizon is always the most densely colonized, primar-ily by Arthropodae. The litter layer is often glued together like a carpet. The dense, loamy H horizon is usually intersected by earthworm channels filled with casts. Although most cases show a mull formation, this is rarely perfect and resembles more a transition to mull-like moder, due to the accumulation of small, little decomposed plant remains and the unevenness of its formation. As it is difficult for many organisms to penetrate into the mineral soil, a thin mineral deficient (sterile) H horizon (i. e. H_0 horizon, the mull being the H_1 horizon) of moder form is found in the deciduous forests above the mull-layer. With extensive drying out of the surface soil, fungae appear in the F horizon and later in cracks in the mineral H and (B) horizons (partly in large, white colonies). The greater the drying out of the upper soil layers and the opening of fissures in the mineral soil the more the small soil animals are driven into the still humid interior of the soil. The *terra fusca* is essentially a meadow soil and is used most profitably in this way. But in spite of the impermeable structure it is frequently cultivated. Mostly, however, it occurs in forests (particularly in beech forests).

Phenology : Even in winters with little snow the soil is generally only superficially frozen. In early spring or with long periods of rain superficial water-logging occurs in depressions. As the water rarely penetrates deeply, the water-logging disappears relatively rapidly. In the late summer and early autumn the *terra fusca* is generally at its dryest.

Erodability : The erodability is considerable and therefore the soil is easily silted up after cultivation. The run-off from slopes can often do great damage in the form of sheet and also gully erosion. The waters of the gullies silt up easily. The material washed down usually produces also a strong compaction and glueing of the surface layer.

Occurrence: In high rainfall areas of Central Europe, preeminently on limestone, dolomite, marl and gypsum. Especially typical formations occur in the Austrian calcareous mountains (Rax, Schneeberg, Schneealpe, Dürrenstein) in the southern Vienna Forest, in northern Alpine foothils, in the Moravian Karst, in the limestone regions of Hungary, Poland, and the Balkan mountains. It is probable in most cases that these are relict and fossil soils (particularly when found in the alpine and sub-alpine regions) whose principal characteristics are better preserved in humid than in dry regions (cf. *earthy terra fusca*).

(46) Bleached Terra fusca (n. f.)

General Specification: *Terra fusca* of high permeability with eluviation of the ferric hydroxide only or colloidal substances in general from the top soil, giving rise to formation of a light yellow, yellowish grey or whitish bleached horizon.

Characteristics:

Profile: The soil usually has a very shallow, humus deficient A_1 horizon (ca. 2-5 cm.) of a yellowish grey or light grey colour. This is followed by a well-developed bleached horizon, about 15-20 cm. deep, which in extreme cases can have a dazzling white colour. Under it, there is always an extremely dense, intense brown ochre coloured B_s horizon which usually passes without transition horizons into the hard parent rock (C horizon).

Dynamic: The soil dynamic is similar to the normal *terra fusca* except that not only are its binding substances highly mobile but also its permeability is high enough to allow strong movement of colloidal substances. The ferric hydroxide has the highest mobility, so that in many structures only the iron is eluviated while the residual colloids are retained in the bleached horizons. In other very sandy varieties the eluviation is so strong that all the finely dispersed material is removed and the bleached horizon consists almost exclusively of a bare sand framework. It is important that humus sols (or tannic acids) are not formed in significant quantities and in this way the soil is primarily distinguished from the always strongly dystrophic *molken podsol* (No. 87).

[8]. **De-ironized Varieties:** As it is the iron which mainly suffers translocation, it is obvious that the bleached horizon of this variety will be composed to a great extent of finely dispersed constituents and have a boluslike behaviour (like the bolus alba or the very iron deficient *terra bianca*).

It is pure white or slightly yellowish in colour, when moist, plastic, when dry almost as hard as rock (however easily scratched with a finger nail and has a greasy feeling). With a microscope numerous fluidal structures are seen in the B horizon and also the A_e horizon. The mobile peptized ferric hydroxide is removed to a high degree from the A_e horizon, while the round, deep brown concretions remain in it unchanged.

[9].   **Sandy bleached Terra fusca** : In the strongly bleached A_e horizon consists of a more or less bare sand framework usually of quartz granules. The bleached layer is loose, when dry, and non-plastic, when wet. Microscopically also here only the smooth-washed deep brown iron concretions are seen. A thin section preparation of the B horizon contains numerous fluidal structures (doubly refracting streaks under crossed nicols).

Humus Form :   Both sub-varieties usually show a humus deficient mull, in neither case raw humus or other dystrophic humus sol producing form. It is this which distinguishes them from *podsols* with which they might be easily confused, both having strongly developed bleached horizons. The eluviation of the finely dispersed constituents occurs because by the formation of the braunlehm they show from the beginning a strong mobility which has been preserved to a great extent by the humid climate.

Occurrence :   The soil is found nearly always in isolated small areas in the region of the humid *terra fusca*. The most perfect forms of the de-ironized varieties are found in Lower Austria in the region of the Dürrenstein.

(47)   Earthy Terra fusca (n. f.)

General Specification :   In the top soil, loose to slightly compacted, usually dark matt brown [16]) coloured *terra fusca* with good crumb structure. Occurring in the dry regions of the south.

Characteristics:

Profile :   Shallow (2-10 cm. thick) humus deficient grey-brown A horizons, followed by moderately thick (i. e. 30-50 cm.) (B) horizons which usually lie directly on the C horizon. The (B) horizons are generally of a deep to reddish brown colour. Light colours appear to be missing, also the intense colouring, characteristic of the *typical terra fusca* is absent.

Structure :   The soil can exhibit a certain degree of silting-up and compaction yet the structure of silted-up soil is also porous and friable. On drying out numerous irregular, sinuous cracks appear which break up the soil into irregular, rounded separations. With further break down and at the same time, the lexiviation of the edges, small rounded aggregates are formed. The soil has a marked tendency to form crumbs. Its plasticity is strikingly lower than that of the *typical terra fusca*.

Microscopic Characteristics: Striking flocculation of the ferric hydroxide into small granular to crumbly precipitates of a deep-brown colour which influence strongly the actual soil colour. Fluidal structures or fabric parts with birefringence due to particle arrangement are strongly repressed and in many soils non-existent. Their presence in transition forms indicates that the earthy form has developed from the loamy *terra fusca,* further presence of numerous iron concretions points to a former strong mobility of the ferric hydroxide. In earthy forms occasionally there is a strikingly high content of foreign minerals as well as a preponderance of minerals of the fine sand and silt fraction in general. This is certainly due to addition of wind-borne sediments [17]) in dry regions. Much powdered calcite is also blown in with the foreign minerals, which is partially dissolved so that the calcium carbonate may be found in nearly all places in the form of calcite granules and as secondary linings of the cavities.

It is especially characteristic for the earthy form that there is no coherent structure in a thin section preparation in which the mass is composed entirely of apparently unattached, irregular, rounded aggregates of about 2-5 mm. in diameter. Further the interiors of the aggregate are usually loose and contain numerous small cavities. The soil never has a bolus-like appearance to the eye or with a magnifying glass but with higher magnification the waxy character of the *braunlehm* is usually still quite apparent.

Dynamic: The soil is composed partly of strongly weathered relict soils, partly of little-weathered new structure elements (foreign minerals). This indicates that the weathering now is considerably slowed down by the dry climate. The relatively high content of secondary chalk indicates a low rate of leaching.

Plant Cover: Open rocky steppe, dry maquis and scanty stone oak scrub.

Humus Form: Generally mull, however not infrequently mull-like moder with well preserved droppings.

Biology: From the numerous, little de-composed plant remains present, relatively incomplete decomposition and humification.

Differentiation from the *Typical Terra fusca:* Braunerde-like flocculation of ferric hidroxides, strong loosening of the structure, a real increase in pore space, higher content of mineral dust, dull, darker soil colour, dry soil climate, xerophytic plant cover.

Differentiation from the Brown Earth: Preservation of essentially *terra fusca* characteristics such as numerous iron concretions in the structure, the remains of doubly refracting fluidal structures, waxy appearance of the binding substances with high magnification in direct light. Usually *typical terra fusca* layers present in sub-stratum.

Occurrence: In dry regions of southern Europe, like the *terra rossa*, frequently on limestone, particularly in Spain, Greece and Crete.

75. *Terra rossa*
(Italian local name, F. ZIPPE 1853)

Synonyms: Crvenica (Croat peasant name).

General Specification: Usually humus deficient, de-calcified, vivid cinnabar red, dark brick red to brown red coloured soil, rich in inorganic colloids containing ferric hydroxide in water deficient compounds, predominately in the shape of concretions and flaky-crumbly granular precipitations which permeate the entire structure.

Characteristics:

Profile: The A horizon is feebly developed and forms little contrast with the rest of the soil. Only where there is a secondary improvement of the water-relations, are reddish grey brown to reddish brown coloured humus layers formed, which, however, rarely exceed a thickness of 5-10 cm. The dazzling red colour, after which the soil is named, is found at its purest in the (B) horizon. As the soil is exposed to repeated displacement, it usually lies directly on the hard parent rock without transition horizons.

Principal Parent Rocks: Primarily it is found on «pure» chalk, whose «dazzling white» contrasts very strongly with the red soil colour. It does not occur on marl rocks due to the soil climatic relations (the *terra rossa* needs an extremely hot and dry summer soil climate for its development which is fulfilled best on pure, highly permeable chalk and least on marl rocks). Moreover, rocks deficient in microskeleton are most suitable as parent material whose non-soluble fraction consists almost entirely of finely dispersed substances. From these arise soils with particularly good conduction for the movement of substances by diffusion.

Texture: The typical *terra rossa* is always rich in colloidal substances and deficient in fine skeleton which corresponds with the kind of insoluble residue from the principal parent rocks. A secondary strong enrichment of mineral powder (particularly in dry regions) may be found in the form of wind-borne sediment and this is easily recognised, usually by the high content of foreign minerals.

Chemical Characteristics: It is normally a strongly weathered decalcified soil. Its iron content is always higher than that of the non-carbonate fraction of the parent rock[18]). The iron is always present in the form of water deficient, therefore dazzling red (in direct light) coloured ferric hydroxide. The soil reaction is slightly acid to neutral. Only secondarily chalk enriched formations are slightly alkaline.

Surface Form: The soil is most widespread in karst landscapes. Due to the strong active erosion in *terra rossa* regions, it does not form a uniform soil cover but is found only in relief depressions, often only in fissures and «karren» formations of the rock. Deeper soil accumulations are often found in the dolinas («red eyes» of the karst country) and where these are cultivated the farmer frequently builds walls around the circular shaped fields. With the lack of soil and the preponderance of bare rock, there is also a great lack of vegetation.

Occurrence: The classic *terra rossa* region in Europe is in Istria and Dalmatia. They are also very widespread in all the karst landscapes of southern Europe, in Spain, southern France, southern Italy, in Corsica, Sardinia, Sicily, in western, central and southern Greece, in Turkey and in Crete. Isolated occurrences of particular interest to the soil scientist are found in central Europe but there are almost none in the cold northern zones. In many occurrences the *terra rossa* are relict soils, even in the temperate zone where the summer dessication and heating essential for their development is missing, and further in most of the southern European regions where it is most widespread, in which the present soil climate has become so dry that owing to the low eluviation and weathering, they are at best, *xerorendsinas* developed as climax forms. In spite of this, the relict soils can be well preserved in both regions of occurrence (in which secondary varieties may develop). On the other hand, in the cold, humid northern regions, the terra rossa, in spite of its high stability, gradually undergoes retrogressive development into brown soil formations.

(48) Siallitic Terra rossa

Synonyms: Limestone rotlehm, lehmige *terra rossa;* Hasselerde = fossil *terra rossa* of the Thuringian limestone mountains. Bollo (ital.) = reddish brown local variety in Apulia.

General Specification: *Terra rossa* with high colloid content, when wet highly plastic, viscous, characterized by a dense ground mass rich in silicic acid.

Characteristics:

Profile: Mostly shallow, humus deficient A horizons formed over the generally dazzling red-coloured (B) horizons. In humid regions, these are dense, highly impermeable, with almost no cavities; in dry regions, strongly split up, intersected by numerous cracks and fissures, often consisting entirely of loose, up to 5 cm. in size, rough surfaced to scrubby separation complexes.

In the numerous cracks and fissures of the C horizons (also in the finest, often also in the structure of the rock itself) deposits and fillings from the highly mobile mass of the (B) horizon are seen.

Chemical Characteristics: The ground substance is rich in silicic acid and in humid regions, contains considerable quantities of active, hydrolized silicic acid. This may be isolated to a great extent already by puddling and filtering fresh soil samples. Part of the peptized ferric hydroxide always goes through the filter with the silicic acid.

Physical Characteristics: The soil mass swells strongly on wetting, is always plastic, mouldable to a high degree and in most cases shows high adhesion.

Microscopic Characteristics: The ground mass of the soil is generally of an intense egg-yellow colour in thin sections, due to the peptized ferric hydroxide (protected by silicic acid). The ground mass nearly always contains, in addition, ferric hydroxide in flocculated crumbly form, in reflected light dazzling red in colour, which permeates the whole fabric (plate XIX). The ground mass is highly mobile so that the thin section preparations are always crossed by numerous streaks due to movement in it. Often an eluviation of the highly mobile, silicic acid rich part of the egg-yellow ground mass may already be observed, leaving behind a porous framework of flocculated ferric hydroxide gels. Similar to the *terra fusca* the soil contains numerous rounded to oval shaped ferric hydroxide concretions, which can also have smooth surfaces and cross sections with sharp contours, however in reflected light they have always a dazzling red colour (in thin section they appear black owing to their low transparency) *). Occasionally these become large enough to be seen with the naked eye and are called «crvenaci» by the karst peasants. In addition to the smooth concretions, under a microscope some are seen which have a strongly serrated cross section. They are a transition to the pronounced spotty precipitates.

Dynamic: Peptization of ferric hydroxides by hydrolized colloidal silicic acid, irreversible precipitation of ferric hydroxide, various movements produced by diffusion in the highly conducting fabric. Partial washing away of the silicic acid rich ground mass (accompanied by various displacements of the highly erodable soil), producing an increasing relative iron enrichment. Due to the strong summer heating and drying, the iron gels suffer an almost irreversible loss of water.

In humid regions the colloidal silicic acid preserves its effectiveness as peptizator. Due to the greater quantities of percolating water here the silicic acid rich ground mass becomes more strongly moved. Not only do stronger fluidal structures appear (doubly refracting movement streaks) but

---

*). Besides concretions of ferric hydroxide, manganese hydroxide ones occur too, which appear black also on examination in reflected light.

with a sufficiently percolated soil eluvial horizons may arise in the topsoil and illuvial in the subsoil.

[11]. **Bleached terra rossa**: A variety characterized by strong iron removal or strong general eluviation of the entire mineral colloidal substances from the topsoil whereby a yellow to whitish bleached horizon has formed. The bleaching appears without the presence of raw humus or any other dystrophic humus form by which acid humus sols could be developed, but occurs owing to the high mobility of the silicic acid rich ground mass even with the greatest humus deficiency. Strongly leached eluvial horizons are sandy and are really composed only of bare mineral grains and more or less smooth-washed iron concretions. Merely de-ironized, bleached horizons contain still, practically all the remaining colloidal material and are plastic and kneadable. They can occur occasionally as eroded sediment, isolated from the rest of the soil, in cavities and fissures in the parent rock (white *terra rossa, terra bianca*).

Humus Form: All varieties show primarily mull-formation. Isolated mull-like moders rich in droppings occur. In humid regions there are often very thin mineral deficient layers above the mull-layers which contain most of the soil life.

Biology: As many *terra rossa* soils are relict formations, their biology is very dependent on the new environmental conditions. In humid regions the soil life is confined more or less to the surface and penetrates little into the compact interior of the soil. In dry regions where, due to the high shrinkage an extensive breakdown into separation complexes and with it a strong loosening occurs, the soil life penetrates considerably into the interior of the soil, although it is strongly impeded by the lack of water. In humid regions, the decomposition and humification in spite of the mull formation is usually very incomplete, in arid regions, due to the low accumulation of plant remains, humus formation is scanty.

Occurrence: Most occurrences of *terra rossa* are of the loamy form, the earthy form being relatively rare. The high stability of *terra rossa* characteristics means that the numerous soils formed in earlier geological times are well preserved as relict soils.

Recognition of Relic Character: Whether the *terra rossa* is a recent formation, a relict, or fossil soil, cannot in general be determined from the characteristics of the soil itself. Often, however, the recent development sequence can be easily recognized in all its phases up to the climax (which in present dry regions does not reach *terra rossa* *). It is sometimes possible to recognize the relict character of a limestone rotlehm directly from the

---

*) Even in the long grass steppe, on loess, and essentially more favourable parent material, soil development does not reach the A (B) C formation.

fabric, if the silicic acid, the peptizing agent in the ground mass, has aged
and become insoluble. This aging has the effect that the fabric part concerned
with its fluidal structures and movement streaks become completely congealed
and is not destroyed with further eluviation and rearrangement. Therefore
numerous fragments of the strongly aged former soil fabric are found, now
no longer active, in which all the morphological characteristics of the *terra
rossa* are preserved, imbedded in a new still peptizable rotlehm or braunlehm
ground mass.

Occurrence according to habitat: As the *typical terra rossa* is easily
eroded, frequently the soil cover is washed down almost completely from
the slopes of hills with poor vegetation, so that it is found principally on
the lower slopes and slope bases. The original arrangement may have been
that the *terra rossa* was formed primarily on hill-tops strongly dessicated and
heated up in summer where conditions were most favourable for its development. Thus in the Adriatic karst country one frequently finds the arrangement
that the *terra rossa* is found on the summits and the *terra fusca* on the slopes
of the hills. The occurrence of the *terra rossa* apparently depends also on
height, so that in calcareous high mountains in which *terra rossa* occurs, the
following catena with increasing height is found: *terra rossa, terra fusca,
rendsina.* In any case the *terra rossa* formations are just as rare in the high
alpine regions as in the far North. The upper limit of the *terra rossa* **)
may be taken, for the Austrian Alps, as about 2.000 meters.

(49) Allitic Terra rossa

Synonyms: Kalkstein-roterde, earthy *terra rossa;* red earth; Istria
rossa (MORLOT 1848) = designation for occurrences in Istria: Mediterranean
roterde = used till now not only for earthy, but also for loamy siallitic *terra
rossa.*

General Specification: Loose, well crumbled *terra rossa*, with low
silicic acid, but high iron and aluminium hydroxide content and low to
negligible plasticity.

Characteristics:

Profile: Shallow, humus deficient A horizons on usually dark red to
brown red, loose (B) horizons, which always lie directly on the hard C horizons.

Chemical Characteristics: Normally completely de-calcified neutral
to slightly acid reaction. Extremely high Fe_2O_3 and Al_2O_3 and low silicic
acid contents, hence deposits of allitic *terra rossa* are utilized partly as bauxite.

**) Micromorphologically almost always recognisable as fossil soil remains or as
relict soils.

Physical Characteristics : The soil is loose, crumbly, with high pore space and has an extraordinarily strongly divided spongy fabric with little coherence. The particles show no affinity for each other when puddled with water, the mass remains loose and cannot be kneaded to a dough.

Micromorphology : A thin section is composed almost completely of a scabby crumbly porous gel framework of ferric hydroxide precipitates. These are opaque so that the preparation of a thin section is difficult. The preparation remains almost completely dark under crossed nicols. In reflected light the precipitates are dazzling red. Besides these, strongly aged (completely opaque) round concretions are found which appear also dazzling red in reflected light. Light coloured remains of the silicic acid rich soil mass with doubly refracting movement streaks are either completely missing or present only to a very small extent.

Dynamic : As the ferric hydroxide has lost almost all its mobility by irreversible precipitation and also there are no mobile colloidal substances present, practically no movements of material take place in the soil.

Occurrence : Known occurrences are in Istria and Croatia.

CF. Bolus-like Silicate Soils
(Plastosols)

General Specification : Generally humus deficient, strongly weathered, intense ochre yellow, ochre brown, brown red, to dazzling red coloured soil formation of the tropics and sub-tropics usually with a highly plastic, extraordinarily easily puddled clay substance, peptized by colloidal silicic acid which in Europe occurs only in the form of sometimes deep deposits of fossil soil formations or in the form of relict soils, but as such, very widespread.

Microscopic Characteristics : *Braunlehms* and *rotlehms* are very stable in their properties so that their individuality has been extensively preserved in most deposits and relict formations. Correspondingly, the micromorphological characteristics of the European occurrences bear a great similarity to those of the tropical and sub-tropical soils and often they are scarcely distinguishable. The main characteristics are: dense structure, peptization of the ferric hydroxide in a dense, rich in colloidal silicic acid ground mass; high mobility of the ferric hydroxide, occasional precipitation in the form of concretions, flecks, deposits, in special cases of flocculated precipitates; high mobility of the ground substance, formation of numerous doubly-refracting streaks and fluidal structures by alignment of the particles. Extensive parallels also exist between their physical character as well as in their chemistry, so

that a distinction between the *braunlehm* relict soils and the externally similar
Central European brown earths is particularly important both for the practical
soil scientist and for the agricultural engineer.

Key for the Determination of Sub-types.

1.   Soil red to brown red coloured   3
1*. Soil ochre yellow, ochre, ochre brown to red brown coloured   2
2.   Soil with light grey to whitish bleached layer under the humus horizon.
                                                  77. Bleached braunlehm.
2*. Soil without bleached layer.
                                                  76. Common braunlehm.
3.   Soil easily puddled and eroded with tendency to form a dense, hard struc-
     ture when dry.
                                                  78. Typical rotlehm.
3ˣ. Soil with good crumb structure, loose even when dry, easy to dig, crumbles
     easily in one's hand.
                                                  79. Earthy rotlehm.

XXXIV. *Braunlehm*
(Harrassowitz, 1926)

Synonyms: Brown loam *), Gelblehm (Harrassowitz 1926) = designation for more iron deficient or bleached varieties, partly also for those
containing the more strongly hydrated ferrous hydroxides; tropical yellow
earth (Wohltmann 1892); insubrian braunerde (Pallmann 1931) = local
soil form in Tessin, apparently closely related to *braunlehm*.

The designation *braunlehm* has been created from consideration of the
designation *rotlehm* which in tropical soil science (c. f. Wohltmann, Marbut and Shantz, Vageler, etc.) distinguishes the highly plastic, silica rich
red soil formations (*plastic soils* after Bennett) from the unplastic, low silicic
acid, alumina and iron rich soil formations, the *red earths* (*friable* soils of
Bennet mostly latosols of Kellogg). The *braunlehms* are the corresponding
silica rich, highly plastic, brown soil formations. The designation -*lehm* (never
used by itself but only in the above combinations) never refers to a particular

---

*) The English expression «brown loam» has been rejected by some recent
authors to avoid confusion with the textural designation loam. It may be mentioned
that the word loam in this case does not refer to texture but means only that the soils
of this group are highly plastic in contrast with the latosols which show little or no
plasticity. The same applies to the expression «red loam», wherefore I have given preference to the original name «rotlehm» of Wohltmann (1892) and «braunlehm»
(Harrassowitz, 1926) without translation. Being nouns they conform more to the
nomenclature rules and are nothing but names, i. e. do not refer to a single property,
but to the soil as a whole. They correspond also to the original concepts and not
to some of the altered concepts of recent years.

kind of texture or structure but, like the designation -*erde*, refers always to a distinct total character.

76. *Common Braunlehm*
Common brown loam

General Specification and Delimitation: Generally humus deficient, dense soil with braunerde-like profile, of a vivid brown, ochre brown to reddish brown or ochre yellow colour with highly mobile, silica rich clay substance in which the ferric hydroxides occur in general in a peptized, easily diffused form and partly precipitate in the form of rounded, deep brown, preponderantly microscopic concretions.

Important external diagnostic characteristics are: the intense, vivid soil colour, the abnormally dense structure, extreme heaviness, low permeability, pasty jelly-like swelling on wetting strongly, high cohesion on drying (frequently angular breakdown). The surest diagnosis is given by a thin section preparation.

Characteristics:

Profile: A (B) C profile, as with the brown earth, humus horizons almost always very shallow and humus deficient. In Europe, on hard parent rocks, *braunlehm* generally occurs only in the form of relict soils. In the usually deep erosion deposits of fossil *braunlehm* the C horizon is missing. With sufficient sand content, the soil nearly always shows eluviation so that the (B) horizons are frequently appreciably heavier than the A horizons. In such cases they are not designated (B) but B horizons. They are usually followed by (B) horizons in which a stronger enrichment of colloidal substances compared with the A horizons can no longer be determined.

Humus Form: Almost always mull, even with *bleached braunlehm*.

Dynamic: Intense chemical weathering, always tendency to compaction, slight damming up of surface water and upper soil water after heavy rainfall, strong shrinkage of the soil mass on drying or freezing, often breakdown into smaller sharp-edged fragments, with sufficient sand content slight eluviation, high mobility of the peptized ferric hydroxide and its irreversible precipitation in the form of concretions.

Microscopic Characteristics: These assume particular importance, as in doubtful cases, they decide whether it is *braunlehm* or another soil formation. The principal characteristics are: peptization of the ferric hydroxide, fluidal structures, appearance of doubly refracting streaks in the highly mobile binding substance, formation of conducting paths filled with binding substance in the dense soil structure, formation of rounded, dark brown coloured, iron concretions (plate XIX).

Explanation for plate XIX

(Micromorphology of the (B) horizon)

1. **Thin section of the (B) horizon of a very well crumbled** *Central European braunerde.* Iron hydroxide considerably flocculated, immovable, not forming concretions or local depositions. Structure rich in cavities and coherent (spongy fabric). By insertion of a gypsum plate and parallel Nicols the mineral grains (blue) can be well distinguished from the cavities (white).

2. **(B) horizon of a** *meridional braunerde.* Low content in fine earth, brown coloured iron hydroxide partly flocculated, partly peptized or precipitated in form of small concretions or dense depositions.

3. **(B) horizon of a** *braunlehm.* Thin section, ordinary light. Ground mass strongly capable of swelling, intersected by shrinking cracks. The iron hydroxide of the ground mass is peptized with a bright ochre yellow colour. Its strong mobility, the uniform through moistening and the perfect conductibility of the fabric cause the formation of well rounded, deep brown coloured concretions.

4. **The same thin section with crossed Nicols.** In the extremely mobile ground mass numerous double refractive fluidal structures.

5. **(B) horizon of** *rotlehm,* thin section ordinary light. The iron hydroxide is peptized and well distributed in the light ochre yellow to egg yellow coloured dense ground mass. Its precipitation takes place primarily in deeply red flecks and depositions. The fabric contains furthermore fragments of strongly aged concretions of iron hydroxide which are almost completely opaque, therefore with transmitted light blackish, with incident light dazzling red coloured.

6. **The same thin section with crossed Nicols,** strongly developed double refractive fluidal structures.

7. **(B) horizon of a** *rotlehm* **with Iwatoka precipitations,** thin section, ordinary light. Coarsely flocculated precipitations of iron hydroxide of deep red colour which are distributed throughout the entire fabric. The strongly mobile, silica rich, egg yellow coloured ground mass is completely washed out with the exception of a few residues in some protected fissures. Spongy fabric with sporadic shrinking cracks and residues of strongly aged concretions.

8. **(B) horizon of a** typical *sialitic terra rossa,* thin section, ordinary light. Residues of the dense silica rich ground mass which is liable to strong eluviation. In it numerous shrinking cracks, beginning formation of a spongy fabric. Iwatoka precipitations of iron hydroxide, also strongly aged, well rounded concretions, which are reddish black with transmitted light, with incident light dazzling red in colour.

Chemical Characteristics: Lack of bases and nutrients, low content of nutrient reserves (almost only quartz grains in the micro-skeleton), usually feeble acid reaction, silica rich colloidal complex, presence of peptizing hydrolized colloidal silicic acid. The soil is normally completely decalcified. Any chalk present (or perhaps salts) is due to secondary enrichment (deposition on calcareous sediments or alternating with them, mixing with chalk debris, etc.). Moderate chalk content in *braunlehm* produces a real improvement in chemical and biological relations, but generally does not neutralize its heaviness.

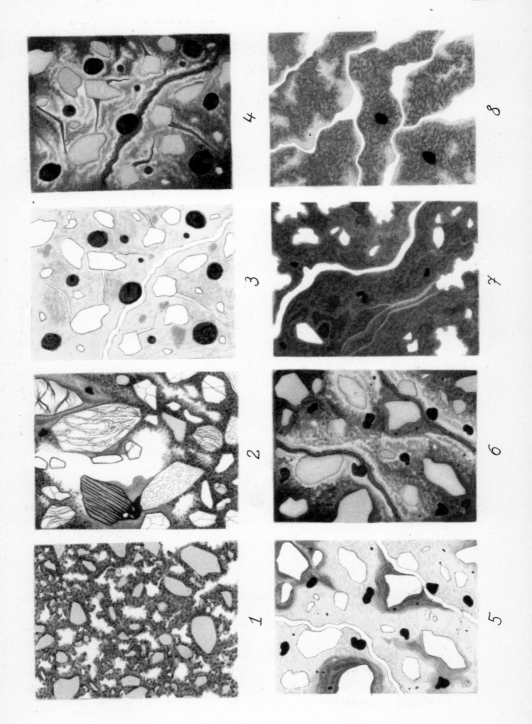

XIX

Biology: Decomposition and humification are such that they lead already to mull formation. Otherwise relatively low in soil life which is often concentrated in a thin surface layer, due to the dense soil structure.

Phenology: In wet periods, waterlogging, then pasty swelling of the wetted layers, usually giving the soil mass a particularly striking stickiness. In dry periods rock-like hardening of the compacted soil parts (especially in dry summers) or break down into small angular fragments (angular breakdown is particularly striking with freezing and thawing in winters with little snow). On slopes, the soils are dry, due to the rapid surface run-off.

Texture: All textures from loamy sand to the heaviest clay occur. Nearly all physical characteristics, particularly heaviness and cohesion, do not run parallel with texture as in most other soils; *braunlehm* is considerably heavier, denser, less permeable and, when dry, more coherent than other soils.

Variability: In humid climates (also in cool northern locations) the original characteristics in sediments of *braunlehm* are better preserved than in dry or dry summer regions. These are very similar to recent sub-tropical *braunlehms*, particularly in their physical relation. Many occurrences of these soils ((50) *humid braunlehm*) are strongly bolus-like in appearance and exhibit an extraordinarily vivid colouring and almost waxy appearance. In regions with dry summers, a more or less strong earthiness can appear in the uppermost soil layers ((51) *earthy braunlehm*), which may be recognized as it crumbles more easily and has a less intense colour. The colour is generally darker, browner and duller. Thin section preparations show a more or less strong secondary flocculation of the ferric hydroxide in the form of brown coloured fine-crumb precipitates, besides the remains of peptized ferric hydroxide and numerous deep brown rounded concretions. The underground layers usually retain a strong braunlehm character. In the dry regions of Southern Europe the great lack of vegetation allows strong erosion effects in the soil surfaces, in small differences of relief, a considerable separation of the soil particles takes place with the formation of a hard, platey crust of deposits of the finest colloidal material intersected by drought fissures; in other places further loosening and strong removal by wind can occur. By secondary enrichment of the soil with chalk, gysum or easily soluble salts, surface enrichment of these materials is often seen. These soil forms ((52) *dry braunlehm* or *Calvero-braunlehm* [19]) are characterized by very scanty humus formation, often by an extensive loosening (dust formation) in the surface layer, while in the sub-stratum all the braunlehm characteristics are well preserved.

1. **Bleached braunlehm** (in the picture *betic gelblehm*, an Andalusian local variety below *Rhododendron baeticum* and *Quercus suber* on siliceous sandstone.
2. **Slightly bleached rotlehm** relict soil on clay schist below *Cistus laurifolius*. (Sierra Morena, Puerto de Despeñaperros, Spain).

77. *Bleached Braunlehm*
Bleached brown loam

General Specification : *Braunlehm* with high water permeability, in which a strong impoverishment of the topsoil in colloidal material and the formation of a light yellow, light grey to whitish bleached horizon has occurred without the influence of dystrophic acid humus forms and acid humus sols.

Characteristics :

Profile : Particularly characteristic is the grey to ochre grey uniformly humified, generally humus deficient A_1 horizon, which contains almost no recognisable plant remains and usually shows distinct marks of intense earthworm activity. In sandy soils it can reach a depth of 35 cm. Following it is a light coloured to almost white bleached horizon (A_2 or A_6 horizon), about 10-15 cm. thick and frequently permeated by yellowish to greyish flecks (faded remains of deposited earthworm casts of soil material from the A_1 or B horizons). The succeeding usually dazzling ochre-coloured B horizon is an illuvial horizon with an extremely dense structure but, in spite of this, it can exhibit considerable marks of earthworm activity. The profiles are formed in general on thick sediments of displaced fossil *braunlehm* which are identical in all characteristics with the (B) horizon of a sub-tropical *braunlehm*. Therefore the B horizon (perhaps consisting of a B_1 and B_2 horizon) is normally still followed by a (B) horizon showing none of the characteristics of an illuvial horizon, and also its chemistry and micromorphology are not those of a C or B/C horizon *).

Humus Form : Almost always mull, no dystrophic humus form.

Dynamic : The bleaching can so develop that the colloidal substances (peptized and protected by colloidal silicic acid) are washed out of the A_2 horizon, or that essentially only the highly mobile ferric hydroxide is removed from it. In the latter case ((53) *de-ironized braunlehm*), colourless, colloid rich, in the former ((54) *sandy bleached braunlehm*), a more or less smooth washed, quartz sand remains.

---

*) So dynamically active a soil as the braunlehm immediately assumes a complete fabric again even in sediments, which differs little from the original.

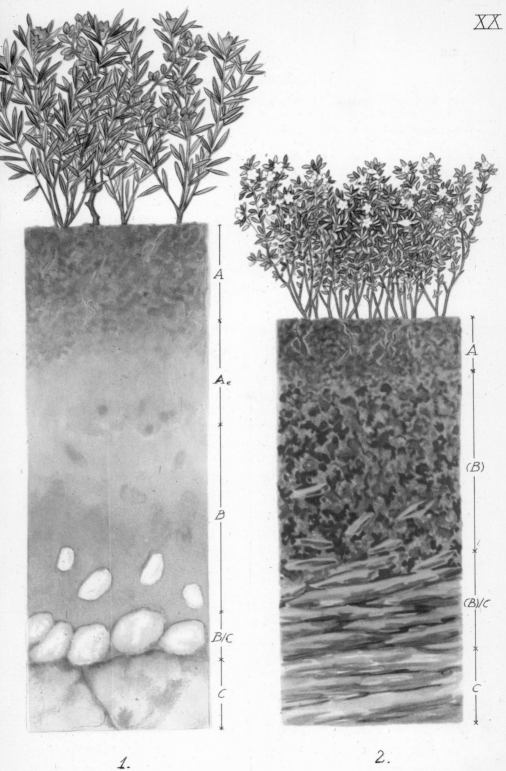

XX

1.

2.

Structure of the B horizon : The horizon is extraordinarily rich in the most different kinds or fabric elements pressed densely into each other. All the intergranular spaces of the ground structure are filled with colloidal substances derived from the topsoil. The formation of new conducting spaces (conducting paths) such as earthworm channels, plant root channels, shrinkage fissures, infiltrated by percolating water, is sufficient to start the movement of colloidal substances again. The parts of the fabric near the conducting paths show an impoverishment of colloidal material recognisable by the much paler colouring to almost complete bleaching. All these phenomena can be partly seen even with the naked eye but become much more distinct under microscopic investigation with reflected light (binocular), and in thin section preparations where, due to alignment of particles in the mobile fabric sections, the formation of doubly-refracting fluidal structures and the finest details of the displacement of substances may be observed. Besides the fluidal phenomena in the colloidal complex, the individual movement of the ferric hydroxide, including the development of concretions and flecks, may almost always be distinctly recognized.

The high mobility of the binding substances (without the assistance of humus sols) is also distinctly apparent in the B horizon, e. g. dug-out material exposed to the rain, after a short time already allows an impoverished zone to develop on the surface, producing, above this, a rind of completely smooth washed mineral grains is formed.

Physical Characteristics : Fragments of the B horizons become as hard as stone on drying, but immediately soften again on moistening and gradually show deliquescence. After heating (rendering the silicic acid insoluble) they soften no longer on wetting. The binding substances are difficult to dissolve both in dilute HCl and also dilute alkali.

Texture : *Braunlehms* in which a displacement of all the colloidal material has occurred are normally sands to sandy loams. Only *de-ironised braunlehms* always consist loamy to clayey textures.

Differentiation from Podsols : The bleached soils are easily confused with *podsols*. They are however distinguished from them by the absence of raw humus or dystrophic moder formations, usually by lack of humus in general, by the intensely coloured binding substances of the B horizon, rich in colloidal silicic acid, under a microscope, with reflected light, shining like wax and which, when dry, break up into angular fragments.

Differentiation from the Molken podsol : Colloidal rich, bleached *braunlehms,* whose bleached horizons are entirely de-ironized, can show a great similarity to the *molken podsol* (No. 87). They are distinguished from them by the absence of vertical displacement of humus sols. The acid humus sols, serving as peptizators in the *molken podsol*, produce the distinct or unequivocal formation of a dark flecked humus enriched horizon (B_h horizon) in the upper parts of the Be horizons, which never occurs in a *bleached* braunlehm. The absence of raw humus and of raw humus plants in its vegetation cover, as well as the formation of mull humus is always a valuable indication. It is to be noted, that *molken podsols* can be derived from *braunlehms* by the development of dystrophic humus forms and acid humus sols.

Occurrence: In high rainfall areas on deposits of fossil *braunlehm*. Particularly frequent are transition formations from the normal to the bleached form, with signs of increased percolation. Typical *bleached braunlehms* with richly developed micromorphology are found in the Paris basin, above all in the Sablière, near the Agricultural Research Centre at Versailles. Strongly *bleached braunlehms* occur as relict soils (partly with elements of the corresponding relict flora), in South Andalusia, particularly in the Sierra de Algeciras.

XXXV. Rotlehm
(WOHLTMANN 1892)

Synonyms: Red loam (MARBUT 1923), Kresslehm (HARRASSOWITZ 1926), krasnosem (AFANASIEFF 1928); ferretto (Italian folk name = *rotlehm* on deluvial shingle); nyirok (Hungarian folk name = fossil and relict *rotlehm* on hard silicate rock.

General Specification: Tropical to sub-tropical soil occurring in Europe only in the form of relict soils or of deposits of fossil formations, resulting on silicate rocks, rich in silic acid, intense brownish red, yellowish red to deep red in colour, with higly advanced weathering.

78. Typical Rotlehm

General Specification: Generally heavy, dense *rotlehm* with highly mobile, silica rich colloidal complex, in which the ferric hydroxide occurs partly in peptized, easily diffusible form and partly precipitated into red concretions, deposits and flecks.

Characteristics:

Profile: The type is also frequently preserved as a relict soil in Southern Europe and then shows a complete A(B)C profile on silicate rocks (chlorite schists, serpentine, basic igneous rocks, also clay schists, even phyllite) and humus deficient A horizons. Also the (B) horizons are usually of only a relatively low thickness (about 40-100 cm. *). These relict *rotlehms* occur in addition to relict *braunlehms* usually simultaneously with recent soil formations

---

*) Relatively shallow profiles occur also in the tropics besides the known deep soil covers.

on the same parent rocks (*Central European* and *meridional braunerde*) and usually contrast with them in very striking manner. On steep slopes not infrequently a *rotlehm* (or *braunlehm*) is overlain by a recent *braunerde*. The *rotlehm* can also occur further in more or less thick sediments of fossil formations which micromorphologically, chemically and physically are practically identical to the relict *rotlehms* *) with more or less complete profiles). The C horizon is missing in both. In forms with strong leaching an illuvial horizon (B horizon) is formed which passes below into a (B) horizon of considerable thickness, usually showing no signs of enrichment.

Humus Form: Almost always mull, even with *bleached rotlehm.*

Chemical Characteristics: Advanced weathering and leaching, therefore extreme base deficiency and low reserves of nutrients, colloidal complex rich in silicic acid, with the presence of mainly still active, highly peptizing colloidal silicic acid. Any chalk or easily soluble salts present are due to secondary enrichment as in the *braunlehm* (page 222). Of the clay minerals, kaolinite preponderates by far, partly also micaceous clay minerals. Free aluminium hydroxide is strongly reduced or completely missing. As in the *braunlehm*, heaviness and cohesion do not run parallel as, e. g. in the brown earths so that sandy soils can often exhibit a striking heaviness, plasticity, coherence, partly even stickiness. The *rotlehm* characteristics appear most strongly in fine textured soils.

Dynamic: Intensive chemical weathering, strong leaching, strong movements of the colloidal complex which can lead to an advanced leaching of the upper soil horizons, strong migration of the ferric hydroxide peptized by silicic acid, which precipitates in the form of concretions, flecks and deposits. The extensive loss in water of the irreversibly precipitated ferric hydroxide is due to the original dynamic of the soils in former geological ages.

Structure: Strong tendency to silting up and the formation of a badly aerated soil structure with low water permeability. Strong swelling of the soil on wetting, development of numerous shrinkage fissures on drying, at the same time often a rock-like hardening. Occasionally a breakdown into small sharp-edged aggregates can occur.

Microscopic Characteristics: Uniformly diffuse dispersion of the ferric hydroxide in the ground mass, formation of concretions, deposits and flecks, which show a dazzling red colour in reflected light (concretions often black with transmitted light as they are more or less opaque). The ground mass in thin section preparations is usually intensely egg-yellow in colour, although dazzling red colours also occur. In the formation of numerous

---

*) The *rotlehms* in soil sediments behave similarly to the *braunlehms*. Cf. note on page 224.

fluidal structures and doubly refracting streaks the *rotlehm* resembles considerably the typical *braunlehm* (plate XIX).

Biology: In spite of mull formation, relatively deficient soil life in the interior of the soil, due to its usually dense structure.

Variability: The fossil formations have a high stability, and are well preserved in Southern and Central Europe. The physical *rotlehm* characteristics, heaviness, cohesion, silting up, are particularly strongly pronounced in humid regions. It appears that in the Far North, the red colouring is considerably repressed and *braunlehms* appear in place of the previous *rotlehms*. The *rotlehm* is extraordinarily variable according to its recent environmental conditions. In the same way as in the *braunlehms* one can distinguish (55) *moist rotlehm* (in humid regions), (56) *bleached rotlehm* *) with stronger leaching of colloidal substances from the topsoil and (57) *dry rotlehm* (*Calvero-rotlehm* [19])) with scanty soil life and open, sparse plant cover.

Occurrence: *Rotlehms* are especially widespread in Southern Europe. Relict soils with A(B)C profiles or with profile remains overlain by recent soil formations are frequent in Greece and Spain. Deep (partly permeated by chalk sediments) deposits of fossil *rotlehms* occupy considerable areas in Spain. Isolated *rotlehm* regions are found in Central Europe, particularly in conjunction with basalt rocks (Vogelsberg, Burgenland, on the Seindlberg in eastern Styria, etc.).

79. *Earthy Rotlehm*
Earthy Red loam

General Specification: Easily crumbling, loose, iron rich *rotlehm*, hardening little on drying, with low to zero content of free aluminium hydroxide.

Characteristics:

Profile: A, (B) and C horizons as with the *braunerde*. In deep deposits the C horizon is missing.

Physical Characteristics: The striking heaviness, adhesion and puddling of the typical *rotlehm* are missing, also the plasticity is lower. The topsoil is remarkably loose, easily worked and does not form crusts and clods. The earth is crumbled easily in the hand and usually has a deep red colour.

Chemical Characteristics: Advanced weathering and lack of bases, in contrast to the *typical rotlehm*, lower silicic acid and higher ferrous hy-

---

*) In Palestine nasas (MENCHNIKOVSKY, 1932).

droxide content in the colloidal complex. In the clay substance, kaolinite usually predominates.

Microscopic Characteristics: The light coloured, usually egg-yellow, highly mobile, silicic acid rich parts of the ground substance of the *typical rotlehm* are restricted to remnants protected from leaching. The main mass of the structure consists of very fine thrombus-like, deep red deposits of ferric hydroxide gel, whose precipitation occurs so rapidly that it can no longer form collecting concretions (Iwatoka-phenomenon [20])). The greatest part of the ferric hydroxide has therefore become immobile. The structure is rich in cavities and in thin section gives the picture of a uniform spongy fabric (plate XIX). The colloidal complex is not dense and waxy in appearance as with the *typical rotlehm*, but scabby crusty and dull. Besides the Iwatoka-precipitates, the soil still contains numerous rounded concretions *) and flecks precipitates, the soil still contains numerous rounded concretions and flecks which are dazzling red in reflected light.

Water Relations: The water permeability is good to excellent, capilliarity considerably lower than in a *typical rotlehm*.

Dynamic: The water-stable structural framework (filter framework) of the irreversible Iwatoka precipitates makes an extensión leaching of all the mobile colloidal substances peptized by silicic acid possible. A bleaching and complete impoverishment of the colloidal substances cannot occur owing to the insolubility of the ferric hydroxide gels.

Occurrence: The soil has as yet been found in Europe only in the form of isolated fossil soil residues, however, it is possible that its area of occurrence is larger.

CG. Latosols (Kellogg 1948)

XXXVI. *(Lateritic) Roterde*

General Specification: Red brown to red tropical soil formation occurring in Europe only in the form of isolated fossil remains with loose structure, very low to almost negligible plasticity, low silicic acid content and high aluminium and ferric hydroxide content in the colloidal complex.

Characteristics:

Profile: A(B)C profile with well developed (B)/C-Horizons with relict soils. In fossil sediments (B)/C and C horizon missing.

---

*) Remains of a braunlehm prestage of development.

Structure : Rich in cavities and slight hardening with remarkably stable crumbs. There is no possibility of silting up and clod formation. No volume expansion on wetting, no development of shrinkage fissures on drying.

Chemical Characteristics : Advanced weathering, high gel content, particularly of sesquioxides, presence of free aluminium hydroxide, strong removal of silicic acid, $SiO_2 : R_2O_3 < 2$.

Microscopic Characteristics : The ferric hydroxide is present almost entirely in the form of immobile, scabby, crumbly, in reflected light dazzling red gel precipitates which form a very porous spongy fabric. The whole soil mass is only slightly transparent even in the thinnest layer, and therefore difficult to prepare. In thin sections practically all structural parts remain dark between crossed nicols. Only rarely are remains found of small silica rich fissure fillings.

Ocurrence : The soil formation is limited in Europe to only a few fossil occurrences, which for soil science at present are only of palaeopedological interest.

CH. Brown Earths

XXXVII. *Braunerde*
(RAMANN, 1905)

Synonyms : Ramann-Braunerde *).

General Specification : Neutral to moderately acid A(B)C soil of temperate climates with predominately immobile, flocculated colloidal substances; they brown to light ochre coloured B horizons are not enriched horizons, but have been formed by deep reaching chemical weathering with good aeration and abundant but not excessive moisture (i. e. they are (B) horizons).

Delimitation : Between *braunerde* and other soil types there exist various transitions. Strong acidification and coarse moder formation as well as the beginning of humus acid aluviation lead to podsolic braunerde, partial peptization and mobility of the ferric hydroxides and the colloidal substances in general in the presence of free silicic acid sols to *braunlehm* and waterlogging to *gley*.

Characteristics :

Profile : All horizons of the A(B)C profile blend gradually into each other without sharp boundaries.

---

*) To distinguish them from the light brown earths or brown soils of the semi-desert (*burrosem*, page 197) of the Russiam school

Dynamic: In general intensive chemical weathering with good clay formation (in which important differences exist between the main forms), characteristic precipitation of little peptised to intirely unpeptized, flocculated, immobile, limonitic ferric hydroxides. The carbonates are leached, braunerde profiles with secondary enrichment of calcium carbonate are always exposed to fresh intense chalk removal. There are no movements of colloidal substances. The soils show good water permeability and aeration. With permanent or long period waterlogging the braunerde character becomes lost.

Chemical Characteristics: No strong acidification or alkalisation. The silicic acid sesquioxide ratio is the same throughout the whole soil profile.

Parent Rocks: Occurring on all parent rocks, except those which due to their chemistry, lead to the development of braunlehm-like soils or which already contain fossil remains of *braunlehm* or *rotlehm*. Very unfavourable for *braunerde* formation are sterile siliceous rocks (quartzite, siliceous schists, siliceous sandstone, pure quartz sands).

Key for the Determination of Sub-types and Varieties.

1. Occurring only in southern dry regions, colour light brown, soil humus deficient, dry, usually sandy, with relatively low chemical breakdown of the parent rock (plate XXII).
    81. Meridional Braunerde

1*. Not only occurring in southern dry regions   2
2. Only occurring in the alpine region of high mountains, loose, low in peptizable substances with restricted clay formation, however usually rich precipitation of free ferric hydroxides.
    82. Alpine Sod Braunerde.

2*. Occurring outside the alpine region of high mountains   3
3. Soil effervescing with HCl or only containing a whitish chalk enriched layer (Ca horizon) underneath the (B) horizon (plate XXII).
    (60). Calc Braunerde.

3*. Soil not effervescing with HCl and without Ca horizon   4
4. The soil, in spite of a high colloid content usually shows a strikingly low plasticity, i. e. when moist it is only sligtly kneadable or formable. The soil mass is mostly dark rust brown in colour, very rich in iron, very loose and is developed primarily, on limonite, siderite and ore yielding limestones.
    (61). Ferritic Braunerde.

4*. Soil not occurring on the above parent rocks, with sufficiently high colloid content always distinctly plastic   5
5. Soil generally dark brown to almost sepia brown, loose, crumbly, humus-rich, fertile, and with tendency to develop a relatively deep profile (plate XXI).
    (58). Eutrophic Braunerde.

5*. Soil usually light ochre coloured, shallow, with dense structure, low in humus, with shallow humus horizons, occurring on base-deficient siliceous and silicate rocks (plate XXI).
    (59). Oligotrophic Braunerde.

80. Centro-European Braunerde

Synonyms: Silvester (MURGOCI 1909), brown forest soil (BALLENEGGER 1916), derived from it: Waldbraunerde. Also a part of the rostfarbener Waldboden (rust coloured forest soil) of STREMME (1930) belong to this subtype, i. e. as far as they are unbleached and show no dystrophic humus forms; it includes primarily very sandy varieties.

General Specification: *Braunerde* with good moisture relations of the humid deciduos and mixed forest region, characterized by intense chemical weathering and clay formation and a close luxuriant vegetation cover.

Characteristics:

Profile: Usually characterized by mull formation, in natural profiles always distinctly pronounced humus horizons. Owing to the intense chemical weathering and clay formation the soil has a certain ability to swell, which can lead on drying to the development of fine shrinkage fissures which particularly in the somewhat denser (B) horizon, occasionally can lead to the formation of irregularly rounded separation complexes, which have been described as «nut shaped» or by other authors as «polyhedrical» (STREMME).

Water Relations: Good water permeability and aeration, as well as good water retaining power which gives the soil a lasting moistness without in general leading to surplus water.

Dynamic: Intense weathering and clay formation, high capacity for sorption and base exchange, strong leaching of the carbonates, but no migration of colloidal substances *), none or only slight acidification.

Texture: The typical characteristics of the «silvester» only attain their full development with a certain loam content, which caused H. STREMME to split off the clay deficient, very sandy forms **). It is to be noted that the chemical weathering in *braunerde* of humid, warm regions is usually more intense than for example in *podsols* in particularly cold habitats (high moun-

---

*) Occasionally by mechanical or chemical analysis (sesquioxide determination) a slight enrichment of finely dispersed substances may be found in the (B) horizon caused by repeated washing down of fine earth into fissures, burrows of animals, root channels, earthworm tubes, etc., i. e. into a changing system of larger cavities, which are filled and re-developed in other places. Such phenomenon alone does not indicate podsolization. A certain enrichment of finely dispersed substances must be tolerated if other unequivocal braunerde characteristics are present and pronounced characteristics of *semi-podsols, podsols*, etc., are missing.

**) They are composed essentially of sand grains with coatings of iron rust (hydrolized iron hydroxide gels) with a very small admixture of clay. According to the thickness of the coatings and the degree of hydrolization of the ferric hydroxide the overall colour of the soil changes from a light rust yellow up to deep rust brown. H. STREMME designated the variety described above as rostfarbener Waldboden (rust coloured forest soil).

tains, tundra forest zone). Parent rocks, on which loamy soils can be found
in the braunerde region in many podsol regions show the development of
pronounced sandy soils.

Humus Form: Predominately mull.

Vegetation: The natural plant cover is deciduous and mixed forests.
Meadow and cultivated soils are always found in this region and in the
absence of human influence they would gradually revert back to forest soils.

Phenology: At no time of the year suffering from excess moisture or
waterlogging. In summer as a rule, never drying out severely and causing
drought damage. In winter moist throughout and also under a snow cover
almost never frozen, therefore even then biologically active. The relatively
considerable snow cover almost never lasts the whole winter, but thaws
repeatedly and in this way the soil always absorbs the thaw-water without
waterlogging. In the relatively warm, long spring the soil is at its moistest
and warms up gradually and continuously.

Region of Occurrence: In general in regions of deciduous and mixed
forests, in Southern Europe also of coniferous forests (*Pinus silvestris, Pinus
halepensis, Pinus pinaster,* etc.). Principally in Central Europe, to a somewhat
lesser extent in Northern Europe, in isolated parts of Southern Europe (Bulgaria, Jugoslavia, Northern Italy, Northern Spain, forest region of Spanish high
mountains, etc.). In the mountains of Central Europe the upper boundary
of the *Centro-European braunerde* lies at about 700-850 m., in Southern
Europe at 1.800-2.000 m.

Variability: This is particularly large here and therefore for a more
precise characterization a further subdivision is especially important. In the
following, the most important varieties will be described.

(58) Eutrophic Braunerde

Synonyms: Nutrient rich braunerde, Eubraunerde, Erubasboden (VON
HOYNINGEN-HUEHNE 1930) = essentially for forms on basic igneous rocks *),
brown forest soil of high base saturation (LAATSCH 1937).

General Specification: In general dark brown to almost sepia brown
coloured, humus rich *Centro-European braunerde* of high mineral and nutrient
content and high biological activity on easily weathered base-rich parent rocks
and which when mature has a deep sod and humus layer.

Characteristics:

Profile: The difference between the *eutrophic* and *oligotrophic braunerde* (page 236) appears most strongly in soil formations on hard parent

---

*) Includes also AC-soils (*ranker*) on such rocks.

234

Explanation of plate XXI

1. **Eutrophic (Centro=European) Braunerde** below beech forest on basaltic lava (Paulusberg, Burgenland, Austria).

2. **Oligotrophic (Centro=European) Braunerde** below mixed forest on sandstone shale (Admont, Styria).

---

rocks. Mature *eutrophic braunerde* has deep, humus rich, loose A horizons (up to 30 cm. and more in depth) which owing to their dark colouring contrast little with the (B) horizon, so that the boundary between the two is occasionall difficult to determine. Further the (B) horizons are relatively deep, loose and rich in cavities. They are followed in general by a strongly developed (B)/C horizon.

Soil Colour: The generally dark brown to sepia or coffee brown colour is usually due to the high ferric hydroxide content of the soil. The mostly dark coloured parent rocks, rich in bases and containing large quantities of mineral nutrient reserves also have, in general, a high content of iron rich minerals.

Parent Rocks: Predominantly easily weathered, base rich igneous rocks and their tuffs and base-rich crystalline schists, such as basalt, basanite, diabase, gabbro, basalt tuff, pumice sand [21]) and amphibolite.

Micromorphology: Usually porous, spongy structure with marks of intense earthworm activity. All peptizable substances are almost completely immobile, therefore absence of any fluidal structures and signs of movement. All the free ferric hydroxide is present in flocculated, immobile form. Gel precipitates in the form of concretions, flecks and localized deposits are missing. The fine crumbly iron precipitates are dark brown coloured and, as seen in thin section preparations, more or less uniformly permeate the whole soil fabric. The degree of flocculation is, however, very variable and depends on a series of different conditions whose intensity of operation has not yet been studied in detail. Apparently it depends on the one hand on the content of bases and ferric hydroxide and on the other hand environmental relations may have particular importance. Thus in areas with a dry summer and warm soil climate, the degree of flocculation appears to be particularly high. In any case here one encounters braunerde with relatively low base content which show an extraordinarily high degree of flocculation, while in uniformly strongly moistened soils with a colder soil climate, even with higher base content, it is relatively low. The extent of the flocculation of the ferric hydroxide is of great influence on the heaviness, peptisability and with it the crumb stability of the soil. The high stability of the crumb structure in braunerde regions with warm and dry summers (*braunerde* on the margin of the steppe or within the steppe zone) appears to be connected with it (plate xix).

XXI

A

(B)

(B)/C

C

A

(B)

(B)/C

C

1.   2.

Structure : All horizons of the *eutrophic braunerde* have a loose structure rich in cavities; the soil is therefore usually much superior to the *oligotrophic braunerde.* The individual aggregates (investigated with a binocular micros- cope) consist in general of morphologically well preserved complexes of earthworm casts.

Water Relations : Excellent water conduction with plentiful aeration, lasting water storage.

Humus Form : Excellent mull.

Mineral Composition : The soil has a high base mineral index (TAMM) and contains, according to the parent material, considerable quantities of biotite, augite, hornblende, olivine, ores, etc. Among the feldspars, calcium rich plagioclases are prominent.

Vegetation : The natural plant cover consists usually of well developed deciduous woods. In level or slightly sloping places usually transformed to cultivated soils, it can be profitably used for field crop and orchard at the same time.

Biology : Intense soil life indicated by the richness in species and individuals of the flora and fauna under the dominating influence of the activity of mull forming earthworm species. Excellent decomposition and humification with perfect formation of clay humus complexes. The only disadvantage consists in that *eutrophic braunerde* is developed almost always only on hard parent rocks and rarely (practically only on loose tuffs and pumice sands) on deep, uncompacted sediments, which imposes a certain limitation on their depth.

Ocurrence : Known extensive occurrences are found in the Bohemian Mittelgebirge and in the Vogelsberg region (Hessen) smaller in Northern Ireland, Odenwald, Burgenland, South-eastern Styria, Carintia, etc.

(59) Oligotrophic Braunerde

Synonyms : Nutrient deficient braunerde; Oligobraunerde; brown forest soil with low base saturation (LAATSCH 1937).

General Specification : Usually yellow ochre to light ochre coloured, nutrient deficient, generally dense soil with strong base removal on base deficient silicate rocks or base deficient loose sediments; if occurring on hard parent rocks shallow, stony and humus deficient (plate XXI).

Between the *oligotrophic* and *eutrophic braunerde* exist transition forms *(mesotrophic braunerde)* which exhibit the characteristics of both formations to a lesser extent.

Explanation of plate XXII

1. (Centro=European) **Calc=braunerde** below meadow on loess (Fernitz, Lower Austria).
2. **Meridional braunerde** on gneiss below dry vegetation. In the picture *Quercus Ilex, Thymus vulgaris* and *Stipa juncea* (Santa María de la Alameda, Sierra de Guadarrama, 900 m.).

Characteristics:

Profile: The difference between the *oligotrophic* and the *eutrophic braunerde* appears most strongly in soil formations on hard parent rock. The A horizons are very shallow, often only a few centimeters thick. The (B) horizons remain of low thickness. In cultivated soils the (A) horizon usually becomes completely lost due to mixing with parts of the (B) horizon.

Parent Rocks: Acid granite, gneiss, syenite, liparite, quartz porphyry, porphyry, sandstones, quartzite schists, muscovite schists, sericiticphyllite, etc., deep forms on base deficient loose sediments.

Characteristic Minerals: Owing to the intense weathering, practically only quartz and muscovite with other minerals particularly difficult to weather are still found.

Soil Colour: Base deficient parent materials are generally also very iron deficient, so that only little free ferric hydroxide can be formed which causes the usually light ochre, ochre yellow to brown ochre colour of the soil.

Structure: Relatively dense, however not so badly aerated that the oxidation weathering is impeded or gleying can occur. Owing to the low base content (and low ferric hydroxide content) the ability to form crumbs as well as the stability of the crumbs is lowered. Of the brown earths, *oligotrophic braunerde* has the strongest erodability; loamy soils may show considerable clod formation.

Water Relations: With loamy soils, a strong water run-off occurs on slopes with little penetration into the soil interior, so that the soil is often supplied with insufficient water.

Microscopic Characteristics: In a thin section preparation the ferric hidroxide does not perhaps appear peptised, but its degree of flocculation is strikingly low, the structure deficient in cavities and much denser than with the *eutrophic braunerde*. It differs from *typical terra fusca*, in that in the latter the ferric hydroxide appears extraordinarily mobile and is precipitated in rounded concretions, which is not the case with the *oligotrophic braunerde*. The colour of the finely dispersed braunerde ground mass in thin sections is extremely light.

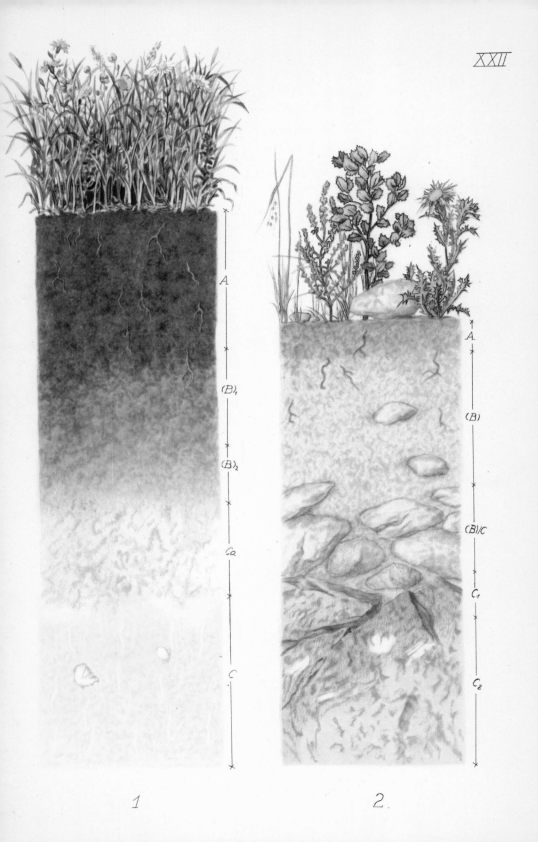

XXII

1   2.

Biology: The activity of the soil is relatively low, its density of organisms is greatly inferior to that of the *eutrophic braunerde*. The soil life is usually concentrated in the superficial layer, in forest soils the most intense activity is seen in the F horizon. The decomposition and humification is considerably more inactive than that of the other *Central European braunerde*. A considerable intensification of the soil life of braunerde on loose sediments may be obtained by liming and organic and mineral fertilizers. The fertility of soils on hard parent rocks always remains influenced detrimentally by the low depth of soil.

Humus Form: Usually mull. Acid soils, approaching the podsolic braunerde, often show moder formation.

Chemical Characteristics: The soil has the strongest tendency to acidification of all brow earths and is at the same time also the most deficient in iron.

Extent: The soil form is very widespread in Central and Northern Europe. Particularly typical occurrence are seen in the Northern Viennese Forest, as well as on acid hard parent rocks in places below about 700-850 m. above sea level.

(60) Calc-Braunerde

Synonyms: Chal-Braunerde.

General Specification: Usually loose *braunerde* with good crumb structure generally good mull formation which, by a calcareous topsoil or at least by the presence of a chalk-enriched horizon in the profile, contrasts distinctly with other brown earths.

Characteristics:

Profile: The normal profile consists of four horizons, A, (B), Ca and C horizons. Occasionally the (B) horizon or even the A horizon already shows a heightened lime content and distinct effervescence with dilute hydrochloric acid. In this case it is always a question of secondary chalk enrichment. This occurs on slopes often by continuous supplying of the soil with chalk powder, chalk sand, chalk debris or calcareous washings from higher parts of the slope where limestone, calcareous sands or marl occur. Frequently it is also the mixing of braunerde sediments with chalk deposits, during the course of deposition. The thickness of the chalk horizons depends in the first place on the maturity of the profile and on the level of the chalk contained in the parent material. The lower part of the (B) horizons often shows calcite efflorescences in the form of needles and filaments similar to those in chernosem, which have grown out from the pores of the colloidal deposits on the cavity walls (see page 201). This pseudo-mycelium layer or (B)/Ca horizon (which is always formed under the chalk free (B) horizon) is almost always to te found with *loess-braunerde*.

Parent Rocks : In the first place, calcareous sandstone, marl, calc-silicate schists, calkphyllite, calc-conglomerate, calc-breccia, sandy chalks, dolomite and gypsum rocks, calcareous loose sediments, etc. The best and most valuable soils are formed on loess (*loess-braunerde*).

Preliminary Stages of Development : The pre-stages to *calc-braun-erde* which have not been formed on mature soil deposits (*braunerde* sediments) are *rendzinas* or *para-rendzinas*. Therefore *calc-braunerde* occurs frequently in association with *rendzinas*. The *loess-braunerde* begins in the brown earth region with a shallow chernosem-like *rendzina* which can be frequently found as a young soil formation on soil refuse from road and railway constructions on the raw loess.

Humus Form : Mull.

Biology : Good decomposition and humification. In soils with calcareous A horizons, humus-rich rendzina-like humus formations which contain calcium humates ([*12*] *rendzina-like calc-braunerde*).

Characteristic Minerals : These can be extraordinarily varied according to the kind of parent material. Pure calc-sandstone soils lead often only to accumulations of quartz grains ([*13*] *oligotrophic calc-braunerde*). After decalcification they form very nutrient deficient, biologically inert soils, which podsolize easily. A mere diverse mineral composition is shown by the *mesotrophic calc-braunerde* (like the *loess braunerde*). [*14*]. *Eutrophic calc-braunerde* is formed particularly on basalts and other basic igneous rocks with high content of chalk yielding silicates, which can form by weathering, considerable quantities of $CaCO_2$.

(61) Ferritic Braunerde (n. f.)

General Specification : Rust brown, dark ochre brown to almost sepia brown, strikingly well-crumbled, little plastic to almost unplastic *braunerde* with strong enrichment of flocculated ferric hydroxides.

Characteristics :

Profile : The soil is usually relatively deep. Besides well-developed loose (B) horizons, in very dark forms only little distinguished from the A horizon, deep reaching (B)/C horizons occur . Ca horizons usually reach deeply into the parent rock (Ca/C horizons).

Parent Rocks : The occurrence of the soil is limited to particular parent rocks, primarily to siderite, limonite and ore-yielding limestones.

Physical Characteristics : The strong crumbling of the soil, its strong flocculation of the ferric hydroxides and low plasticity depend to a great extent on the content of clay substances and easily-weathered iron ores in the parent material. Lack of clay intensifies the characteristics of the soil.

Dynamic: Intense solution weathering which produces decalcification and consequently liberation, weathering and concentration of the iron ores. Due to the concentration, almost complete flocculation of the ferric hydroxide occurs, which takes place also in cool and moist habitats. Even in the regions of the podsolic braunerde and the forest podsols, there is no podsolization.

Chemical Characteristics: High content of ferric hydroxide, extensive decalcification, but only moderate acidification.

Similarity to Ferritic Roterdes: These are tropical soils having another genesis and are not characterised unconditionally by their occurrence on the above parent rocks. They are, however, at the same time loose, strongly crumbled, little plastic soils, which can be recognixed by their exclusive enrichment of flocculated ferric hydroxides with a much lower water content.

Humus Form: Almost always mull.

Biology: Good decomposition and humification, deep-reaching soil life, limited however by lack of nutrients. Their cultivation is mostly limited by their occurrence in strongly articulated, often rocky landscapes.

Phenology: The soil has a high permeability but low capillary conductivity. Its surface dries out rapidly and warms up quickly in spring. Although it is generally low in sandy constituents, it behaves in many ways like a sand soil.

Ocurrence: Widespread in iron ore rich regions of Central, Southern and also Northern Europe. Particularly typical occurrences are found on siderite and ore-yielding limestones in West Styria and on limonite in Attica, Greece.

81. Meridional Braunerde

Synonyms: Brown dry forest soil (HUGUET DEL VILLAR 1927); Mediterranean braunerde; Southern braunerde (LAATSCH).

General Specification: Light-coloured, humus deficient, usually sandy *braunerde*, retarded in its chemical weathering, showing micromorphological characteristics both of the *braunerde* and the *braunlehm* and occurring in the drier regions of Southern Europe.

Characteristics:

Profile: Generally shallow A(B)C profile with shallow, humus-deficient A horizons (often only a few centimeters) and shallow (B) horizons. Between these and the C horizon a usually well-developed (B)/C horizon of the same colour as the (B) horizon is seen. Owing to the open, often very sparse plant cover, as well as the strong erodability of the soil the upper parts of the profile are easily removed. But such erosion does not alter its character. Owing to the slight humus formation and the mixing of the A horizon with the upper part of the (B) horizon in ploughing, humus horizons are usually only very indistinctly developed or almost completely missing.

Soil Colour: In general a dull light desert brown, in particularly iron deficient soils up to a brownish drab. These colours almost never occur in the *Centro-European braunerde,* so that they are a useful easy diagnostic character. Deeper brown colour and reddish-brown colours may occur with a higher iron content in transition forms to *Centro-European braunerde, braunlehm* and *rotlehm.*

Parent Rocks: As parent material hard silicate rocks occupy the first place. Granite and similar igneous rocks, gneiss, mica schists, chlorite schists, phyllite and clay schists are the most important. On loose sediments braunlehm-like formations predominate.

Texture: Almost always sandy textures, deficient in colloidal material (with the exception of forms on clay schists).

Structure: Owing to the lack of structure-forming constituents the structure is generally dense. Occasionally cementation occurs in conjunction with intense drying-out, producing a hardening of the soil which makes it somewhat difficult to work (probably colloidal silicic acid acts as the principal binding substance in this case).

Plant Cover: Usually very sparse dry vegetation in which today open covers of dwarf shrubs such as *Quercus ilex, Juniperus oxycedrus, Thymus vulgaris,* etc., appear prominently. Sometimes secondary dry woods of *Pinus pinea, Pinus halepensis,* etc.

Micromorphology: In thin-sections the soil shows at the same time structure parts with brown earth characteristics such as completely flocculated, immobile ferric hydroxide, and others with braunlehm-like characteristics such as complete peptization and mobility of all the colloidal substances, peptization of ferric hydroxide and its accumulative precipitation in the form of dark brown flecks and small concretions. The fabric character is much changing and areas of low chemical weathering alternate with small intensely weathered (plate XIX).

Phenology: The soil is dessicated for the greater part of the year and only becomes moist temporarily from individual showers of rain. Drying out occurs rapidly. The occasional winter snow cover is always thin and of short duration. The snow lies on the unfrozen or slightly frozen soil and becomes completely absorbed by it. The phenology of the soil also distinguishes it from the *Centro-European braunerde.*

Dynamic : The considerable heating of the moist soil during a great part of the year causes intense braunlehm-like weathering to begin, which, however, owing to the rapid drying-out of the soil, has little effect on its general character and remains confined to small spots. On the other hand the intense mechanical weathering causes the rock to break down to gravel or fine gravel and grit. Signs of the chemical weathering extend deep into the parent material, but, in contrast to the *Centro-European braunerde*, little clay formation, clay enrichment or liberation of free ferric hydroxide occurs. There is practically no movement of substances.

Humus Form : Mull.

Biology : The relatively intense soil life during the short moist periods is almost completely suppressed during dry periods. In spite of comparatively good decomposition and humification, however, there is only little humus enrichment due to the low amount of plant remains.

Erodability : Owing to the low content of colloidal material and the absence of stable binding substances the soil mass is easily eroded. Because, there is generally no protecting closed plant cover, it almost always shows many signs of erosion, so that this may be regarded as a typical characteristic in which it differs essentially from the *Centro-European braunerde*. On the south-east slopes of the Guadarrama mountains, a complete removal of the soil cover up to the (B)/C horizon often occurs. Where recolonization has occurred on the strongly eroded surfaces *rankers* are usually formed and are widespread in these regions even in the hill phase.

Ocurrence : In the hilly dry regions of Southern Europe, particularly Greece, Southern Italy and the Iberian peninsular, it is the main soil formed on silicate rocks.

82. *Alpine Sod Braunerde*

General Specification : Loose *braunerde,* deficient in colloidal substances, with supressed clay formation, but rich in precipitated ferric hydroxides, occurring above the tree line in the cushion plant region (Central Europe) or in the grass heath region (Southern Europe) on high mountains.

Characteristics :

Profile : Shallow A(B)C profile with distincly developed, frequently humus rich, dark brown grey to blackish A horizons and intense rust brown, on very iron deficient parent rocks ochre coloured (B) horizons. Between these and the C horizon occur usually well developed (B)/C horizons.

Parent Rocks : Practically only hard silicate rocks, primarily plutonic rocks and crystalline schists are concerned.

Texture : Predominately sandy to gritty textures. Heavy soils are practically non-existent.

Structure : Strikingly loose and easily dug soils.

Micromorphology : The micro-structure consists principally of loosely arranged, slightly weathered mineral grains with generally scabby-crumbly deposits of ferric hydroxide. The arrangement of the fabric elements is loose and porous, and with a high mica content bulky. The cavities consist predominately of inter-granular spaces in which only small quantities of deposits of colloidal substances are found.

Dynamic : The varieties occurring in the Alps have a sufficient moisture content but the temperature is too low for intense chemical weathering. For this reason and due to the long inactive winter period, only little clay formation occurs. However, the conditions are adequate for the formation and precipitation of a large quantity of free ferric hydroxide. The soil has a high water permeability but owing to the insufficient rainfall and absence of humus sol formation, podsolization does not occur and at most transition formations to podsolic braunerde may be found.

Phenology : Continuous winter snow-cover over the frozen soil, interruption of life processes as well as the processes of decomposition by a rest pause of 6-8 months. Thorough moistening when the snow melts in early spring, moderate moistening in summer and early autumn.

Humus Form : Generally humus with mull-like moder and with droppings mostly well preserved in shape.

Biology : Relatively good decomposition and humification, but complete absence of clay-humus complex formation.

Ocurrence : The soil occurs in the Alps as climax formation above the zone of the *alpine sod podsols,* and in the Austrian Central Alps at a height of about 2.800-3.000 m. As a prestage to the *podsols* it descends into the dwarf shrub zone. In Southern European high mountains it is most widespread in the grass heath zone usually above a forest girdle, in which (in the absence of a podsol girdle) *Centro-European braunerde* is formed.

CI. Gley-like Soils

XXXVIII. Pseudogley

Synonyms : Gley-like soil *), gleiartiger Boden (G. KRAUSS 1928), extended by (LAATSCH 1938).

---

*) The modification of «gley-like soil» to *pseudogley* has been made here to make it conform to the rules of nomenclature, whereby the type designation should be expressed by a noun.

General Specification: Densely packed, silty soil with gley-like appearance which is characterized principally not by water-logging, but by alternative conditions of superficial water-logging and rapid drying out, in which the latter predominates. It is essential that solution and movement of hydroxides occurs to a greater or lesser extent under the influence of peptizing plant acids (primarily tannic acid).

83. Krauss' Pseudogley

Synonyms: Gley-like soil, gleiartiger Boden (G. KRAUSS 1928); Krauuss'scher Pseudogley; marbled gley-like soil (LAATSCH 1937) = for transition forms between marbled soils and gley soils; Melmboden = frankish local variety on fine Keuper sand with dust loam covers.

General Specification: *Pseudogley* with very varying moisture content, easily dried out, which, under the humus horizon, usually shows a uniform pale layer with numerous dark brown concretions or a pale horizon reaching into the subsoil; the solution and movement of the iron compounds in these horizons, due mainly to the action of soil carbonic acid, occurs in ferrous form.

Profile: The soil is formed on the foundation of a well or feebly developed Centro-European braunerde or a dense structured (ganter-like) *grey ranker* (see page 171). Immediately under the A horizon, which generally shows dystrophic humus formation, a narrow zone of humus substances of a dark grey colour often with a lilac to bluish tint is frequently formed. This corresponds to the «klebsandschicht» *) of the *molken-podsol* (A/g_h horizon). This zone passes gradually into a light pseudogley layer (g horizon) **), which has a pale grey, whitish grey, or in transition forms flecked pale brown colour, and is generally permeated by numerous, dark brown concretions of about pin-head size. It may only be a few centimeters thick in feebly developed *pseudogley*, but in extreme cases it can extend deep into the substratum. The change into the usually brown to ochre coloured, dense, only slightly permeable substratum ((B) horizon) occurs gradually and frequently there is a grey and brown flecked transition horizon (g/(B) horizon).

From *pseudogley* there are not only transition forms to *braunerde* and *molken-podsol* (page 255), but also to genuine *gley*, particularly to *anmoor*.

Texture: Almost only silty to fine sandy texture, in which both coarse sand and clay are completely missing or very unimportant.

Parent Material: De-calcified silt loams (mealy sands) derived from loess covers, dust sands, rocks which weather to similar material such as fine

---

*) See page 255.
**) To distinguish it from a G horizon = gley layer.

---

grained bunter sandstones or silty erosion sediments. Such silty covers usually lie on heavy clay sediments or other impermeable substrata.

Structure: Extraordinarily dense packing of the soil particles, so that only very fine pores can be formed between them. Thus there develops a very homogenous, fine pored uniform fine fabric, very conductive to capillary movement, which in its upper parts is saturated entirely with colloidal humus substances. However on drying no shrinkage fissures are formed, but at best, there is a tendency for horizontal laminae to separate. Dry fragments of the topsoil may be easily crumbled between ones fingers.

Water Relations: The fine-pored fabric of the pseudogley layer has a high capilliarity, but a low permeability. On soaking, all the pores become completely filled with water causing deficient aeration. The movement of water downwards is impeded by the low permeability of the substratum so that the primary movement is lateral, especially on gentle slopes. With surface evaporation, an intense capillary rise occurs which accelerates the impoverishment of the soil in available water. The capillaries of the A/g_h horizon are reduced in size by the adhesion of mobile humus substances. After intense drying there occurs in addition a considerable reduction in the moisture capacity so that the rain water only penetrates slowly into the soil and stagnates in the surface. The sealing of the soil by the dense humus cover and the klebsand layer of the A/g_h horizon impedes aeration even in dry periods. The soil is sufficiently aerated, however, for the formation of ferric hydroxide concretions.

Morphology of the Concretions: The formation of concretions is a consequence of the high conductivity of the soil fabric, which is completely filled with water, in which movements of substances by diffusion readily occur. In typical *pseudogley* the concretions are extremely numerous and are readily visible to the naked eye. They are dark brown to blackish coloured (in partly due to manganese), soft and form streaky smears on cutting the soil *). They are rarely well-rounded, but have irregular, extraordinarily variably shaped cross-sections and often indistinct contours.

De-ironization of the g horizon: The light ground mass of the

---

*) Such soft rust granules were already known to the older Russian soil scientists and were designated as «bobowinas».

XXIII

A_1

A_2

A_e

B

C

A_1

B_h/B_s

B_s

B/C

C

1.

2.

pseudogley horizon often shows an extensive iron impoverishment, recognisable by its whitish colour. Iron-rich gley layers, in which the iron has not been carried away but is present in ferrous form, show bluish to greenish grey, olive-green, brownish, green to greenish brown colours. The degree of iron impoverishment may be easily ascertained by calcining small fragments of the ground substance. Whitish iron deficient fragments show only little or no reddening on heating in air. Fragments rich in ferrous iron from true gley horizons give an intense reddening. The iron impoverishment is due either to lateral conduction or to the concentration of almost the entire iron content of the pseudogley layer in the concretions.

Surface Relief: The soil formation is favoured in level or shallow trough-shaped topography where practicly no water inflow and no lateral water supply is possible within the soil. Such locations produce a strong alternation of water-logging and drying out.

Chemical Characteristics: Extreme de-calcification and base removal, advanced acidification.

Humus Form: Dystrophic acid moder to raw humus-like coarse moder. In the lower parts of the A horizon the coprogenic constituents are greatly dispersed and therefore the shape of small animal droppings is poorly preserved.

Phenology: Due to the winter being relatively deficient in rain and snow, the soil can store up only little winter moisture. The superficial water-logging in spring only allows slow warming of the soil. *Pseudogleys* are formed in a relatively dry summer climate, which is essential for their development since they are located on level or only slightly depressed country. In this way the intense summer drying out of the soil occurs which is typical for its phenology. In a moist summer climate and in deeper troughs with good water supply *gleys* to *anmoors* with continuously water-logged upper layers are formed. Summer rainstorms may produce great pools of stagnant water on the soil surface, as its penetration into the soil is restricted by the low moisture capacity and low permeability. Thus, the greater part of the water evaporates unused by the vegetation.

Dynamic: The very apparent solution of iron complexes in ferrous form under the influence of carbonic acid is accelerated by the tannic acids nearly always present, or by humus sols and their peptizing effect. Partly, too, transport of iron is possible in the form of ferric hydroxide. The movement of iron, also of a part of the humus substances, occurs only within the individual horizons, primarily of the topsoil, and does not lead to the formation of illuvial horizons (B_{hs} and B_s horizons) as in the *molken-podsol* (page 255). A very narrow seam-like illuvial enrichment horizon of humus substances, which is paralleled by similar formations in the stesopodsolic braunerde (page 251) and in the glebsand layer of the *molken-podsol*, occurs only immediately underneath the humus horizon in the upper part of the g horizon (therefore A_{gh} horizon and not B_h horizon).

Biology: Owing to the lack of bases and nutrients, acidification and other biologically unfavourable relations, there is incomplete decomposition and humification as well as a tendency to produce dystrophic, acid humus sol-producing humus forms. The soil is primarily a forest soil and the drying out is the primary decisive biological factor. Lack of moisture reserves in summer, difficulties of root-penetration, restriction of the lateral spread and thickening of roots in the extremely hard dry soil, lack of air and slow warming-up in spring are the principal disadvantages.

Plant Cover: Open peduncular oak birch woods with a scanty shrub layer and a ground vegetation very poor in species (principally *Molinia coerulea* is typical). Stunted spruce plantations are frequently encountered.

Ocurrence: The classical region of occurrence lies in North-West Saxony. However, the soil is also found not infrequently in other areas in Central Europe on similar parent material and with similar conditions.

84. Marbled Pseudogley

Synonyms: Marbled soil, marmorierter Boden *) (LAATSCH 1937), terre bigarrée et striée (P. TREITZ 1912).

General Specification: Soil occurring in forests with trees rich in tannins (particularly *Quercus pedunculata* and *Quercus sessiliflora*) with temporary water-logging, by which tannins are extracted from the tree-roots, and this subsequently causes a partial solution and local translocation of the ferric hydroxide present and the development of light coloured bleached zones, flecks, striations and veins.

Characteristics:

Profile: The soil has essentially an A(B)C profile like the *braunerde*, i. e. the formation of illuvial layers, designated as B horizons, cannot be determined. The brown (B) horizon, however, is strikingly permeated by light grey, whitish grey to yellowish flecks, striations and veins. The top-soil usually shows an increased content of light flecks which may coalesce to form a complete light grey horizon (g horizon). In this horizon particularly there are numerous dark brown to blackish concretions of ferric hydroxide (up to pea size) visible to the naked eye.

Morphological Characteristics: Dense structure, when well mois-

---

*) The word «soil» is replaced here by the type designation «pseudogley».

tened of pasty consistency, on drying out becoming almost rock-like. The bleaching due to tannic acid solution and translocation of the ferric hydroxide occurs primarily in the marginal zones of conducting channels, i e. of root channels, in which the roots have been wholly decomposed (bleached channels), cleavage surfaces of shrinkage fissures, in close proximity to fresh oak roots, etc. All these phenomena give the profile surface the appearance of a marble-like flecking and veining. A uniform bleaching occurs where the iron complexes can either be transported laterally or where they can be precipitated as iron concretions.

Surface Relief: The soil is to be found principally in shallow troughs, level places or less frequently on slight slopes on silty sediments with impermeable substrata. On steeper slopes it is absent.

Chemical Characteristics: Complete removal of chalk and bases; under the influence of ferric tannic acid sols, the pH value falls below 5 (pH 4.8-3.6).

Humus Form: Strong tendency to develop dystrophic humus forms, however, mull-like moder also, in many cases even acidified mull can be found.

Plant Cover: Acid-tolerant oak forests (in part oak-hornbeam forests) are typical as they are not highly sensitive to temporary water-logging.

Dynamic: Strong chemical weathering, formation of free aluminium hidroxide. The solution of the ferric hydroxide occurs in the form of tannic acid ferric sols which have violet hues. The gel precipitates are dark blue and on aging turn black. Therefore, in the soil substrata (particularly in the B/g horizons) blackish flecks often appear. The ferric tannic acid sol moves usually only short distances in the soil fabric and penetrates for example in root channels only a few millimeters into the soil mass and is here soon changed back to brown ferric hydroxide. A dark coloured enrichment skin develops at the edges of the pale grey bleached channels. The movement of ferric hydroxide can also occur without oxygen deficiency and therefore the presence of reducing conditions is not necessary. Stagnant water however extracts more tannic substances from the oak roots (also spruce roots, fallen leaves, etc.). The tannic acid sol solutions penetrate into the water conducting channels of the dense soil structure, from which they are absorbed by capilliarity by the channel walls. Further, the formation of concretions can occur entirely under the influence of tannic substances without reduction of the ferric hydroxide. Formation of the concretions is due entirely to the transfer of substances by diffusion i. e. movement towards the concretion nucleus in whose neighbourhood the concentration of mobile iron is continually reduced due to precipitation, while the marbling is due to the formation of bleached zones by capilliary displacement an re-precipitation. The tannic substances, which are highly hydrated colloids, generally also have a strong peptizing and protective colloid effect, therefore they have great influence on the formation of the structure and its hardening on drying. It is essential that the movement of substances in *marbled pseudogleys* should occur within relatively small regions and that intense vertical eluviation with the formation of complete illuvial horizons should not exist. Besides tannic substances, humus sols, however, are able to some extent, to contribute to the mobility of substances as well as to intensify reduction resulting in a solution of part of the iron in the ferrous form.

Phenology: Alternation of short period water-logging and extreme drying out, accompanied by extraction of tannic substances, and ensuing solution and precipitation of the iron.

Biology: Interrupted and irregular decomposition and humification. The unbalanced water economy, dense structure, the tendency to acidification and development of unfavourable humus forms generally act very detrimentally on the vegetation.

Delimitation: Differentiation from the *Krauss' pseudogley* is difficult as both soils overlap to a great extent. The simple term *pseudogley* should be used in doubtful cases, and where strong marbling and easily recognisable tannic acid effects are present *«marbled pseudogley»* should be applied.

Ocurrence: Very widespread in Central Europe, also in parts of Northern Europe, particularly know in Germany where it is absent only in the driest regions.

CJ. Podsol Class

XXXIX. *Semipodsol*

Synonyms: Podsolic soils (GLINKA 1908) = forms with light bleached flecks, without uniform bleached horizon; feebly podsolic soil (GLINKA 1908) = similar soils with no development of horizon-like flecked zone; cryptopodsol (NIKIFOROFF 1937) = soils in which translocation of colloidal substances (embryonic podsolization) is not externally apparent, but can only be detected by chemical analysis *); concealed podsol (GORODKOFF and NEUSTRUEFF 1923) = podsol-like soils without bleached horizons at the boundary between tundra forest and treeless tundra (*Northern semipodsol*).

General Specification: Soils with dystrophic humus forms, acid humous eluviation **) and development of illuvial horizons, without however

---

*) The opposite concept is called phaneropodsol (NIKIFOROFF 1937) = podsols with distinctly apparent podsolization [22]).

**) Displacement of colloidal substances under acid reaction and the peptizing action of acid sols of humus.

the presence of a uniform, distinctly developed bleached horizon (eluvial horizon).

85. Podsolic Braunerde
(RAMANN, 1917)

Synonyms: Degraded braunerde (LUNDBLAD 1924) = braunerde which has become podsolic by unsuitable forestry managment.

General Specification: Soil with similar external appearance to *braunerde*, frequently derived from *braunerde*, with moderate humus sol movement and, in contrast to the *podsol*, moderate acid humous eluviation.

(62) Eupodsolic Braunerde

Synonyms: *Eumorphic semipodsol;* podsolized braunerde, micropodsol = soils with uniform thin seam of bleached sand (to be distinguished from podsolic braunerde in the narrow sense, where the bleached sand occurs only in isolated flecks); weakly bleached brown forest soil (STREMME 1930) = for loamy soil forms; weakly bleached rust coloured forest soil (STREMME 1930) = extremely clay-deficient, sandy and iron hydroxide rich forms (cf. page 232).

General Specification: Podsolic braunerde with bleached sand flecks or with a seam of bleached sand at the lower edge of the humus horizon.

Characteristics:

Profile: The best profile development is to be found in forests, particularly coniferous forests. It is therefore always advantageous, when examining arable or grassland soils, to study the adjacent profiles under forest remnants under similar conditions, particularly similar parent material. In this way it is often easy to recognise changes caused by man. In forest there is a moderately thick förna above a dystrophic humus formation between whose lower edge and the B horizon appear grey to whitish grey shallow lens-shaped bleached sand flecks or a uniform very thin (ca. 1/2-2 cm.) layer of bleached sand (A_e horizon). Even with low-power magnification it can be seen that all the mineral grains in the natural, unprepared humus layer itself are completely bleached. Bleached grains may be easily detected in cultivated fields where the profile has been disturbed and coherent bleached flecks are not found. The B horizon, which is in most cases ochre yellow, but brown to rust brown in colour when the parent material is rich in iron, in contrast with the *braunerde* is a true B horizon (illuvial horizon), showing a considerably higher content of finely dispersed substances than the A horizon. A podsolic braunerde whose upper soil horizons have been disturbed by cultivation can generally be recognized between ones fingers by the higher content of colloids in the B horizon, so that chemcial analysis is only necessary as a diagnostic acid in exceptional cases. The C horizon and B horizon are usually connected by a well developed B/C horizon.

Parent Rocks: The soil is easily formed on base deficient loose sediments with sufficient sand content or on hard rocks which break down to similar weathering products, like sandstone, mica-schist, gneiss, granite, etc. On base rich rocks, podsolic braunerde is formed as a climax althought well developed *podsols* on other parent material may also occur in close proximity. The soils on hard parent rocks are always stony and shallow and have an average, profile depth (up to the B/C horizon) of 25-40 cm.

Humus Form: Usually dystrophic coarse moder (of less thickness than in the *podsol*); in many forests auflagetorf (page 36); rarely raw humus, sometimes mineral rich acid fine moder, however, practically never mull.

Dynamic: Intensive chemical weathering, wasteful decomposition of all mineral reserves. In the podsolic braunerde chemical weathering predominates over the slow eluviation, while in the *podsol* eluviation occurs more rapidly than the weathering so that, for example, bleached sand formation occurs on granite before the feldspars are weathered. As a consequence of the complete bleaching of bases, there is increasingly intense acidification and solution by acid humus sols. Eluviation effects humus substances and inorganic colloidal substances to an almost equal degree. A separate or preferential precipitation of humus substances in particular parts of horizons does not occur or occurs only to a limited extent (no formation of B_h horizons).

Biology: Slow or practically no decomposition and humification.

Vegetation and Occurrence: The podsolic braunerde is primarily a forest soil and is especially typical of spruce forests rich in cranberries and bilberries. In the Alps they become a climax formation in the high region between 700-1.500 m. They also extend inside the podsol zone (generally as development prestages), and often also as a climax form on the southern slopes of the higher spruce forest region and grassy parts rich in *Calamagrostis villosa*. It is a frequent soil formation Northern Europe. In Southern Europe it occurs on relatively small areas in high mountains.

Alteration by Cultivation: Fundamental changes occur in the soil under arable and grassland cultivation, the principal effect being that the raw humus and coarse moder layers become disintegrated and mull-like formations appear in their places. Bleached zones and flecks disappear, and a kind of braunerde with increased acidity, dense structure, easy silting up, high surface water run-off and strong erodability is formed, in which the subsoil is always heavier than the topsoil (cryptopodsolic braunerde). In cultivated soils owing to mixing of the A horizon with the upper B horizon and to little new humus formation, a distinct humus horizon can often no longer be detected.

[15]. **Crytopodsolic Braunerde**: This can occur also as a natural soil and, lilke the soils disturbed by cultivation, shows no bleached flecks nor bleached sandy seams. It may be recognized by the humus form (predominately acid moder), the usually distinc difference in the texture between the surface soil layer and the substratum for there is a considerable increase in the content of colloidal substances with depth, and by the predominance of bleached grains in the humus layer.

(63) Stesopodsolic Braunerde [*)]

Synonyms: *Stesomorphic semi-podsol.*

General Specification: Podsolic braunerde, usually rich in colloidal substances, with dense structure and no bleaching but with striking signs of the migration of humus sols in the upper part of the B horizon, which leads to the formation of a characteristic humus enriched zone.

Characteristics:

Profile: Forest profiles show a moderately rich förna above a dystrophic humus formation, with distinc division into F and H layers. Immediately underneath the usually shallow A horizon there is a migration horizon of humus substances (B_h horizon), by which the soil is primarily characterized. It has a chocolate to cocoa brown colour and varies in thickness from about 3 to 8 cm. It is followed by a usually ochre yellow to brown ochre coloured, dense B_s horizon. Humus sols (which generally also contain ferric hydroxide) in very loamy soils can further migrate into dry fissures and produce dark brown coatings on the surfaces of the cleavage aggregates. On hard parent material between the C horizon and the B_s horizon there is a well-developed, hard, but intensily brown B/C horizon. The profile is usually thin on hard parent rocks.

Texture: Principally loam to clay-loam textures, although at the same time the soil may have not only a considerable stone content, but depending on the parent rock, a certain content of grit or small, slaty rock fragments well embedded in the fabric.

Parent Rocks: Primarily clay schist, easily weathered gneiss rich in feldspars, chlorite schist or loamy sediments.

Humus Form: Dystrophic coarse moder to raw humus, usually rich in humus and almost always with a well developed, predominately coprogenic

---

*) The soil is a stesomorphic variety i. e. arrested in its formation, its dynamic not having attained full development; hence the name (stesomorphy = arrested formation, stagnating in a lower phase).

H layer in which, however, the droppings have to a great extent lost their form due to silting-up and eluviation.

Structure : Always dense with low permeability, so that a loose structure is generally found only in the humus layer. The soil shows a strong tendency to silt up, and is strongly erodable.

Water Relations : The soil is usually moist but shows almost no water-logging. Since the water only penetrates slowly, the surface water run-off is considerable.

Relief : The soil is primarily a mountain soil and occurs almost only on slopes.

Dynamic : Intense acidification and chemical weathering; all colloidal substances are highly dispersed under the peptizing effect of acid humus sols but relatively low eluviation owing to the dense soil structure and low permeability. Predominately capillary migration of humus sols in the upper part of the B horizon. This occurs in a similar way as in the klebsand horizons of *pseudogleys* and *molken podsols* (page 255) and has certain parallels with them.

Biology : Soil life is restricted more or less to the humus layer and is most highly developed in the F horizon. The B horizons are generally lacking in life, but sometimes striking, extremely humus-deficient, small fragments of droppings of cylindrical to rounded shape (of the same ochre yellow colour as the B horizon) can be found, whose genesis is not yet clear. There is a definite structural loosening in these sections.

Ocurrence : Frequent in the subalpine spruce forest region of the East Austrian Alps above 700 m. and in Northern Europe.

XL. *Podsol* *)

(Russian peasant name. DOKUTSCHAEFF, 1879)

Synonyms : Bleached earth, bleached sand, bleisand; grey earth (RA-MAN)=has been used for other soil types; Bleicherdewaldboden (STREMME)= =only for podsols in forest regions (e. g. not for the alpine sol podsol).

General Specification : Strongly acid, nutrient, deficient, ABC soils, which generally show raw humus or dystrophic moder formations, as well as an intense acid humous eluviation, which has led to the formation of a strongly pronounced bleached layer in the top soil and one or more enriched layers (illuvial horizons) in the subsoil.

---

*) Sola = ash.

Key for the Determination of Sub-Types.

1. Occurring only at the tundra boundary or in the alpine region of high mountains   6

1*. Occurring in other regions   2

2. Showing periodic surface water-logging or more or less continous water stagnation in the subsoil   5

2*. Profile without periodic or continuous water-logging   3

3. Soil profile usually containing in the illuvial zone only a coffee brown, iron deficient, humus enriched layer (plate xxv)

                                                 88. Humus-podsol.

3*. Containing not only humus enriched illuvial horizons   4

4. Soil profile containing in the illuvial zone not only a coffee brown humus enriched layer but also a light ochre yellow to rust brown iron enriched layer (plate xxvi) or both, combined into a mixed horizon.

                                          89. Iron-humus-podsol.

4*. The illuvial zone consists only of light ochre yellow to rust coloured iron enriched horizons (plate xxvi).

                                          90. Iron-podsol.

5. Showing periodic water-logging in the top-soil. The bleached layer has a gley-like nature, is very dense, fine sandy-silty to loamy with high capillarity and low permeability (plate xxiv).

                                          87. Molken-podsol.

5*. Soil with normal bleached sand layer, however showing gley layers in the subsoil, occasionally also raseneisenstein layers.

                                          86. Gley-podsol.

6. Soil usually loose, with markedly decreased chemical weathering and tendency for the formation of relatively thick humus horizons, but thin reduced bleached layers and illuvial horizons. Occurring in the alpine region of the Alps under a plant cover consisting predominately of grasses.

                                          91. Alpine sod-podsol.

6*. Soil developed from forest iron podsol with decreased chemical weathering and reduced, dwarf profile, occurring at the tundra boundary (plate xxvi).

                                          92. Nanopodsol.

86. *Gley-Podsol*
(FROSTERUS, 1912)

Synonyms : Gley podsolic soil (J. WITYN 1911), pakihi soil (RIGG 1929).

General Specification : *Podsol* with partial water-logging and gleying, however with permeable surface soil and sufficiently intense acid humous eluviation for the formation of a pronounced bleached horizon.

Characteristics :

Profile : The complete profile consists of a humus horizon, a bleached

Explanation of plate XXIV

1. **Krauss Pseudogley** below spruce forest; thickets of *Aira flexuosa* on weathering sediments of sandstone (Elbesandsteingebirge).

2. **Molken=podsol** under spruce forest with cranberry and bilberry bushes on moraine (Serfaus, Tyrol, 1.800 m.).

---

layer and the illuvial horizons, which end in a gley layer. Not infrequently a part of the illuvial horizon is developed as a raseneisenstein layer (Fe horizon), a rust brown to red brown precipitation layer of ferric hydroxide, hardened like rock, at the height of present or former ground-water levels. Unconsolidated precipitations of a similar kind are designated raseneisenerde horizons. The illuvial horizons consist either of a humus or an iron enriched horizon (B_h and B_s horizon), in other cases there are only iron enriched layers (64). *Iron-Gley-Podsol*), rarely do they consist of humus enriched layers (65). *Humus-Gley-Podsol*, see also *peat-podsol*, page 127). Various variations in profile structure are possible due to different heights of the prevailing ground-water level. Therefore signs of gleying can be quite extensive even in the illuvial horizons. However the surface soil itself remains beyond of, at most is only very temporarily under the influence of water-logging.

Texture: As with other *podsols*, sandy textures predominate in the surface soil, with a high coarse sand content in contrast to the *molken-podsol* (page 255), in which the coarse sand fraction is very low or completely missing. In the subsoil there is either a rapid increase in silty or clay constituents or the profile lies on an impermeable substratum.

Humus Form: Raw humus or strongly acid coarse moder to moder. Old peat remains, which are usually overlain by raw humus formations, lead, in conjunction with *gley-podsols*, to a variety which has already been treated under *peat-podsols* as a transformation form of old peat layers (page 127).

Dynamic: Intense acidification, chemical weathering, and humus sol formation which gives rise to intense eluviation, reaching however only to the ground-water layers. In these, ferric hydroxide is reduced and dissolved in the form of acid ferrous carbonate. Precipitation of ferric hydroxide in the surfaces at ground-water level by contact with air or in oxygenated structural parts (root channels, loose parts of the fabric) of the gley horizon.

Differentiation from Molken-Podsol: The *gley podsol* combines subsoil gleying with true gravitational eluviation produced by percolating waters. The *molken-podsol* stands closer in its dynamic and dense structure to a *pseudogley* and shows only little true eluviation, since migration of substance is primarily due to capillary movement and owes very little to gravity.

Ocurrence: Limited to certain habitats with water-logged subsoils in podsol regions, mostly on slopes at the edge of water-logged depressions and

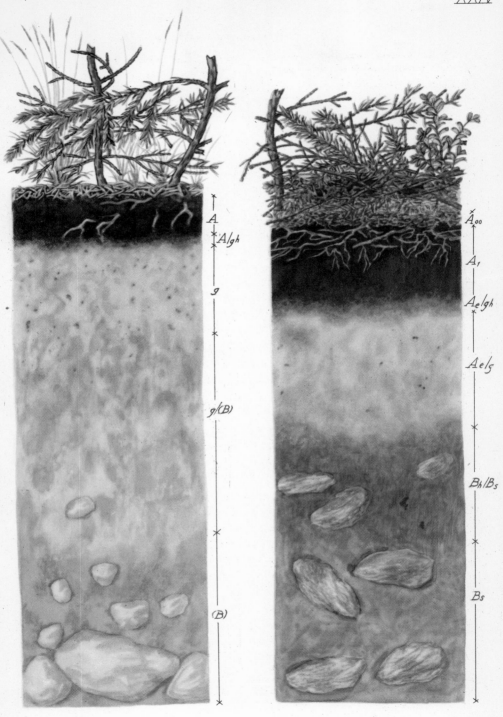

XXIV

1   2

valley basins. Lower down the slopes they generally pass over *gley*, *dystrophic anmoor* or *peat moor*, upward into ungleyed *podsols*.

87. *Molken-Podsol*

Synonyms: Clayey podsol (GIORGEWSKI 1888) = not restricted solely to clay soils, as the concept of clay i. e. the fraction capable of being elutriated, included much coarser fractions at that time than today [23]); Molken soil (Central German folk name, O. GRUPE 1909) = some of the molken soils without definite podsol character being closer to *pseudogley* because of the absence of pronounced illuvial and eluvial horizons [24]); Misseboden, Missenboden (Württemberg local name, RAMANN 1908) = also partaking of podsol character, but very much of the *pseudogley*.

General Specification: Silty and fine sandy *podsol* with very dense structure showing good capillary conduction, forming not only a light coloured to whitish, gley-like eluvial horizon, but also illuvial horizons, consisting usually of a humus and iron enriched layer (B_{sh} horizon) and a humus deficient, iron- (sesquioxide-) enriched layer (B_s horizon).

Characteristics:

Profile: Compared with most other *podsols*, the profile consists of narrow, thin horizons. The A horizon shows a dystrophic humus formation and is generally divided into a mineral deficient A_0 horizon of brownish colour and a well developed, predominately coprogenic, blackish A_1 horizon. The shape of the small animal droppings in it is very rarely preserved, and the droppings are, to a great extent, completely dispersed, resulting in a dense anmoor-like structure which when wet is almost muddy. At the lower edge of the A_1 horizon occurs an immigration of peptized humus substances into the bleached horizon and a zone, designated as klebsand layer *), is thus developed. This is dark grey to almost blackish in colour, often with a reddish violet to bluish violet seam, and has a thickness of about 5 cm., in many cases even 10 cm. and more. It is followed by a greyish yellow, light straw yellow to almost white bleached sand layer (the characteristic molken layer), which has a thickness of about 5-10 cm. (sometimes more). It contains a few humus flecks and at the same time has a pseudogley character which is often distinctly expressed by the presence of small, dark brown iron concretions. It is advantageous therefore to designate it by the letters A_e/g horizon, while the klebsand layer, glued by humus sols in its fine pores, has the character of an A_e/gh horizon.

The molken layer is followed by an iron-humus layer (B_{hs} horizon), a dark brown coloured, dense horizon, which usually contains, on a brown

---

*) «Klebsand» is a Central German folk designation.

---

ferric hydroxide ground colour, dark, cloudy, more or less uniform humus flecks or shows a general dark brown tinting from deposited humus substances. Occasionally this admixture appears like a veil of humus. The horizon passes gradually into the brown, humus deficient B_s horizon, which has a more intense and vivid colour. The subsoil often lies over a layer of the parent material, entirely coloured brown by chemical weathering ((B)/C horizon), which, however, can occasionally show water-logging and consequently greenish grey to olive coloured gley flecks.

Texture: Predominately rich in silt and fine sand, partly loamy, however always low in coarse sand. Usually the whitish molken horizon also shows a certain plasticity and can be moulded when wet, so that the soil is easily distinguished from other *podsols* even by the layman.

Structure: Due to the extraordinarily dense packing of the fine soil particles, a dense, fine pored structure of great uniformity arises.

Water Relationship: High capillarity, low water permeability, therefore slow water movement. The water content of the soil is very variable but owing to the high humidity of the air and frequent falls of rain a complete drying out hardly ever occurs (distinction from the *pseudogley*).

Parent Material: Fine sandy-silty to fine-sandy loamy sediments or hard parent rocks (fine grained bunter sandstone, Bündener Schiefer), which break down easily to similar weathering products.

Relief: On slopes, on edges of depressions, on the elevations of rolling topography and on flat hill-tops. In neighbouring troughs and depressions *dystrophic anmoor* is generally formed with strong gleying reaching to the surface.

Humus Form: Raw humus with well developed, blackish, coprogenic H horizons or dystrophic, strongly acid moder formations, usually of a blackish colour.

Dynamic: Intense acidification, and therefore, under the influence of acid humus sols, intensive chemical weathering, with regard to the movements of substances it shows not only the characteristics of the dynamic of a *pseudogley* (page 243) i. e. the precipitation and concentration of ferric hydroxide in the form of concretions (although not so numerous), but also the vertical

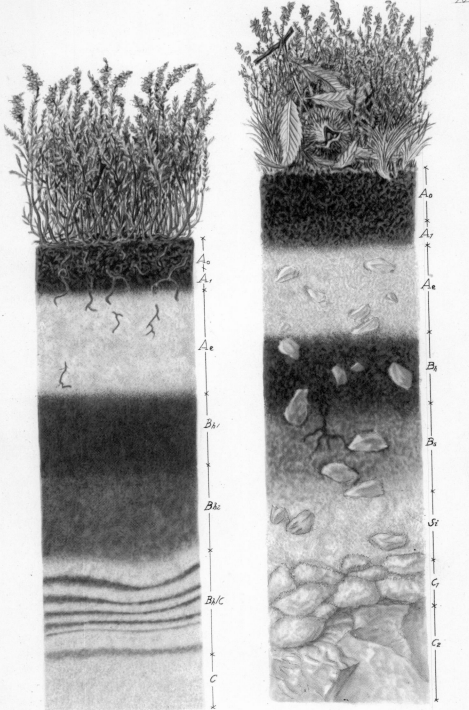

XXV

A_0
A_1
A_e
B_{h1}
B_{h2}
B_h/C
C

A_0
A_1
A_e
B_h
B_s
Si
C_1
C_2

1.

2.

translocation of colloidal substances and the formation of illuvial horizons. Peptization of the ferric hydroxide and the formation of concretions primarily take place under the influence of humus sols, although reduction effects (which are possible in all *podsols* to some extent, see page 265) and the formation of soluble ferrous bi-carbonate are much more likely here than in the following *podsol* types. The vertical translocation of substances is not, or only to a small extent, a consequence of eluviation, i. e. a simple gravitational washing-out of the finely dispersed substances, but occurs by capillary movement. The highly peptized substances are moved in a similar way as in fine rock fabric. The unilateral movement from above to below is established because the new wetting and the new supply of substances always occurs from above and return capillary movement is reduced for climatic reasons. In addition, in the illuvial horizons there is a more or less irreversible fixation of the deposited colloidal substances, so that a return movement by capillary rise is hindered or strongly restricted. Still little is known about the nature of the fixation.

Biology : Due to intense acidification, lack of nutrients, cold soil climate, bad aeration and dense structure, soil life is very restricted decomposition is slow and humification incomplete.

Ocurrence : Frequent on the above parent materials in extreme podsol regions of Central Europe.

88. *Humus Podsol*
(FROSTERUS 1914)

General Specification : Extremely acid and base deficient *podsol* usually formed on iron deficient parent material, with intense humus sol formation, in whose illuvial zone only the development of a true humus-enriched horizon is found (plate xxv).

Characteristics :

Profile : The A horizon, usually differentiated into an A_0 and A_1 layer, is mostly dark grey in colour, generally followed by a bleached horizon (A_2 or A_e horizon) due to simple eluviation and consisting primarily of loose sand. The underlying humus enriched horizon (B_h horizon) has a striking coffee brown colour and often a sandstone-like cementation (humus-ortstein layer). Such horizons uncompacted or only slightly compacted are designated as orterde layers. Frequently two humus enriched layers occur together, of which the upper is dark coffee brown in colour (B_1 horizon) and the lower, light coffee brown (B_2 horizon). Occasionally a striking series of thin (about 3-8 mm. wide) dark brown bands may be found reaching into the C horizon from the B_2 horizon which generally become lighter with depth and finally disappear. Isolated dark bands can also occur within the light B_2 horizon. The thickness of the ortstein and orterde layers varies enormously. Thus the entire illuvial horizon of a humus podsol may attain a total thickness of up to 1 1/2 m. In other cases the ortstein layer is seen only as an intense, dark brown band about 10 cms. wide which runs either level or in various up and down convolutions. The convolutions are often pocket-like (ortstein pockets) or deepened pots widening out below like bottles (ortstein pots). In the accessible parts within the B_2 horizons (conducting paths) more or less pipe-shaped bleached zones can develop, whose walls are frequently coated with cemented and dark coloured ortstein crusts (bleached pipes). The humus-ortstein is very readily distinguished by its colour from the iron-humus-ortstein and the iron-ortstein (261). It contrast to the iron-humus-ortstein it is usually less strongly compacted, corners and edges of fragments are easily rubbed off, small pieces may generally easily be crushed between on's fingers.

Parent Material: The most typical *humus-podsol* is formed on bare loose dune sands which consist mainly of coarse grains.

Plant Cover: Profile development is favoured most strongly under old heath vegetation (particularly *Calluna* heath).

Humus Form: Raw humus with well developed coprogenic A_1 horizon with a coal-like appearance. Occasionally practically all the raw humus is transformed into dystrophic coprogenic moder.

Water Relationship: The normal *humus podsol* shows no water-logging at all but has a high water permeability on which the rapid drying out of the soil and the wide variation in moisture relations depends. The ortstein itself even in thick layers is not impermeable to water provided it has a regular coating fabric (see below). The raw humus and moder layer has a relatively high water capacity, and in wet periods, completely soaks up the water which it enriches with humus sols. But this water, in so far as it not percolates with the humus sols into the subsoil, is, on the one hand entirely used by the plant cover, on the other hand the humus cover easily dries out because it is an isolated surface layer in the open heath. Various transitions may be seen from the normal soil, which is the most extensive, to *peat podsol* (page 127) which also frequently appears as *humus podsol* with similar ortstein or orterde layers, and also to *gley podsol*.

Micromorphology of the Humus Layer: As in all raw humus for-mations there is a predominance of plant remains difficult to decompose together with a relatively low amount of coprogenic elements. The droppings of small animals are preserved but have usually become brown mostly inside plant residues where they have been deposited by mining animals (usually horny mites). The droppings are usually characterized by a certain rawness and incomplete humification which may be already recognized by their mostly brown colour. Coprogenic elements predominate in the A_1 horizon. The fragments of the droppings are however extensively destroyed so that their forms have become indistinct. The humification within the droppings is incomplete; they also contain many undecomposed although strongly browned plant splinters.

Micromorphology of the Bleached Sand Layer: This consists largely of smooth washed quartz grains, strongly reflecting in direct light. Only a few grains here and there showing a coating of humus are found, i. e. originating from a former B_h horizon. Remains of former humus coatings may be detected also in the fissures and in dentations of the grain surfaces. In the inter-granular cavities there is found, with intense eluviation (grey coloured bleached sands), an increased content of washed-in remains of droppings, often, however, only the undecomposed, insoluble plant splinters which they contained are seen (dropping skeleton).

Micromorphology of the Ortstein Layer: This is extraordinarily characteristic, so that a coated ortstein formation can generally be determined from a single quartz grain. Each sand grain is painted as with a dye and shows a uniform skin of sepia brown, highly dispersed humus substances. Owing to the great shrinkage of the skin, drying out causes its breakdown into irregularly formed tiles separated from each other by a network of light fissures which allow the bare grain surfaces to be seen. In thin section, the humus coating appears as a dark brown line round the contour of the grain. The inter-granular spaces are completely empty. With a very high soil permeability and with intense eluviation the remains of droppings and more or less washed dropping skeleton also are carried by the percolating waters and become deposited between the sand grains. In the normal humus ortstein formation they are missing. The individual sand grains are glued to each other for their coatings show a collar-like thickening at the points of contact, due to the precipitation of more humus colloidal substances at the corners. The coatings are iron and mineral deficient. The mineral substances contained in them are readily apparent if the humus substances are ignited. The individual tiles of the coatings are then seen to consist only of sparse remains of mineral substances. They are usually only slightly reddened (ferric oxide colour) and often are completely white.

Dynamic: Strong acidification, intense chemical weathering by the action of acid humus sols on the few constituents which are not quartz. Transport of all finely dispersed substances by the percolating water which is highly enriched with humus sols, particularly acid soluble humus substances (fulvic acids). Precipitation of the finely dispersed humus substances in dense skin-like deposition structures in the illuvial horizons.

Biology: Owing to the extreme lack of nutrients, acidification, the presence of substances impeding decomposition and plant residues, which are very difficult to decompose, inert, highly specialised and species-deficient soil life with slow decomposition and incomplete humification (unilateral formation of fulvic acids and pre-products of humification). The activity of micro-organisms, which consist mainly of a few species of fungi, is very restricted. Therefore the pre-decomposition of plant residues, essential for many soil animals, is missing. Nevertheless, the decomposition and humification is mainly performed by a specialised soil fauna. Even in cultivated soils there is an apparent accumulation of undecomposed plant remains and a very slow decomposition of stable manure and green manuring plants.

Changes by Cultivation: Humus-podsols remain easily recognisable even when cultivated. The sandy topsoil, easily blown about by the wind, has an ashy, light grey ground colour (hence the name «ash soil» = podsol) which usually contains dark flecks of incompletely mixed humus constituents with a coal-like appearance and undecomposed plant residues. Wind erosion can occasionally cause a local accumulation of bleached sand so that in a profile, unusually deep A_e horizons may result. Further, owing to the easy silting up of the humus layers which are deficient in binding substances, extensive displacement of bleached sand layers due to run-off may be observed on slopes. By digging below the grey sand layer the humus-enriched horizon may be found intact. A thin ortstein band close to the surface may have been destroyed by cultivation. In any case the iron enriched layers typical of the other *podsols* are missing, i. e. in the subsoil rust brown to ochre yellow colours are not found or are only weakly developed.

Ocurrence: The most typical occurrences without the least influence of subsoil water-logging are found on the heaths of the North Sea and Baltic Sea cost. However the soil is found on corresponding parent materials in all podsol regions of Northern Europe.

89. *Iron-Humus-Podsol*

General Specification: *Podsol* with strong humus sol formation in whose illuvial zone not only humus enriched horizons are developed but also iron enriched horizons may be determined.

Characteristics:

Profile: The A horizon is differentiated generally into A_0, A_1 and A_e horizons (bleached sand layer, A_2 horizon). The blackish, predominately coprogenic A_1 horizon, often with a coal-like appearance, is usually well developed and frequently projects far into the A_0 horizon. Not infrequently the A_0 horizon is completely missing, so that the soil profile begins with a mineral-rich, mainly coprogenic, blackish A_1 horizon, and the A_0 horizon

is almost completely missing. The differentiation of the illuvial zone is particularly characteristic. It generally begins with a more or less deep brown,
blackish to sepia brown coloured, in other cases light coffee-brown humus
enriched layer (B_h horizon), which passes gradually into the ochre yellow,
brown ochre to rust brown coloured iron enriched layer (B_s horizon = sesquioxide enriched layer). On hard parent rocks between this and the C horizon
there is usually a well developed extensively browned B/C horizon. The soil
in this case is almost always shallow and very stony.

B_{hs}-Podsols: Many iron-humus podsols are distinguished from the normal
form in that the B_h and the B_s horizons are combined to form one or two
B_{hs} horizons, which are both rich in iron (rich in sesquioxides) and contain
visible amounts of humus. This may be easily recognized by the strong
admixture of the colour of ferric hydroxide in the colour of the humus substances.

Ortstein Formation: The B horizons are often built up as ortstein
layers. The B_h horizon can occasionally consist of a pure, slightly cemented
humus-ortstein with a relatively low iron content. In other cases it has a
considerable iron content, which is expressed in the colouring. Such iron-
humus-ortsteins usually have a considerably greater tenacity than the pure
humus-ortsteins. Also, the B_s horizon can be hardened to a certain degree
(iron ortstein), however in this case it always contains humus substances too.

Parent Rocks: Base and nutrient deficient materials rich in quartz,
favour and accelerate podsol formation to a high degree, while it can be
retarded considerably with a certain content of bases and nutrients. Preferred
parent materials are: loose sands, sandstones, quartzite, mica schists, strongly
acid gneiss and granite, etc.

Texture: In the surface soil almost always sandy, in the subsoil usually
sandy-loamy.

Plant Cover: Iron-humus-podsols are formed more readily outside
forests, where the humus layer is not continually moist, but is subjected
to a continuous alternation of wetting and drying out. Therefore the
activity of the soil fauna is increased and the humification is more intense.
Preferred plant covers are heathers and dwarf shrub associations. However,
the soils may also be found in forests.

Humus Form: Raw humus with tendency to be transformed into
dystrophic acid moder.

Occurrence: The principal regions of occurrence are the Northern
Calluna and Erica heaths and the dwarf shrub region of high mountains
adjoining the forest zone ((67) sub-alpine iron-humus-podsol). Further, the
Asturian podsols are found chiefly on extrasylvatic Erica-heaths.

Micromorphology: The iron-humus-podsol on the Atlantic dune sands and also on the North and Baltic Sea coasts shows a similar micromorphology to the *humus podsol*. Further, the iron-ortstein layers and uncompacted B_s horizons similar to the humus-orsteins have a regular coating fabric with empty inter-granular spaces. With particularly strong eluviation however the B_h horizons can contain considerable deposits of undissolved or half peptized fragments of droppings.

In the Central European *podsols* the development of the coating formation is rather irregular, the Southern Asturian *podsols*, even in the B_s horizon, have flocculated precipitations in the inter-granular spaces.

Dynamic : Strong acidification, intense chemical weathering (increased especially by the action of humus sols), breakdown of the silicates and formation of aluminium hydroxide. Intense humus sol formation in the percolating water whereby its content of acid soluble humus substances (fulvic acids) is considerably increased. Peptization and transportation of all finely dispersed substances into the subsoil, and particularly of free ferric and aluminium hydroxides (sesquioxides) and clay substances.

Biology : Due to lack of nutrients, strong acidification, exclusive favouring the luxuriant development of raw humus plants which supresses the growth of other more valuable plants. The activity of the micro-flora is considerably restricted by the high acidity, the difficulty of decomposing the plant residues, and the presence of decomposition-impeding substances. On the other hand, there is a somewhat better development of a specialized soil fauna adapted to this kind of nutriment and these environmental conditions. In general decomposition is slow and humification incomplete.

Changes by Cultivation : Soils with sufficiently deep-lying humus-enriched horizons on cultivation show the uniform light grey ashy colour of the bleached sand horizon which, due to mixing with the humus cover, has become the principal material of the surface soil. The B horizons in the substratum are usually well preserved. A strong admixture of material rich in iron from a B_{hs} horizon will alter the colour of the surface soil with thin bleached layers. The soil character, however is generally easily recognisable by the large quantity of bleached sand grains in the surface layer. It is a considerable help to the understanding and systematics of the soil to study the uncultivated, undisturbed, profile in the neighbourhood of the cultivated area.

(68). *Asturian Podsol:* A particular form of the iron-humus-podsol is found in the Asturias, in a district with a moist oceanic climate which is warmer than normal for a podsol region and where chestnuts and *Quercus sessiliflora* grow at low altitudes reaching almost to the sea. The soils are formed preeminently on Devonian siliceous sandstone or on sandy-gravelly moraines usually under *Erica* heather, of which the Atlantic *Erica ciliaris* is particularly characteristic. The principal areas are on the unwooded, heathy, domed foot-

hills of the Cantabrian Cordillera at a height above sea-level of about 300-
1.000 m. and more. The principal characteristics are as follows: the A_0
horizons are extensively permeated by the droppings of small animals, all
raw humus layers appear to be undergoing intense decomposition, are easily
friable, blackish, with brownish red plant remains, and pass into well-
developed blackish coprogenic A_1 horizons. In many cases raw humus forms
are completely missing and are entirely replaced by blackish dystrophic
moder. The bleached layers have a thickness of about 15 cm. and pass into
a pure blackish brown orterde layer (slightly cemented), whose inter-granular
spaces are strongly filled with washed-in remains of droppings. The iron
enriched layer is intense ochre brown in colour and is often intersected by
humus veins. The inter-granular spaces are filled with crumbly colloidal
substances rich in iron. Occasionally in soils on siliceous sandstone the iron
enriched layer has the character of a B_s/C horizon as the rock structures as
well as the rock fissures (encrusted with humus substances) have remained
completely preserved in it. The mass only has been softened by intense acid
humous weathering so that it can be easily cut with a knife. The siliceous
cement of the rock fabric has been completely dissolved and removed. In
thin section one sees that it has been replaced by iron-containing humus substances. The development of a silicic acid enriched layer is of particular
interest and can be found almost always between the B_s horizon and the
hard sandstone. It has the appearance of a chalk-enriched layer, as the silicic
acid precipitated in white finely-dispersed masses acts as cement in a similar
way as the calcium carbonate in Ca horizons. The parent rock, when moist,
is light grey in colour and has a conchoidal to splintery fracture, whereby it
forms extraordinarily sharp flinty edges and corners. Weathered pieces become
whitish ochre, lose their hardness, do not splinter, and are easily friable so
that small fragments may be readily crushed between the fingers.

90. Iron-Podsol
(FROSTERUS, 1914)

Synonyms: Stark gebleichter rostfarbener Waldboden (STREMME 1936).
General Specification: *Podsol* with moderate humus sol formation in
whose subsoil only an iron enriched layer (sesquioxide enriched layer, B_s horizon) may be found.

Characteristics:

Profile: The soil is primarily a forest soil and as such (*forest iron-
podsol*) develops into a form with the following characteristics: the förna is
rich and consists of the accumulated leaf fall over several years. The F layer
also is usually strongly developed, while the predominately coprogenic H hor-

Explanation of plate XXVI

1. **Iron=podsol** under pine forest (*Pinus silvestris*) on moraine (Heinavesi, Finland).
2. **Northern Nanopodsol** (Northern dwarf podsol) under tundra forest with Betula nana and *Cladonia rangiferina* on syenite (Petsamo, Finnish Lappland).

---

izon is reduced. All layers are almost always damp and are practically never completely dried out. The F horizon always has a sharp boundary to the H horizon. The blackish H horizon (A_1 horizon), in which the forms of the animal droppings are rarely preserved, is usually rich in minerals that are predominately smooth, and washed like those in the A_e horizon. In many cases the H horizon is so weakly developed that it is almost completely missing. The A_e horizon (A_2 horizon) according to humus content (mostly washed-in undispersed humus fragments such as brown plant splinters and blackish remains of droppings) is grey, whitish grey to almost pure white in colour. The B_s horizon is dense and yellow ochre to rust brown in colour. On hard parent materials, between it and the C horizon, there is a similarly coloured B/C horizon which is either solid or consists predominately of rock fragments (plate XXVI).

Parent Rocks: As with *iron-humus podsol*, here too podsolization is encouraged by parent materials deficient in bases and rich in quartz.

Texture: Almost always sandy in the surface soil, sandy-loamy to loamy in the subsoil.

Ortstein Formation: This is very rare in the true *iron-podsol*. Most of the ortsteins described are raseneisenstein formations in transition forms of the *iron-podsol* to *gley-podsol*.

Humus Form: Under forest, strong tendency to develop moist raw humus and dystrophic coarse moder. In spruce woods, dense, easily cut auflagetorf (page 36) frequently appears as a particularly unfavourable humus formation. In clearings dry humus covers develop; on grassland a gradual transformation into mull-like moder occurs.

Plant Cover: Primarily spruce forest, however, also some beech woods, rich in bilberries, acid-tolerant oak forest and, in the far North, birch forests. *Iron podsols* are also to be found in broad stretches of the white pine forests (Finland, Sweden). In the sub-alpine region of the Alps they are primarily spruce woods rich in bilberries and cranberries, nearer the upper tree-line larches and sembra pine forests. On southern high mountains *iron podsol* is still not yet known; they appear to be missing there or very rare. Great parts of the podsol region of the temperate zone have been transformed into meadow or cultivated land and have more or less strongly retained their podsol characteristics.

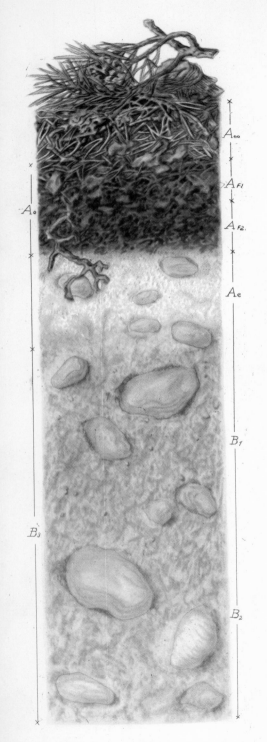

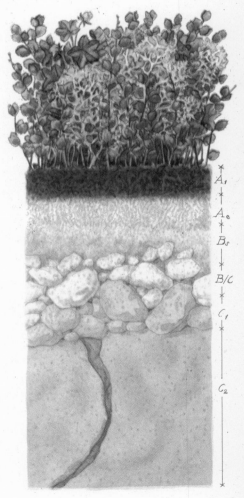

A_{oo}

A_{F1}

$A_{F2.}$

A_e

A_o

B_1

B_3

B_2

A_1

A_e

B_s

B/C

C_1

C_2

x

1.

2.

Ferrous Oxide Test: Due to the reducing effect of acid humus sols and the impeding of good aeration by dense moist raw humus layers, a certain formation of water soluble ferrous oxide compounds almost always occurs. This can easily be demonstrated if one takes a wet sample from the bleached sand layer and ignites a small quantity from it in the air. The apparently completely bare grain surfaces show after the treatment a reddish to deep red film. The reddening is the stronger, the stronger the acidity and the lower the aeration of the soil and can already be partly detected in bleached granules of podsolic soils which are free from coatings of ferric hydroxide. The correlation with soil acidity is explained by the fact that the lower the value of the pH [25]) the more humus substances are desolved and the less ferrous iron is precipitated as ferric hydroxide.

Dynamic: Strong acidification, intense chemical weathering, intense eluviation of all finely dispersed substances into the subsoil. The eluviation can occur because of the high dispersion and erodability of most *iron-podsols* even without the assistance of acid humus sols. However these are almost always present and therefore involved too. The humus sol formation in the percolating waters is never as intense as in *humus-podsol* and *iron-humus-podsol*. Still it may nearly always be recognized.

Brown Water Formation: The formation of brown percolating waters, which can already serve as a diagnostic characteristic for the *semi-podsols,* may be determined in mountains after heavier rainfall in profile sections on slopes (road cuttings on mountain sides) where they flow out laterally from conducting paths in the B horizon (route channels, loose structural parts between deposits of rock débris). In level places, brown water formation is seen in pools (in the bottoms of which dy-formation may usually be detected), usually also in many channels and streams in the forest.

Biology: The raw humus cover in normal soils which is almost always moist (never water-logged), shows, particularly in the F layer, stronger growth of fungae than in most other soil types. The fungal flora is relatively deficient in species but in places may lead to a luxurious development of fungus growth (mostly very extensive, white, yellow or dark brown colonies). It always has a strong restrictive effect of the activity of the micro-fauna and is connected with a lower rate of humification. Soils with A_0 horizon, which are drier and looser, can form H layers relatively rich in humus substances or develop coarse moder. The humification however is almost always less intense than in the *humus* and *iron-humus-podsol*. The humus of the *iron-podsol* is generally lacking in total nitrogen, very deficient in root soluble nitrogen, strongly acid, contains decomposition impeding substances, is deficient in bacteria and shows a low nitrification.

Changes by Cultivation: If the bleached sand layer is sufficiently deep, the surface soil, which is loose and sandy, has the typical light ash grey colour of mature *podsol*. The B horizon in this case is retained undisturbed. If parts of the B horizon are broken up by the plough, the surface layer either has a flecky appearance or it shows nests and clods of materials from both the A and the B horizons. This is because the mixing, soil-homogenizing work of earth-worms is almost completely missing as they do not find favourable living conditions in *podsols*. Further with better mixing of the horizon by cultivation implements the surface soil is always considerably more sandy, lighter in colour than the subsoil and is characterized especially by its high content of bleached sand grains. These are particularly accumulated after showers of rain on the soil surface.

The soil has a high erodability which in mountain regions particularly leads to extensive loss of the surface layer or whole parts of the soil cover. The cultivated soil shows an extraordinary inertness with regard to decomposition of stable dung and green fertilizers. They are acid, cold, deficient in nutrients, easily silting up, tending to a dense structure, little permeable to heavy rainfalls, and with a small clay content already difficult to work. In general they show low plant stands and low crop yields.

Occurrence : *Iron podsols* are very widespread in the great forest regions of Northern Russia south of the tundra boundary down to about the latitude of Smolensk, in the North and Baltic sea regions, in Scotland, Fennoscandia as well as in the Alps. In the mountains of Central Europe they are found on base-deficient igneous rocks and metamorphic rocks, sandstone and sandy sediments, occurring in comparatively small areas.

91. Alpine Sod Podsol

General Specification : Shallow *podsol* with decreased chemical weathering and tendency to form humus rich, relatively thick, humus horizons but also with reduced bleached layers and B horizons, occurring in the alpine regions of high mountains under a plant cover consisting predominately of false grasses.

Characteristics:

Profile : The profile, usually of little thickness, shows either a well-developed, but compared with other soil horizons proportionate A horizon, or the humus layer is distinctly thicker than this, so that between it and the rest of the soil up to the hard substratum (i. e. the bleached sand layer and the B horizon) there may be up to a 3 : 1 ratio [*]). The thickness of the humus horizons varies between 5 cm. and 40 cm. (in many cases even more). The bleached sand layer is usually ash-grey in colour

---

[*]) H. JENNY designates a soil in which the humus horizon dominates over the other horizons as *alpine humus soil*.

and has a thickness of 3-8 cm. With regard to the illuvial zone the soil can develop either only as an *iron-podsol* ((69). *Alpine Iron-Podsol*) and contain a B_s horizon only or it is an iron-humus-podsol and shows a B_h as well as a B_s horizon ((70). *Alpine Iron-Humus-Podsol*). The B_s horizon varies in depth from about 8-20 cm. The B_h horizon is usually developed only as a narrow seam. Next to the B_s horizon a browned B/C horizon can be found, either compacted or consisting of coarse rock débris and in addition an entirely mechanically loosened C horizon. The colour of the B_s and B/C horizon varies from ochre yellow to rust brown according to the parent rock. In the sub-alpine dwarf shrub region the profile deepens, and the thickness of the horizons increases. The contrary occurs at the upper boundary of the *alpine sod podsols*, near the region of occurrence of the *sod braunerde* and *ranker*.

Parent Rocks: Primarily hard silicate rocks (particularly acid ones), as well as débris and moraines of such rocks. However, also calcareous silicate rocks which easily become decalcified and then behave as a parent material in a similar way as the other silicate rocks. In the eastern Austrian Central Alps, calc-mica schists and calc-silicate schists are podsolized particularly easily after a short rendsina and ranker prestage. On the other hand, on dense limestone and dolomites *alpine sod-podsol* is almost completely missing.

Texture: Usually coarsely dispersed, sandy-gritty soils, which are relatively deficient in colloidal substances even in the B horizons.

Structure: Loose to bulky. The last occurs particularly with crystalline schists as parent material, as in this case small plintery rock fragments predominate, giving in the thin section a kind of ophitic fabric *). This is particularly true of the B horizons. Also it is usually characterized by a certain looseness which distinguishes it from the B horizons of *forest iron-podsols* and is due to the reduced intensity of chemical weathering and the low content of finely dispersed substances.

Phenology: Due to the long duration of the winter the soil is frozen and covered with snow for a great part of the year. In late spring melting and gradual strong water-logging due to accumulation of snow water. Strong water run-off, strong winds, high permeability of the soil due to its permeable structure and usually strong débris formation in the substratum make continuous water-logging impossible in spite of heavy rainfall. The warming up of the interior of the soil in spring takes place very slowly. The strong temperature variations between night and day and the rapid warming up by direct sunlight refer only to the uppermost part of the humus layer. The yearly temperature average is extraordinarily low (often below 0° C). In places strongly exposed to wind, a strong drying out of the humus layer often occurs

---

*) A rock fabric consisting predominately of splintery to stalky constituents showing a bulky, interlocked arrangement.

in dry weatner, and this can occasionally have a considerable influence on the kind of humus formation.

Humus Form : Generally strongly coprogenic mull-like moder or dystrophic fine moder to coarse moder rarely raw humus. In places strongly exposed to wind a particular kind of dry humus formation is found which is characterized by an externally peat-like *) matted accumulation of undecomposed plant remains (*Eilag humus*). The cavities are filled with blackish droppings of small animals usually well preserved in shape. In many places, particularly under grasses with more or less tufted growth (particularly with *Festuca dura*) the drying out by wind is so strong, that in conjunction with other unfavourable biological conditions the plant remains in the humus cushion are almost completely preserved. It is also almost completely free of animal droppings.

Dynamic : The strongly active frost weathering gives rise to a rapid and intense mechanical breakdown. In rocks with schist structure, important in the Central Alps, this is shown to a particular extent. However, the frost weathering is no longer effective on small splintery rock fragments, so that the soil becomes strongly enriched with them. The long freezing and complete winter calm the usually low soil temperatures, the relatively short fine weather periods with better warming up all have a reducing effect on the chemical weathering and clay formation. Although the strong browning and ferric hydroxide precipitation (particularly with the presence of ore grains in the rock) simulate strong weathering, microscopic examination shows only a relatively low decomposition of the orthoclase and Na-rich plagioclase, often only a slight baueritisation of the biotite. All these conditions lead to the development of shallow soil profiles with relatively thin horizons. The acidification is moderate in comparison with other *podsols* (usually pH values of 5). Occasionally the effects of the presence of pyrite in the parent rock causes a local strong reduction of the pH.

Usually closed alpine grass heath which provides predominately good, easily decomposed parent material for humus formation and consists of Graminae, Cyperaceae and alpine shrubs. In the first place twisted sedge swards are characteristic (lawns of *Carex curvula*) in dry high locations with strong reduction of the thickness of the horizons, swards of *Elyna myosuroides*.

Biology : The activity of the micro-flora (although detectable) is of little consequence due to the predominately low temperatures and the acid soil reaction. The soil climate is particularly cold on the shady sides. The long freezing and complete winter calm causes a preservation and rich accumulation of plant residues. As in the arctic humus soils, decomposition by the micro-

---

*) The humus form is however in no way related to peat.

flora is distinctly duked. The activity of soil animals (as long as the soil is not frozen) is not restricted by the lower temperatures. Due to this and to the accumulation of easily weathered plant remains, habitats with good development of the micro-fauna show a relatively good humification by the accumulation of animal droppings, usually still well preserved in shape. Because of the favourable conditions for the soil fauna, deep humus horizons develop, which to a great extent are almost entirely of a coprogenic nature (alpine moder).

Occurrence: The soil is known by its occurrence in the Central Alps where it is very widespread in the alpine region and must be regarded as the predominating soil form (climax formation).

(71). *Alpine Nanopodsol* and (72). *Alp. Semipodsol:* In high elevations the *alpine sod podsol* can show a similar considerable reduction of the bleached horizons and B horizons as the *dwarf podsol* (No. 92) at the tundra boundary and is characterized then by horizon depths of only a few centimeters. From this *dwarf podsol* transitions to the *alpine sod braunerde* may also be determined which correspond to the *northern semipodsol* (the «concealed podsol» of NEUSTRUEFF and GORODKOFF, see note 22). They no longer have bleached layers and bleached flecks, but the same humus formation and a higer content of colloidal substances in the B horizon.

92. *Northern Nanopodsol*
Northern Dwarf Podsol

General Specification: *Forest iron podsol* occurring at the tundra boundary with decreased chemical weathering and reduced, strikingly dwarfed profile (plate XXVI).

Characteristics:

Profile: The entire profile often has a depth of less than one decimeter and in this case consists of horizons only 1 1/2-3 cm. thick. However, the thickness of profile and horizon varies strongly, yet the mineral soil rarely reaches a depth of more than 25 cm. on hard parent rock. On loose parent material it shows much deeper B horizons, although the bleached layers still remain thin. A strongly developed herb and bottom vegetation in the tundra forest (dwarf bushes, mosses, lichens) may give rise to a considerable increase in the humus horizon. This increase does not occur uniformly, but the whole surface shows numerous hillocks, cushions and knolls of raw humus, which give rise to an extremely strongly articulated micro-relief. The bleached layer is light grey to almost white in colour. The illuvial zone shows almost always only a pure iron-enriched layer (B_s horizon), usually of an ochre-yellow colour.

Parent Rocks: In the first place acid igneous rocks and crystalline schists or rock débris rich in stones and gravel. Strongly loamy soils always have deposits of fossil soil remains for parent material and it may be only partially possible to recognize the influence of recent factors of soil formation.

Texture: Predominately sandy textures, rich in gravel.

Phenology: The soil is frozen and covered with snow for a great part of the year and usually even in the short summer shows a permanently frozen layer in the subsoil.

Humus Form: Generally raw humus in the case of shallow humus horizons (preeminently in wood clearings) coarse moder or acid, mineral-rich fine moder with higher content of coprogenic elements.

Dynamic: More or less strong acidification, low humus sol formation enhanced physical, however reduced chemical weathering due to the permanent coldness of the soil. In particular this results in a very low transformation of substances by hydrolysis, while the oxidation and liberation of free ferric hydroxide is only slightly impeded.

Biology: Low activity of the microflora due to the coldness of the soil, but unrestricted activity of the soil fauna in soil layers not too strongly soaked. For this reason, in favourable environmental conditions, formation of coprogenic humus horizons or sub-horizons in which the animal droppings (usually only terrestrial Arthropodae) to a great extent are well preserved in shape and recognisable.

Occurrence: Predominately at the tundra boundary in Northern Russia and Northern Finland.

Notes

1) According to the first Russian alphabetical nomenclature, all eluvial or impoverished horizons were designated as A horizons, and alluvial or enriched horizons as B horizons, irrespective of whether these were humus horizons or not. In this way no provision was made for humus horizons which are not eluvial horizons. Their distinction however must be regarded as extremely important for the aims of soil diagnosis. (A SOKOLOWSKI has therefore proposed the mode of description H = humus, layer, E = eluvial layer, I = illuvial layer, but this has not been preserved.) Equally, no provision was made for those non-humus horizons, which, perhaps are coloured by ferric iron yet which are not illuvial horizons, but formed entirely by deep weathering, like the (B) horizons of *braunerde, roterde,* and unbleached *braunlehm* and *rotlehm.* The simple designation B horizon makes no distinction further between enriched horizons of $CaCO_3$ (today Ca horizons) or water soluble salts (Sa horizon) and those of colloidal substances, which is particularly important for soil systematics. The designation B horizon could also be applied within the accumulative humus horizons (today A/Ca or A/B), without thus indicating the true depth of humus formation. All these circumstances have led to various new manners of designation.

2) To avoid confusion with the designations «moor» (peat moor) and «moortorf», the original designations of P. E. MÜLLER «mor» and «torf» for raw humus are not felicitous. On the same grounds the designation dry peat (trockentorf) is also of little advantage and is always the cause of misunderstandings.

3) As here also it is not a peat formation but a raw humus or a humus formation close to coarse moder, the designation «auflagetorf» is not very advantageous. However, for the present there exists no more suitable synonym.

4) The designation of P. E. MÜLLER «insect mull» is no longer used as, among other reasons, the droppings in moder generally were found to consist to a greater extent of those of non-insects.

5) Mull-like mor and mull-like peat are unfavourable on the above-mentioned grounds (note 2). From MÜLLER'S designations (insect mull, mull-like peat) it is apparent that he counted it neither as a species of mull or as a species of raw humus, but recognised it as an independent *third* terrestrial humus form standing *between* raw humus (torf) and mull.

6) Ranker is derived from «rank» = steep mountain slope. Ranker is therefore called «the coloniser of steep slopes». Ranker is frequently to be found on steep slopes in the Austrian Alps, as there soil erosion is generally strongly active, and thus soil formation must always be starting afresh and can never get beyond the initial phase. A further explanation is given by the meaning of the word «ranken» in the sense of «to cling», «climbing up steeply», as the young *ranker (protoranker)* can often develop adhering to a very steep rock surface, a peculiarity which they have in common only with the *protorendsinas.* The name was later applied to all AC soils on chalk-deficient parent materials (with the exception of chalk-deficient steppe soils).

7) No soil type in the literature has been defined and delimited from other soil types in such a contradictory way as the *rendsina*. In regard to the meaning of the name, that of MIKLACZEWSKI must be regarded as the most authentic. Rendsina is derived from «rzedcic» or «rzezic» (Polish) = to roar, and is derived from the noise which the plough makes as it grinds through soils usually very rich in stones. The Russian name «chrap» for stony *rendsina* which means «the snorer» is of similar origin and indicates this characteristic even more strongly. In every case the original name refers to very shallow, little-weathered and usually stony soils. In contrast to this, GLINKA explained that the word *rendsina* means a «tenacious» clayey soil. However, in the same section of his book he states that there is also a dusty form of the *rendsina* (popylucha). GLINKA'S explanation «tenacious» clayey soil for *rendsina*, owing to his great authority, has given rise to a very widespread erroneous viewpoint in the literature that only heavy soils can be designated as *rendsinas* and the characteristic of a true *rendsina* is its formation of sharp-edged angular aggregates (and in some cases this kind of aggregate formation has been especially designated «rendsina structure»). Such a structure is only possible with higher clay content and with lower ability to form crumbs (extensive peptization of the ground mass rich in colloidal substances) i. e. only in transition formations from *rendsina* to *braunlehm*. In this way the so-called «typical rendsina structure» can only apply to a very small part of the *rendsinas*. A. STEBUTT says, to quote a contradictory opinion, that the word *rendsina* means «ash-soil» and gives the explanation that the rendsina is perhaps well-crumbed but often powdery and then shows an ashy appearance (cf. popylucha, page 189). There is a great lack of uniformity also in the division of *rendsinas* according to their occurrence. Many authors have wished to designate soils with rendsina-like profile as *rendsinas* only if they are to be found in the podsol regions, others if they occur at least in forest regions or in certain forest regions. Also GLINKA asserts in a similar way and is of the opinion, that *rendsinas* do not appear in the steppe region, because even soils on limestone there take on a *chernosem* character. However, he emphasises, at the same time, that the above mentioned popylucha occurring in the black earth region of Saratow (very little like a black earth) is a *rendsina* and cites in this connection DIMO who equally emphasises their *rendsina* character and mentions that these loose, ashy-coloured soils must be particularly striking in the *chernosem* zone, because all the remaining soils there are black in colour. In contrast to the limitation of the *rendsinas* to podsol regions, there is also the opinion that *rendsinas* are «endodynamorphic» i. e. in the first place influenced by the parent material or «intrazonal» i. e. soils not restricted to particular climatic zones. According to this conception there is no reason why the soil should occur, only in the podzol zone, and not also in the steppe zone. By a summary of all the various concepts (leaving out the contradictions) and by careful delimitation from the *braunerde,* the *braunlehm, rotlehm* and *roterde* on limestone, one arrives without difficulty however at the synthesis of a concept of *rendsina* which leaves no gap in the systematics of soils (see page 178). If this synthesis had not been possible from what is as yet known, a new concept would have to be created.

8) That no *rendsinas* are formed on crystalline limestones and calcareous crystalline schists is a very widespread error in the literature.

9) In Russian literature these soil formations have been designated partly as brown loams or podsolic soils which reach far into the steppes. In this connection it must be observed that the designation, when Ramann's concept of *braunerde* was still not known or still not recognized, had another, wider significance in the sense that one regarded the formation of *braunerde* already as a phase of podsolization. In this connection I exclude those individual findings of forest soils in the region

of the *chernosem* steppe, whose profiles according to accounts show bleached layers (apparently they are *pseudogleys*, c. f. page 242).

10) H. KURON, who has conducted erosion studies or a series of soils in Rumania maintains that the light *braunerdes* on the left bank of the Don are erosion remains of chestnut coloured soils (personal communication).

11) As long ago as 1771 M. I. AFONIN, one of the first Russian soil scientists and teachers of agriculture, recommended in his work on the *chernosem* that the Russian soil surface should be accurately investigated both for easier application of experimental results in cultivation and the improvement of particular soils: «one ought not to collect the black earths only but also the other kinds of soil, to study their properties and to pay attention to their origin—regions and villages—even the field from which the collected earth is derived». Quoted from S. S. SOBOLIEW, Agronomija, July 1908, Die Bodenkultur 1948, Vol. 3, No. 4, p. 607.

12) The statement that no *chernosem* is formed on pure sands was first made by RUPPRECHT in 1886 who wrote «if one takes broad stretches of sand in the steppe they would normally become covered with forest, but under these, podsolic soils would develop» (cf. GLINKA 1914, page 122). With regard to the designation of podsolic soils cf. note 9.

13) The *dregraded chernosem* is shown as a «degraded» formation in regard to its characteristics of humus content, humus depth, level of nutrient and chalk content. It shows, however, owing to its better water relations in summer and the reduced danger of drought damage, a greater safety in its cultivation. Therefore in many regions (e. g. Muntenia) the *degraded chernosem* is often considered more valuable than the *chernosem*.

14) The class designation *Terra* goes back to the Italian (*terra rossa*, terra gialla) on the one hand, but on the other hand has its roots in the designation for earth used in medicine and craftwork particularly in the Middle Ages, taken from the Latin, for predominately bolus-like material closely related to the terrae calxis (e. g. terra lemnia, terra alba, terra miraculosa Saxonia, terra de Siena, terra sigillata, terra fullonum, etc.). The strongly braunlehm- or rotlehm-like, dense, wavy, greasy-lustrous forms, which often have a conchoidal fracture on drying out are directly designated as bolus (e. g. Bolus alba, Bolus flava, Bolus rubra).

15) It has often been considered that the terra gialla is a «degraded *terra rossa*» i. e. in which in moist locations the red ferric hydroxide, due to a secondary increase in water content has been transformed back into ochre yellow limonitic iron compounds. The exact proof as to whether it is really a regressive formation or not just a pre-stage to *terra rossa* like the rest of the limestone braunlehms has still not yet been given.

16) I became well acquainted with the earthy form of *terra fusca* only on my second visit to Spain (1949/50), hence the observation in my «Entwicklungslehre» page 84, that the *terra fusca* only occurs in the highly peptized forms, is no longer true. On page 113 (§ 106) of the «Entwicklungslehre» I had already mentioned that flocculated ferric hydroxide precipitates (similar to those of the Iwatoka form) in the *Mediterranean terra fusca* are more frequently to be found than in the *Centro-European terra fusca*.

17) This is shown not only in Spanish occurrences but also with terra fusca in Crete and Greece. One observes in the White Mountains of Crete that the snow is very frequently yellow to brownish in colour due to a covering of dust (coming from Africa). In the same way, in the southern Balkans yellow snow is known which falls to the ground already loaded with fine sand dust from North Africa. The Yugoslav Weather Service has announced that snowfalls of «yellow snow» occurred

in Belgrade even on the 29th January 1947. Of much greater influence however is the supply of wind sediments from neighbouring soil formations on silicate rocks (mostly *meridional braunerde*) as examinations on Spanish *terra fusca* have shown particularly.

18) With regard to the reasons for the higher iron content of many forms of the terra rossa cf. «Entwicklungslehre», page 116.

19) The designation CALVERO (Castillian folk name) was introduced into soil science by HUGUET DEL VILL·AR and refers to all dry soils with sparse open vegetation, limited to rounded clumps and individual bushes only, between which are found the bare soil surfaces (calvas) whose environmental conditions usually only permit a scanty humus formation in the region of the root zones of the plants (whereby similar embryonic soil formations on hard parent rocks are excluded and only those on loose parent materials included in the designation). The ordering of the concept of calvero soil in the soil system has given rise to difficulties and led to very varied opinions. HUGUET DEL VILLAR sees it in the first place as an original rendsina-like soil, whose profile has been to a great extent removed, so that soil formation must start afresh. STREMME spoke of it as a light chestnut coloured steppe soil, DE SIGMOND designated it according to its present dynamic as a kind of light brown steppe soil, ROBINSON refers to the association of many calveros with the *rotlehms* of the Savannah under monsoon forest. Thus there has arisen a series of very different concepts, ranging from the primitive embryonic formations to the most advanced final phases of soil development (characterized by extensive decomposition, gel precipitation, leaching and nutrient impoverishment). What is designated in Spain as «calvero» refers indeed to the most different types of soil formation, according as to whether its parent material is calcareous or chalk deficient or consists of deposits of the most mature fossil soil formations (in which case the reference of ROBINSON is entirely correct). All forms have in common soil life reduced extensively by dryness, a sparse and scattered vegetation and a sparse humus formation. On calcareous sands and marls as parent materials, it has clearly the character of a mosaic of *xerorendsina* and chalk raw soil or a humus deficient semi-desert soil, like *serosem*. With deposits of fossil *braunlehm* and *rotlehm* there is the possibility to obtain with adequate moistening over-night almost all the properties of a highly developed *braunlehm* or *rotlehm*. The calvero is a typical phenomenon of the dry regions of Spain. However, by the above, the distinction between the different forms, in which it appears, is inevitable. It becomes, on calcareous sands and marls a *calvero-rendsina*, on unweathered chalk deficient sands, a *calvero-ranker*, on braunlehm sediments, a *calvero-braunlehm*, on those of rotlehm a *calvero-rotlehm*. The designations «light chestnut coloured» or «light brown» steppe soils are to be used here with care as the brown hue of the soils in Spain is usually derived not from humus but from free ferric hydroxide and appears in the same way also with almost no humus. On braunlehm sediments it becomes a rather intense brown when wet, on little weathered parent material it generally shows a lighter brown, but which corresponds entirely to an iron-deficient *braunerde*. Mostly it is already a question here of distinctly pronounced *meridional braunerde*.

20) This form of precipitation, which has a great influence on the physical characteristics and affects the entire fabric, was first determined in the *Iwatoka rotlehm* of the Anglo-Egyptian Sudan. Therefore, the designation Iwatoka phenomenon. This is due to a periodical intensive heating up and drying out of the *rotlehm*.

21) The *braunerde* on pumice sand rich in bases occupies a special position in regard to several characteristics. Although the soil in the Westerwald contains up to 80 % of coarse sand, around 20 % of fine sand and only 1 % of clay, owing to the high porosity of the sand grains, it shows a high water capacity, excellent humus

formation, 30-35 cm. deep, humus-rich, A horizons and a high growth capacity for exacting tree species (ash, maple, elm, beech, larch). Its colour varies in the profile, owing to the light colour of the parent rock when unweathered, from blackish brown through light brown to almost pure white in the C horizon.

22) The designation *semi-podsol* stands for GLINKA's designation «podsolic soils» in order to conform to the rules of the nomenclature by which the name of the type should be expressed by a noun and the undescriptive or poorly characterizing and therefore unnecessary filling words, such as «soil», «forest soil» (as isolated nouns) should be avoided. The designation «cryptopodsol» was given by NIKIFOROFF only to a small part of the group, namely to those soils in which the characteristics of podsolization are so little developed that they can scarcely yet be determined by morphological investigation, but practically only by chemical analysis. The *semi-podsols* show (including the humus formations) well developed morphological characteristics, so that between the cryptopodsol and the phaneropodsol lies a group of widespread phaneropodsolic soils. In regard to the best known form of the *semi-podsols*, the podsolic brown earth, the facts must be taken into consideration that it is no longer a *braunerde* (even if it is derived from *braunerde*) for it shows another dynamic, other formation conditions, no (B) horizons but true B horizons (illuvial horizons) and the tendency to develop other humus forms. Further it can occur on large areas as an independent climax formation. By all these characteristics it falls distinctly outside the concept of *braunerde* and an alternation of the type designation is necessary but I have not done it here, in consideration of the general use of its name and in order not to overburden the book too much with new nomenclature. The *semi-podsols* have been little worked in as yet and the exact description, definition and delimitation of a number of subtypes is still missing. The «concealed podsols» mentioned by NEUSTRUEFF and GORODKOFF occurring at the northern boundary of the tundra forest appear of particular importance (*northern semi-podsol*). They are evidently parallel to the similar high-alpine forms above the region of the alpine turf podsols.

23) Similar soils were found also in Russia by GLINKA (1914) on dense boulder clay of a red brown colour with concretions in the bleached layer from the district of Luga, province of Petersburg and by TJUMIN (1909) on dust loess with the same concretions up to 1-2 cms. in size from the province of Smolensk. Both forms however pass over easily into *marbled pseudogley*.

24) The name molken soil is derived from the milky cloudiness which the water exhibits after percolation of the highly erodable soil. The new designation *molken-podsol* was created here on the one hand in order to replace «soil» by the type name and on the other hand to make it clear that the designation refers within the group of molken-like soils only to that with distinct podsol character and excludes the others (belonging to the *pseudogley* type).

25) The Russian soil scientists have greatly extended the «group of podsolic soils» and have included in it non-podsolic *braunerde* and even browned *chernosems*. In the interest of a more exact differentiation and division of the phenomenon of soil formation, this is not very advantageous. They have, however, sharply delimitated the type podsol as such, and differentiated distinctly between real podsols and only «podsolic soils», i.e. those without distinctly developed bleached layer. From their descriptions and their reports of the region of occurrence it is evident also that soils with dystrophic humus forms and with the development of acid humus sols are concerned. The essential separation of the *pseudogley* (the gley-like and marbled soils) was only made possible by the work of G. KRAUSS and W. LAATSCH. The concept of *podsol* has unfortunately not been accepted in its original form and in present soil science literature appears to be defined as vaguely as ever. The reason

is primarily that not the totality of the characteristics, but isolated particular characteristics have been used for the designation of the soils as *podsols*. The most frequently used individual characteristics in this sense are the following:

1. Base impoverishment. This is the condition for podsol formation, but podsolization need not necessarily occur. A low base saturation as such is not therefore a podsol characteristics which can be used entirely for diagnosis.
2. Strong acidification. Also this, alone, will still not make a *podsol*.
3. Eluviation. Occurs with numerous other soil types.
4. Formation of bleached horizons. Not every bleaching means podsolization, it is shown also by *braunlehm, rotlehm, solodi* and *pseudogley*.
5. Raw humus formation. This is also possible in conjunction with other types such as *dystrophic forest ranker, tundra ranker, dystrophic tangel rendsina* and *pseudogley* without being coupled with humous acid eluviation and formation of true bleached sand layers.

Appendix

Short Guide to the Arrangement of a Soil Collection

In the same way as one only obtains a knowledge of plants by the arrangement of a herbarium or of coleptera by the collection of beetles, so one only obtains a real knowledge of soils by a correctly laid out soil collection. It is unfortunate that one rarely has the opportunity of having a sufficiently complete soil collection or even one containing the most essential soils, although their arrangement and care can offer so many joy filled hours. A soil collection can indeed only be made enjoyable and fulfil its aim if it is expertly arranged. The easy destructibility of the structure of the soil has induced men all along to regard soils as loose frameworks without particular inner structure and even in Pedology Institutes the activity of the expert began with extracted soil samples, which were pulverized in mortars and kept as powder in glass jars. The first consideration for the collector is the removal of structurally undisturbed samples, even when it is a question of cultivated soils (even in their loosened surface layer they develop a certain very informative inner structure). Pulverization makes the soil just as uninteresting as pulverization makes the most rare beetles, butterflies, mussels, rocks and minerals completely valueless and unsuitable for the aims of the collector. The term soil can only refer to an entirely undisturbed, living soil cover in its natural state undergoing a characteristic yearly change, therefore a collection can never contain «soils» but only samples or sections of soils. They are just dried parts of the soil, lacking life and all remaining functions, in the same way as a herbarium of forest trees can contain only a collection of dried parts, robbed of life and of natural connection. Here as there the parts ought to be chosen so that one obtains the most comprehensive picture possible of the whole. The soil collection must therefore not only contain suitable samples from all parts (horizons) of the soil profile but alto the parent material or better both the parent rock and plant cover. The soil collector is therefore also a collector of rocks, which very much increases the attraction of his work. He collects not only samples of the fresh parent rock but also hand samples showing the changes brought about by the environmental weathering. He is in addition a collector of plants, for in order to make his collection complete, he should take a sample of the plant cover by a particular technique (especially where this has a marked influence on the kind of soil formation) and attach it to the soil profile concerned.

Of all sampling methods the *frame sample technique* seems the most suitable as by its simplicity it leads most rapidly to the goal. It is the only method which can be considered for general collection on journeys. Whole profile sections can be obtained by the *monolith technique*. Very beautiful profile preparations for display may be made by the *lacquer film method*. The profile methods are not suitable for collection on excursions and travel as their preparation requires a long stay at the profile location, and in addition the necessity of having a suitable method of transport at one's disposal (particularly in the case of the monolith technique).

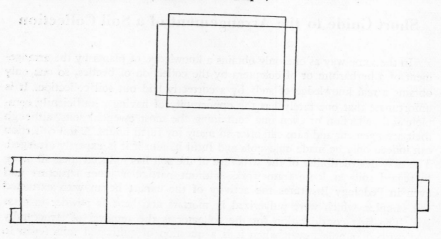

FIG. 4.—Pattern for the manufacture of sample frames.

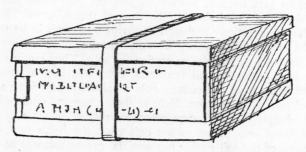

FIG. 5.—Sample frame for taking soil specimen with undisturbed structure.

The *frame sample technique* works with small hand samples. In exactly the same way as a hand sample may be chipped from a rock stratum with a hammer, so hand samples of soil horizons are cut with the soil knife and by slipping over a frame of galvanized tin plate, protected from destruction. If the soil formation lies on a rocky parent material, from the half-weathered, as well as the fresh parent rock (C₁ horizon and C₂ horizon) a rectangular sample somewhat larger than the sample frame is taken with a hammer. With loose parent material, these samples, as well as the individual soil horizons, may be taken with the aid of the sample frame. The most suitable way to take samples of the plant cover is to dig out a sod with an open sample frame from a typical location and to dry it in the air. With shrubs and trees an air-dried unpressed branch of each kind is placed in a black pasteboard carton. These plant samples serve also as working material for the microscopic investigation of humus, the soil and rock samples for the production of thin section preparations. Besides the sample frame, the following tools are necessary: a geological hammer, a soil knife (a strong knife with a stiffened handle, a blade about 15 cm. long and corresponding sheath), a spade fitting in a rucksack, perhaps a small chisel and small scissors. If one does not wish to pay for a tinsmith the sample frames may be easily manufactured by oneself. For this, a sheet of tin plate 0.5 mm. thick is cut with tinsnips in 4 cm. wide strips. These must be cut along the cutting line as in *fig. 4* and formed by bending the 8 cm. by 6.5 cm. side pieces. The edges, using two iron corner pieces with whose help the fillets are clamped in a vice, are beaten with a mallet. The closing of the toothed seal is also done with the mallet (see *fig. 4 and 5*) by bending the edges of the seal. This simple closure makes it possible to open the frame easily by raising the middle tooth and thus remove the sample (which for example is essential for the production of thin section preparations). Many coherent soil samples or peaty humus formations can be taken out of the frame immediately after drying, it being unnecessary to put them into the shallow pasteboard cartons. The two lids belonging to the sample frame are more easily made from somewhat thinner tin plate (0.35 mm.). After the tin piece is cut along the cutting line «b» in *fig. 4*, a piece of wood the size of the cross-section of the frame is laid on it, and using it as a base-plate the edges of the tin may be easily bent up. Under the central tooth of the frame seal, the edge of a label of stiff paper 7.8 × 3.8 mm. in size is inserted. Both lids are now put on the frame, so that the edges also cover the border of the label on both sides. Finally a strong rubber band is slipped over the closed sample frame (see *fig. 5*) to keep the lid firmly imposition.

Before taking samples in the open air, the frame is opened and the label removed. The taking of the sample must not be done by pressing, which is the case with cutting- or forced cylinders for physical investigations. It is produced by cutting and gradual slight pushing of the frame over the sample separated by the knife. The frame is laid on the sampling spot with the upper lid on and it is necessary to have the above mentioned tooth of the seal pointing to the left. The sample frames are then dug out with the knife. The sample is now cut on its lower side about 3 cms. below the frame. This protruding portion of the soil sod is removed by reversing the sample and subsequently cut off. Finally the label is attached, the cover put on and the lid closed by slipping over the rubber band. It is to be noted that the lower lid must be a particularly firm fit, which can be achieved by bending inwards to a greater degree the overlapping side edges. With a slackly fitting lid there is always the danger that loose samples will fall out after removal of the rubber bands and thereby be destroyed. For arrangement in the collection, the sample frames are opened on top and air-dried. With a well-fitting lower

FIG. 6.—Procedure of taking a frame sample.

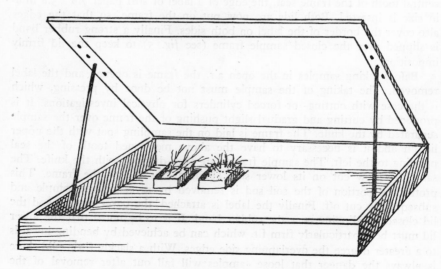

FIG. 7.—Protection case with glass cover for fresh frame samples.

lid, the sample can be preserved without danger. On the ticket of each sample frame the following sequence of details should be noted: Profile number, soil type (or subtype or variety), plant cover, parent rock, name of sample site, height above sea-level, horizon and depth from which the profile was taken and thicknecc of the horizon (in cm. or inch.). The reverse side of the ticket may be used for further information (particular observations, experimental results, etc.). Further samples from deeper horizons which have been previously separated by a spade are cut out in the same way as above, always maintaining the same orientation for each sample. The drying and preservation of the samples before their final inclusion in the collection is carried out in a display frame, which prevnts them becoming dusty. It consists, as *fig.* 7 shows, of a wooden frame which though open on two sides can be closed by a glass lid held by two suports when open. This frame is placed above the samples laid out on the base plate. The samples are best protected in cupboards with drawers. The most advantageous depth of drawer is 10 cms. The samples are most suitably arranged from left to right in the drawer for which the natural system offers the best basis for disposition of the classes and sub-classes. The individual profile begins with the sample of the plant cover and passing through the horizons and sub-horizons of the soil layer ends with the sample of the parent rock. In order to prevent the various sample sequences from sliding about, they are separated by 2 cm. high and 1 cm. wide soft wood strips which are fixed with wire tags. The collector when working on a particular soil group may wish to leave one drawer for a longer time on the work bench. In these circumstances the drawer should be covered with glass in a wooden frame, the latter fitting over the edges of the drawer (see *fig.* 9). This lid should fit all drawers. It is advantageous due to the weight of the contents of the drawer not to make it too large and a size of about 60 × 70 cm. appears to be suitable. For institute and teaching collections it is better to place show glasses on the cabinet drawers (somewhat as in *fig.* 8).

A rich soil collection is by far the most important part of a Pedology Institute and is a most indispensable aid for soil systematists. Soil collections, as well, are often specially useful for teaching. The completion of each collection will become much easier only when the number of collectors has grown to such an extent that samples of exotic soils will be obtainable by exchange or purchase. Obtaining such samples by these means will be particularly valuable to those who are unable to undertake long journeys.

As I am myself a passionate collector, I can say from experience that nothing has deepened my love for pedology more than collecting. It will give pleasure to the beginner to find the most varied evidence of all forms, knowledge of which he has acquired by using this book. Those who have had happiness in rocks and their collection have particular pleasure in seeing the alteration due to the influence of living and environmental conditions. Certain parent rocks are especially felicitous and a visit to the most favourable location is extraordinarily rewarding to the collector. Thus cindery basalts, basanite, or diabase will give a rich yield of most valuable samples even in a temperate climate, beginning with the most primitive *ranker* up to the most variable *eutrophic braunerde,* the most richly coloured fossil *braunlehm,* sub-tropical *rotlehm* or lateritic *roterde.* Very interesting and beautiful collection pieces may be obtained not only from the most diverse formations of olivine rocks (picrites, peridotites, dunites) serpentines, calc-mica schists, calc-silicate schists, calc-schists, but also from commonly occurring rocks as calcareous sandstones. Certain plant covers are especially desirable for the collector, partly on the grounds that he is able, by the above mentioned methods, to obtain partic-

FIG. 8.—Cupboard with drawers and show glass.

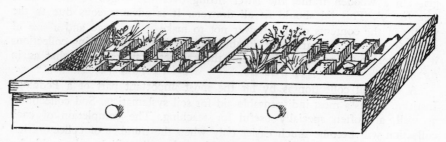

FIG. 9.—Single drawer with dust lid.

ularly beautiful whole samples, such as alpine cushion plants, turf of certain form-preserving grasses, dwarf shrub covers, soil espaliers, moss or lichen covers (particularly of the tundra zone), the association of sclerophyllous or steppe plants, etc. Thus the activity of the soil collector is always an excursion into the four realms of nature, the soil, the rocks, the plants and, as every biologically trained soil scientist knows, also the animals. Many series of samples can be a continual source of rememberance of an unforgettable journey or of a succession of joy-filled hours observing nature. Everywhere one can find sources of interest if one is sufficiently acquainted with the kingdom of soils.

Collection marches in the vanguard of every science and as soil science from this point of view has not yet reached the highest level, much help is to be expected from an increase in collecting activity. An effective, fruitful comparison of forms is only possible by having a rich soil collection at hand. Only the presence of a sufficient quantity of material permits of fundamental systematizing, of the recognition of new forms and of the characteristics which distinguish them from other soils. It makes their corelation and interrelation distinct, and permits an overall view of the great richness of form. The putting together of the similar reveals the variation of a particular idea in nature and with sufficient completeness of the collection even the most divergent shows the inner connection to the whole and appears as a part of it. The attentive collector will find that in certain landscapes or parts of landscapes on the same parent rock, a number of very different soil formations with greatly varying maturity can be found. In which way these belong to a genetic sequence (development sequence), which characteristics a soil form has taken over from its genetical predecessor, which it has altered, to which particular environmental conditions or biological influences these alterations are due, all these are questions with which research in soil development is intensively occupied (cf. Kubiena 1948). To follow its results is not only a stimulating task for every collector but one which leads him through the different branches of the natural system of soils and allows him to recognize the entire soil cover as a unit created by common, law-abiding development and subject to further continual alteration.

While the methods described above for the frame sample technique make it possible to obtain only hand samples of soil sections, the *monolith technique* enables the entire soil section to be removed with all the soil horizons in their natural place and without destruction of their natural connection. This was first done by R. V. RISPOLOSHENSKY * and described in the year 1897. It is used today in a form which K. GLINKA suggested. Although the production of a soil monolith often requires much time and labour on the part of the collector, they greatly enhance the value of a collection and amply repay the labour involved. Only the best and most suitable ought to be removed as monoliths. Generally for this purpose only soil formations on loose parent material may be considered.

The method is founded on a similar principle to the frame sample technique, only the frames consists of strong boards (2 cm. thick) and have a length of about 1 m. (according to the depth of the profile) a breadth of 20 cm. and a depth of about 10 cm. (see *fig. 5*); the removal is also not horizontal but vertical. The frames can be closed on both sides by a wooden lid which may be firmly attached to it by screws, not nails. An edge rail of about 2 cm. is fastened with screws to the front side of the frame which can be easily taken off in the laboratory (see shortening rail in fig. 10). The part of the soil exposed in this way thus projects beyond the edge of the frame, making it possible by careful loosening of the superfluous soil with awl or

---

* Employing a particular apparatus for taking monoliths which today is rarely used.

needle shaped tools (not by cutting with a knife), to obtain a new, carefully prepared profile surface which at the same time also gives a view of the natural structure of the soil. For field work the following tools are necessary: 1-2 spades, 1-2 soil knives (according to whether one or two persons are working) and one screw-driver.

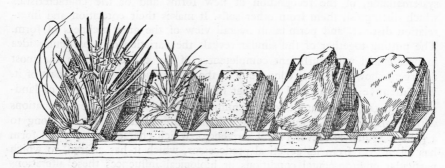

FIG. 10.—Display of frame samples of a soil profile (Plant cover, A, (B), (B)/C and C horizon.

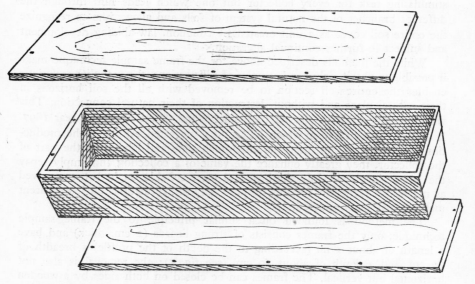

FIG. 11.—Wooden profile frame for sampling after the monolith technique.

For the removal of the profile block, a profile pit is dug, one of its walls smoothed, and from it, with a soil knife, a rectangular soil column is cut out, though still retaining contact with the natural soil at the back and base of the cavity. The column should be about 10 cm. wider than the frame. Then the frame is laid in position, the correct width of soil marked with a knife along its inner sides and the exact monolith cut out by repeated fitting of the frame. Only then can the frame be pushed on to the soil block, in which one carefully lays bare the lower part and prepares the ground surface. At the same time the box must be supported at its lower edge by the insertion of a spade to prevent permature separation of the soil block from the side wall. Now the front surface is levelled so that the lid fits without cavity and can be screwed on. The separating of the monolith from the soil is done by

FIG. 11.—Procedure of taking a monolith sample.

cutting with a soil knife obliquely along the side edges inwards from the back wall of the profile pit, so that a roof shaped surface results. The freed monolith is raised out of the pit, its back face levelled, and the second lid screwed in position, again avoiding cavities. In this way the danger of destroying the structure in transport is reduced to a minimum.

It is recommended that the monolith boxes after final preparation of the profile surface should not be laid upright in the collection but obliquely, in

order to avoid deterioration due to crumbling or sliding off of parts which
have become loose.

With strongly shrinking soil formations the wood frames must be narrowed
afterwards. The somewhat smaller boards are again not attached by nails but
by screws as the risk of damaging the structure must always be avoided.

The *lacquer film method*, which has still to be described, serves only,
although in a very complete way, to prepare the profile surfaces for exhibition,
not for the removal of profile samples which can at the same time be used
for research. For the preparation, a profile wall is exposed and smoothed
with spades and soil knives, then the slightly dried-out wall is brushed free
of loose crumbs and sprayed with a 1:2 mixture of Zaponlack and acetone
with a spray gun. After the Zaponlack has dried out the process is repeated
once or twice and a profile surface about 20 cm. wide is painted with a thick
cellulose lacquer using a broad painter's brush. The most suitable material
for this purpose appears to be the Geiseltal lacquer of E. VOIGT, the originator
of the method, although any other highly viscous cellulose lacquer may be
used. On the somewhat dried-out but still moist wall is laid a strip of
webbing about 20 cm. broad and its surface painted once more with cellulose
lacquer, although E. VOIGT used the method also without the weebing sub-
layer. The lacquer layer must be allowed to dry out completely, which may
require a few hours. Then one takes the webbing strip at its upper edge with
both hands and peels off from the profile wall the resulting lacquer skin, to
which the soil layer is adhering, perhaps with some help from a knife using
the reverse side. The binding part of the cellulose lacquer is so strong that
even stones and roots are held in the lacquer skin. Larger roots are separated
from the profile wall by a small sharp saw so that only their outer surfaces
remain embedded in the profile preparation. It must be also noted that not
only stones and roots but also the edges of the profile must be carefully
lacquered on. The removed profile is best transported in a light case. Only
lacquer films of loose, stone-free soil may be rolled up like a carpet. The profile
is mounted on a plywood frame. The exterior surface is brushed and any
damaged places are repaired immediately with lacquer and broken-off soil.
Finally the upper surface can be fixed again by spraying once more with
strongly diluted Zaponlack (1 part Zaponlack, 6 parts acetone). The profiles
then may be easily hung on the walls of the collection room.

Literature

AFANASSJEFF, J., 1930.—Das bodenkundliche Antlitz der Erde in seinen Grundzügen. (German, Ukrainian and Russian.) Minsk.

ALBAREDA HERRERA, J. M.ª, 1940.—El Suelo. Madrid.

ALBAREDA HERRERA, J. M.ª, 1943.—Clasificaciones y tipos de suelos. Anales del Instituto de Edafología de Madrid; p. 151-192 u. 373-407; ibíd., 1944, p. 142-155.

ALBAREDA HERRERA, J. M.ª, u. HOYOS DE CASTRO, A., 1948.—Edafología. Madrid.

ALBERT, R., 1935.—Bimsteinsandböden des preussischen Forstamtes Montabaur im Westerwald. Forstarchiv, II, p. 129.

BALLENEGGER, R., 1916.—Über die chemische Zusammensetzung ungarischer Bodentypen. Jahresber. Kgl. ungar. geol. Reichsanstalt (1920), p. 509-601.

BLANCK, E., 1919.—Ein Beitrag zur Kenntnis arktischer Böden. Chem. d. Erde, I, p. 438.

BLANCK, E., 1930.—Die Mediterran-Roterde (Terra-rossa). Handbuch der Bodenlehre, Bd. 3. Berlin.

BLANCK, E., 1930.—Krustenböden, Handb. d. Bodenlehre, Bd. III. Berlin.

BLANCK, E., 1939.—Handbuch der Bodenlehre. I. Ergänzungsband. Berlin.

BLANCKENHORN, M., 1901.—Neues zur Geologie und Paläontologie Agyptens. Z. dtsch. geol. Ges., 53, p. 479-484.

BORNEBUSCH, C. H., u. HEIBERG, S. O., 1936.—Vorschlag über die Benennung der Waldhumusdecke. Verh. 3. Intern. Congress of Soil Sci, Oxford, 1935, 3, p. 260.

BRAUN-BLANQUET, J., u. JENNY, H., 1926.—Vegetationentwicklung und Bodenbildung in der alp. Stufe der Zentralalpen. Denkschrift der Schweiz. Naturf. Ges., 63, Abt. 2. Zürich.

BÜLOW, K. v., 1929.—Allg. Moorgeologie. Berlin.

CLAVER ALIOD, M., 1947.—Contribución al estudio de los suelos silícico-húmicos de la Sierra de Guadarrama. Anales Esp. Edafología, Ecología y Fisiología, VI, v. I.

COMEL, A., 1937.—Elementi di Pedologia climatica. Udine.

DARWIN, CH., 1881.—Vegetable Mould and Earthworms.

DEMOLON, A., 1932.—Principes d'Agronomie. I. La Dynamique du Sol. Paris.

DIETRICH, W. G., 1941.—Die Dynamik der Böden in den feuchten Tropen. Berlin.

DIMO, N. A., 1904.—(See GLINKA 1914.)

DOKUTSCHAJEFF, W. M., 1879.—Russian Soil Survey (Russian).

DOKUTSCHAJEFF, W. W., 1879 (dtto 1883).—The Russian Chernozem (Russian). St. Petersburg.

DOKUTSCHAJEFF, W. W., 1893.—The Russian Steppes. Dept. Agr. Min. of Crown Domains for the World's Columbian Exposition. St. Petersburg.

DUMONT, J., 1913.—Etude sur le sol. I. Agrochimie, Paris.

EDELMANN, C. H., 1950.—Soils of the Netherlands. Amsterdam.

EISELEN, J. Ch., 1802.—Handbuch oder Anleitung zur Kenntnis des Torfwesens. Berlin.

ERDMANN, 1926.—Humusformen des Waldbodens. Forstarchiv, II, p. 81-89.

FRANZ, H., 1950.—Bodenzoologie als Grundlage der Bodenpflege. Berlin.

FRASER, G. K., 1943.—Peat Deposits of Scotland. Dept. of Sci. and Indust. Research, Wartime Pamphlet No. 36.

FREI, E., 1944.—Morph., chem. u. Kolloidchem. Unters. subalp. Weide-u. Waldböden der Rendsina-u. Podsolserie. Eein Beitrag z. Humusklassifizierung. Mitt. d. E.T.H. Zürich, 54.

FROSTERUS, B., 1912.—Geologiska Kommissionen in Finland. Geotekniska Meddelanden, Nr. 10.

FROSTERUS, B., 1914.—Zur Frage der Einteilung der Böden in Nord-West-Europas Moränengebieten. V. Geol. Kommiss. in Finland. Geotekn. Meddel., Helsinki, 14.

GEDROIZ, K. K., 1926.—Die Solodierung der Böden. Public. of the Nosowsk. Agric. Exp. Sta., 4 (Russian).

GSDROIZ, K. K., 1929.—Der adsorbierende Bodenkomplex. Deutsch von H. Kuron. Kolloidchem. Beihefte. Dresden u. Leipzig.

GESSNER, H., 1931.—Der Böden das unteren Tessintales. Schweiz. Landw. Monatshefte, 9, p. 28.

GIORGIEWSKI, 1888.—Notes on Russian Soil Investigations. IV. Lief. (Russian) (see GLINKA, 1914).

GLINKA, K., 1914.—Die Typen der Bodenbildung. Berlin.

GRIPP. K., 1914.—Über Frost- und Strukturböden auf Spitzbergen. Z. Ges. f. Erdkunde, p. 7-8.

GEDEWANISHWILLI, D. P., 1930.—Natural conditions on the route from Tiflis to Baturyany. Guide-book for the Excursion of the IInd Int. Congress of Soil Science. Moscow, II, p. 159-194.

GROSSKOPF, W., 1931.—Fortschritte der Humusforschung. Sudetend. Forst. und Jagdzt., Feberheft.

GROSSKOPF, W., 1935.—Stoffliche und morphologische Unterschungen forstlich ungünstiger Humusformen. Thar. Forstl. Jb.. 86, p. 48.

GRUPE, O., 1909.—Die Brücher des Sollings. Z. f. Forts. - Jagdwesen, p. 3.

HALL, SIR D., 1903.—The Soil. London.

HARRASSOWITZ, H., 1926.—Laterit. Fortschr. d. Geologie u. Paläontologie, IV, 14, p. 253-516.

HARRASSOWITZ, H., 1930.—Böden der tropischen Regionen. Blancks Handbuch der Bodenlehre, III. Berlin.

HARTMANN, F., 1944.—Waldhumusformen. Ztschr. f. d. ges. Forstwesen, p. 76-77.

HELLRIEGEL, H., 1862.—Über Analyse einer Modererde der Wublitz bei Potsdam. Landw., p. 149.

HESSELMANN, H., 1926.—Studien über die Humusdecke des Nadelwaldes. Meddel. Stat. Skogsförs., 22, p. 169-552. Proc. IV. Intern. Congr. Pedol. Rome, 2, p. 625-635.

HILGARD, E. W., 1906 u. 1914.—Soils. New York.

HÖGBOM, B., 1914.—Die geolog. Bedeutung des Frostes. Bull. Geol. Inst. Upsala. 12, 308. s. a. Meinardus, Blancks Handb. Bodenlehre, III.

HOYNINGEN-HUEHNE, P. F. v., 1930.—Die Dodentypen Nord-und Mitteldeutschlands bis zum Rhein. Dissertation. Danzig.

HUGUET DEL VILLAR, E., 1927.—España en el mapa internacional de suelos. Ministerio de Fomento. Publicaciones agrícolas.

HUGUET DEL VILLAR, E., 1929.—Suelos de España. Madrid.

HUGUET DEL VILLAR, E., 1937.—Lue suelos de la Península luso-ibérica. Madrid.

HUXLEY, J. S.. u. ODALL, 1924.—Notes on surface makings in Spitzbergen. Geogr. J., 63, p. 207-229.

JENNY, H., 1926.—(see BRAUN-BLANQUET u. JENNY, 1926.)

JENNY, H., 1929.—Klima und Klimabodentypen in Europa und in den Vereinigten Staaten von Nordamerika. Soil Research, 1, p. 139.

JENNY, H., 1930.—Hochgebirgsböden. In Blanck's Handbuch der Bodenlehre, III. Berlin.

JENNY, H., 1941.—Factors of soil formation. New York u. London.

JOFFE, J. S., 1936.—Pedology, New Brunswik, N. J., 1949, II. edit.

KAUFMANN, H., 1929.—Rhytmische Phänomene der Erdoberfläche. Braunschweig.

KELLOGG, CH. E., 1936.—Soil Survey Manuel. Washington D. C.

KELLOGG, CH. E., 1948.—Preliminary suggestions for the classification and nomenclature of great soil groups in tropical and equatorial regions. Proc. First Commonwealth Bureau of Soil Science, 78-85.

KJELLMAN, F. R., 1919.—Om Växtligheten pa Sibiriens Nordkust. Of versigt Vet. Akad. Stockholm, 36, 5-21 s.a. Meinardus, Blancks Handb. Bodenlehre III.

KORSCHINSKY, S., 1886.—Über die Bodenarten u. über geobotanische Forschungen im Jahre 1886 in den Gouverments Kasan, Samara, Ufa, Perm und Wyatka. Arbeiten d. Naturforscher-Ges. Universität Kasan, Bd. 16, H. 6.

KRAUSS, G., 1928.—Die sog. Bodenerkrankungen. Jahresber. d. D. Forstvereins, p. 121.

KRAUS, G. MÜLLER u. GARTNER, 1928.—Standortsgemässe Durchführung der Abkehr von der Fichtenwirtschaft im nordwestsächsischem Niederland (mit grundsätzlichen Bemerkungen über «gleiartige» Bodenbildungen). Thar. Forstl. Jn. 20, H. 7/9.

KRUEDENER, A. v., 1927.—Die Waldtypen, Klassifikation und ihre volkswirtschaftliche Bedeutung. Neudamm.

KUBIENA, W. L., 1938.—Micropedology. Ames, Ia., U. S. A.

KUBIENA, W. L., 1943.—Gefügeuntersuchungen an tropischen und subtropischen Rotlehmen. Beitrag z. Kolon. Forschg. Bd. 3, p. 48-58.

KUBIENA, W. L., 1948.—Entwicklungslehre des Bodens. Wien.

KÜHNELT, W., 1950.—Bodenbiologie mit besonderer Berücksichtigung der Tierwelt. Wien.

LAATSCH, W., 1937.—Entwicklungstendenzen und System der deutschen Acker- und Waldböden. Kolloid-Beihefte Bd., 46.

LAATSCH, W., 1938.—Dynamik der deutschen Acker- und Waldböden. Dresden und Leipzig.

LAUTERBORN, R., 1901.—Die sapropelische Lebewelt. Zool. Anz. 24.

LEININGEN, W. GRAF ZU, 1908.—Über Humusablagerungen in den Kalkalpen. Ztschr. Forst u. Landw. 6, p. 529, 1909; ibid., 7, p. 160 u. 249.

LEININGEN, W. GRAF ZU, 1912.—Über Humusablagerungen im Gebiete der Zentralalpen. Ebenda, 10, p. 465.

LEUENBURGER, R., 1950.—Beitrag zur Kenntnis der Humuskarbonatböden und Rendsinen im Schweizer Jura. Mitt. Agrikultchem. Inst. E. T. H. Zürich.

LOMONOSSOFF, 1763.—Die ersten Grundlagen der Metallurgie. (see GLINKA, 1914.)

MARBUT, C. F., 1927.—A Scheme for Soil Classification. Proceedings and papers of the I. Intern, Congr. of Soil Sci. Vol. IV. Washington.

MECKING, L., 1925.—Die Polarländer. Leipzig.

MEINARDUS, W., 1930.—Arktische Böden. Blanck, Handbuch der Bodenlehre, Bd. III.

MENCHNIKOVSKY, F., 1932.—Pan (Nasa) and its origen in the red sandy soils of Palestine. J. agricult. Sci., 22, 4, p. 689.

MEYER, L., 1943.—Experimenteller Beitrag zu makroskopischen Wirkungen auf Humus- u. Bodenbildungen. Bodenkunde u. Pflanzenernährung, 29, p. 119-140.

MIECZINSKI, T., 1932.—Die Böden der Wojewodschaft Lublin. Materialien zur Erforschung polnischer Böden. H. 2, p. 1-84.

MIKLASZEWSKI, 1922.—Contribution à la connaissance des sols nommés «Rendsinas». C. R. III. Conf. Agropédologique. Prag.

MORLOT, 1848.—Geologische Verhältnisse von Istrien. In Haidingers Naturwissenschaftl. Abhandlungen. Wien.

MORTENSON, H., 1930.—Die Wüstenböden. Blancks Handbuch der Bodenlehre III. Berlin.

MÜCKENHAUSEN, E., 1936.—Die Bodentypenwandlungen des Norddeutschen Flachlandes. Jb. preuss. geol. Landesamt für 1935, p. 460.

MÜLLER, P. E., 1887.—Studien über die natürlichen Humusformen. Berlin. Danish Original 1879.

MURGONI, G. M., 1909.—Die Bodenzonen Rumäniens. I. Conf. Intern. Agrogeol. Budapest.

MURGOCI, G. M., 1924.—Etat de l'étude de la cartographie des sols. Bucarest.

NAUMANN, E., 1939.—Einführung in die Bodenkunde der Seen. Die Binnengewässer, 9. Stuttgart.

NIDDA, ST., 1932.—Die Rendsinen von Polessie. Materialien zur Erforschung polnischer Böden. H. 2, p. 124-156.

NEUSTRUJEFF, S. A. 1908.—(see NEUSTRUJEFF, 1910 u. 1911.)

NEUSTRUJEFF, S. S., 1910.—Über die Böden der Wüstensteppen von Turkestan. Tageb. XLI. Vers. russ Naturf. u. Arzte in Moskau, 10 (Russian).

NEUSTRUJEFF, S. S., 1911.—Über die geologischen und bodenbildenden Prozesse in den Ebenen am Unterlauf des Syr Darja.
   Potschwowiedjenie, 2, 15 (Russian and German).

NOVAK, V., u. PELISEK, J., 1939-40.—Rendsinaböden auf Serpentingestein. Ann. Fac. Agronom. Bukarest, 1, p. 1-25.

OGG, W. G., 1935.—The Soils of Scotland. Excursion Guide Book, 3. Intern. Congress of Soil Science, Oxford.

PALLMANN, H., u. HAFFTER, P., 1933.—Pflanzensoziologische und bodenkundliche Untersuchungen im Oberengadin. Berichte der Schweizer. Botfl Ges. 42, p. 357.

PALLMANN, H.; HASLER, A., u. SCHMUZIGER, A., 1938.—Beitrag zur Kenntnis der alpinen Eisen- u. Humuspodsole. Bodenkunde u. Pflanzenerng, p. 94.

PALLMANN, H., 1942.—Grundzüge der Bodenbildung. Schweiz. Landw. Monatshefte, 22, p. 1-24.

POHLE, R., 1924.—Frostboden in Asien und Europa. Petermanns geogr. Mitt., p. 86-89.

POST, HAMPUS V., 1862.—Studier öfver nutidens koprogena jordbildninger, gyttja, dy och mull. R. Sv. Vet. Ak. Handb., 4.

POST., L. V., 1924.—Das genetische System der organogenen Bildungen Schwedens. Comm. Int. Pedol., 4, Comm. Nr. 22. Int. bodenk. Kongr. Rom., 4, Bd. 3.

PRINCIPI, 1943.—I terreni d'Italia. Soc. Ed. Dante Alighieri.

PROISSL, A., 1949.—Nomenklaturvorschläge für die bei der Bodenkartierung zu berücksichtigenden Moorböden. Arbeitsgem. Oesterr. Bodenkartierung. Vervielfältigtes Manuskript. Wien.

QUERVAIN, A. DE, 1920.—Schweizer Grönlandexpedition 1912/13. Denkschrift der Schweizer Naturf. Ges. 53 b, p. 173-175.

RAMANN, E., 1883 p. 1893.—Forstliche Bodenkunde und Standortlehre. Berlin.

RAMANN, E., 1905 u. 1911.—Rodenkunde. Berlin.

RAMANN, E., 1906.—Z. Forst- u. Jagdwesens, p. 637.

RAMANN, E., 1917.—Bodenbildung und Bodeneinteilung.

RAMANN, E., u. WHITTLES, C. L. (Translator), 1928.—The Evolution and Classification of Soils. Cambridge.

RAMM, K., 1908.—Bestandesverjüngung auf den vielfach zur Rohhumus- und Ortsteinbildung neigenden Böden der Buntsandsteinformation des württembergischen Erzgebietes. Ber. d. Württ. Forstvereins.

REIFENBERG, A., 1929.—Die Entstehung der Mediterran-Roterde (Terra-rossa). Kolloid. chem. Beihefte. Berlin.

RICHTHOFEN, F. v., 1882.—China.

RIGG, T., 1929.—Pakihi lands of the Nelson Province. New Zealand. J. Sci. Techn., 11, p. 231-241.

ROBINSON, G. W., 1932.—Soils. London. (3. Aufl. 1949.)

ROMELL, L. G., u. HEIBERG, S. A., 1932.—Types of humus layer in the forests of Northeastern United States. Ecology, 12, p. 567-608.

ROMELL, L. G., 1935.—Mull and duff as biotic equilibria. Soil Sci., 34, p. 161-188.

RUSSEL, SIR E. JOHN, 1942.—Soil Conditions and Plant Growth, 7. Aufl.

SCHUCHT, F., 1930.—Grundzüge der Bodenkunde. Berlin.

SEE, K. VON, 1921.—Beobachtungen an Verwitterungsböden auf Kalksteinen. Ein Beitrag zur Frage der Rendsinaböden. Int. Mitt. Bodenk., 2, p. 85.

SIBIRZTZEFF, N. M., 1895.—Genetische Bodenklassifikation. Zap. Novo-Alexandr. Agr. Inst. !, 1-23.

SIGMOND, A. A. J. VON, 1938.—The Principles of Soil Science. London.

SHANTZ, H. L., u. MARBUT, C. F., 1923.—The Vegetation and Soils of Africa. New York.

STEBUTT, A., 1930.—Lehrbuch der allgemeinen Bodenkunde. Berlin.

STELZNER, 1827.—Die Marschgegenden im Königreich Hannover. Möglinsche Ann. d. Landwirtsch., 20, p. 200-320.

STREMME, H., 1926.—Grundzüge der praktischen Bodenkunde. Berlin.

STREMME, H., 1930.—Die Bleicherdewaldböden oder podsoligen Böden. Blancks Handbuch d. Bodenlehre, Bd. III. Berlin.

STREMME, H., 1930.—Die Braunerden. Blancks Handb. d. Bodenlehre, Bd. III. Berlin.

STREMME, H., 1930.—Die Steppenschwarzerden. Blancks Handbuch d. Bodenlehre. Berlin.

STREMME, H., 1930.—Degradierte Böden. Blancks Handbuch d. Bodenlehre, Bd. III. Berlin.

STREMME, H., 1930.—Die Böden Deutschlands. Blancks Handbuch d. Bodenlehre, Bd. V. Berlin.

STREMME, H., 1936.—Die Böden des Deutschen Reiches und der Freien Stadt Danzig. Petermanns Mitt., Engänzungsheft, Nr. 226.

STREMME, H., 1949.—Die Böden der Deutschen demokratischen Republik. Berlin.

TACKE, BR., 1930.—Die Humusböden in gemässigten Breiten. Blancks Handbuch d. Bodenlehre, IV, p. 124-184.

TARNUZZER, 1911.—Die Schuttfacetten der Alpen und des hohen Nordens. Peterm. Mitt.

THIENEMANN, A., 1921.—Seetypen. Naturwiss., 9, H. 18.

THIENEMANN, A., 1926.—Die Binnengewässer, 1. Stuttgart.

TREITZ, P., 1912.—Die Bildungsprozesse des Bodens im Osten des pannonischen Beckens. Jahresber. d. Kgl. Ungar. Geolog. Reichsanstalt.

TUMIN, G., 1909.—(see GLINKA, 1914.)

VAGELER, P., 1930.—Grundriss der tropischen und subtropischen Bodenkunde. Berlin.

VATER, H., 1904.—Ein Vortrag über die Bedeutung des Humus für den Wald. 5. Hauptversammlung Deutsch. Forstverein, Eisenach.

VATER, H., 1907.—Einheitliche Benennung der Humusformen. Vers. Sächs. Forstverein.

VILENSKY, D. G., 1924.—The Salt Soils and their Genesis, Composition and Amelioration. Moscow (Russian).

VOIGT, E., 1930.—Ein neues Verfahren zur Konservierung von Bodenprofilen. Z. f. Pfanzenern. Düng. u. Bodenk., 45, p. 111.

WAKSMAN, S. A., 1936.—Humus. Baltimore.

WASMUND, E., 1930.—Lakustrische Unterwasserböden. Blancks Handbuch d. Bodenlehre, Bd. V. Berlin.

WESENBERG-LUND, C., 1905.—Umformungen des Erdbodens. Prometheus, 16, Nr. 816 u. 817.

WHITTLES, 1928.—(see RAMANN-WHITTLES, 1928.)

WILDE, S. A., 1946.—Forest Soils and Forest Growth. Waltham, Mass.

WILLIAMS, W. R., 1919.—(6. Aufl. 1949.) Soil Science. Moscow (Russian).

WITYN, J., 1911.—(see WYTIN, 1924.) Die Hauptphasen des Podsolbildungsprozesses. Riga.

WOHLENBERG, E., 1931.—Die grüne Insel in der Eidermündung. Archiv der deutschen Seewarte, 50, Nr. 2, Hamburg.

WOHLENBERG, E., 1937.—Die Wattenmeer-Lebensgemeinschaften im Königshafen von Sylt. Helgoländer wiss. Meeresuntersuchungen, 11, H. 1.

WOHLTMANN, F., 1891.—Über den Kulturwert der tropischen Lateritböden. Z. Landw,. 39, p. 149.

WOHLTMANN, F., 1892.—Handbuch der tropischen Agrikultur.

WYSSOTZKI, G. N., 1900.—Hydrological and geobiological observations in Velikoanadol, V. Ground waters, Potschwowjedjenie, 2, p. 22-39 u. 99-113 (Russian).

WYSSOTZKI, G. N., 1905.—Gley. Potschowowjedjenie, 7.

WYSSOTZKI, G. N., 1901.—Das Illuvium und die Struktur der Steppenböden. Potschwowjedjenie, 3, p. 137.

ZACHAROFF, S. A., 1906.—Potschwowjedjenie, 1-4 (Russian) (see GLINKA, 1914).

ZIPPE, F., 1853.—Über die Grotten und Höhlen von Adelsberg, Lueg, Planina u. Lasa. Wien.

Explanation of some pedological terms

Active Soil: Soil with favourable biological conditions which is characterized by a rich colonization with organisms, as well as by good and rapid decomposition and humification of organic substances (particularly organic manure and green manure).

Aggregate: (J. DUMONT, 1913). General designation for the small, loose, structural bodies, formed by nature, which have the most different shape and origin, and which in common parlance are designated «soil crumbs». Aggregates are either true crumbs (with flacky fabric and irregular scabby surface), or small fragments, or small clods, or droppings of small animals of the most different kinds.

Allochthonous: (Greek allos = other, chthon = earth). Designation for soils, soil constituents or soil characteristics which have not been formed in the present location but else-where.

Autochthonous: (Greek autós = the same, chthon = earth). Designation for soils, soil constituents or characteristics which have been formed in the present location.

Baueritization: The weathering of biotite to rust brown (bauerite) or lustrous-gold small plates (cat gold) by the formation of free ferric hydroxide.

Biology of a Soil: The composition of life and the totality of the living processes characterizing a particular soil, to be distinguished from its dynamic (q. v.) which includes the totality of all non-biological processes.

Bolus: Dazzling ochre yellow, brown, red, grey, bluish or white coloured, strikingly waxy to greasy-lustrous, very dense clays of different composition, with concoidal fracture and rich in silica, which have various medical and technical uses. They are derived primarily from vesicles in basalts, amygdaloids and cavities in dense limestone.

Classification: In contrast to division (q. v.), an ordering of the usually most accesible objects (e. g. the agricultural cultivated soils of a particular country) which starts from the specialized, and graduay progresses to the general, sorting them into classes already present or to be created, generally according to particular viewpoints (to serve particular branches of agriculture, forestry, engineering, etc., or limited to certain administrative regions).

Clay-Humus Complex: Complex formation between humic acids and clay substances, mechanically inseparable, chemically completely divisible only with great difficulty, whose nature is little known. Microscopically well-developed clay humus complexes, in which the humic acids appear as an adsorbed dye on the clay substance (brown coloured clays), are easily distinguished from simple mixtures of humus and mineral constituents. Its determination is diagnostically of particular importance (for the differentiation of humus forms).

Climax: The maximum attainable end phase of a development sequence (q. v.) in a particular location, owing to the favourableness or unfavourableness of its environmental conditions. In the dry deserts, the desert raw soil is the only phase which is already a climax in its development sequence. In the podsol zone on calcareous sandstone, for example, it may happen that the climax (iron podsol) is reached after a development sequence of eight phases (carbonate raw soil, protorendsina, mull-like rendsina, mull rendsina, brown rendsina, brauerde, podsolic brauerde, iron podsol). In landscapes with strong soil removal climax formations of development sequences with many phases do not appear usually alone but in conjunction with other phases of the development sequence.

Conducting Channels: Predominately vertically running conduction paths in a dense soil fabric, which allow the down-flow of the percolation waters. They are usually derived principally from drought fissures, earthworm tubes and root channels. The substances dissolved or washed down in the percolating waters become deposited in a characteristic way in the conducting paths, so that their contents are of particular importance diagnostically. The fillings most frequently found are calcium carbonate, humus substances or highly peptized inorganic colloids.

Coprogenic Constituents: The part of the humus, generally strikingly dark coloured, characterized by stronger decomposition and humification, as well as by more complete mixing and combination of the organic and mineral substances; it is composed of the excreta of small animals (droppings) either well formed or remains of such.

Crumb Capacity: Property of soils to break down more or less completely on digging, or at slight pressure on dug-out clods, into small, strongly articulated aggregates with rough, scabby surfaces (true crumbs). The concepts «crumbly» and «earthy» are closely related, therefore the expression «earth», as it is used in common parlance, usually designates a strongly crumbling soil.

Development Sequence: Synonymous for genetic sois series (PALLMANN) or development series. Sequence of soils (types, subtypes or varieties), in which each is derived from its predecessor whereby a graduated scale arises progressing from the primitive to the complex (e. g. limestone raw soil, protorendsina, mull-like rendsina, brown rendsina, terra fusca, terra rossa). Many development sequences show a loss of productivity in the end branches, designated as aging.

Diagnosis: Recognition and naming of certain soil formations on the basis of some particularly characteristic and unequivocal (diagnostically applicable) properties, in the first place those which are easy to determine.

Division: The systematical arrangement of a totality (kingdom of soil formations) by the creation of graduated concepts (categories) starting from the most general, and progressing through the intermediate categories to the most specialized. Division is the opposite of classification (q. v.) which does not start from the whole and does not necessarily consider the whole, but creates special units (classes) and advances from these gradually to the more general. The older soil systematics had, predominantly, the character of a classification.

Dynamic: The totality of the effective forces in the soil, as well a the movements and physical and chemical alterations of non-biological character produced by them (in contrast to biology, v. q.).

Dystrophic: (Dys = Greek prefix = un- dis- ill-; trophos = nourishing). Designation for humus and soil formations with particularly unfavourable biological relations, only tolerable by certain organisms.

Eluvial Horizon: (Latin, eluere = to wash out). Washed out or impoverished horizon, deprived of substances by the percolating waters and which are deposited in deeper soil layers (illuvial horizon). The term applies in the first place to the washing of peptizable substances.

Eluviation: The displacement of substances by the percolating waters which move downwards in the space system of the soil from the top into deeper soil layers due to gravity.

Erodability: The very different intensity of removal in the form of washing away by running water, sliding by moistening or carrying of by wind of different soils under the same conditions (equal rainfall, slope, wind force, lack of vegetation protection, etc.).

Eutrophic: (Greek eu = good, trophós = nourishing). Designation for soils with high nutrient content and high biological activity.

Fabric: The arrangement of the soil constituents, not only in the narrower sense of aggregate formation (q. v. aggregate, separation, crumb capacity) but in a general sense, referring also to the variable inner fabric of dense soil masses, the effect of the most varied processes of precipitation and solution, the movement of substances and the alterations due to organisms, etc.

Feeding Marks: Variously shaped cavity formations, gnawed through boundaries, skeleton formation (leaves) and alterations of the otherwise little decomposed plant remains in humus formations, produced by the feeding of small animals. The kind of feeding marks is characteristic of particular animal forms and is therefore a diagnostically valuable characteristic in the microscopic humus investigation in addition to the kind of animal droppings, also for the determination of the intensity of the activity of particular animal groups in the humus formation.

Fossil Soil: (latin fossilis = buried). Fossilized i. e. dead, buried, petrified (transformed to rock) soil, in many cases diagenetically altered (i. e. hardened by cements, transformed to coal or carboniferous sandstone by carbonization). The term is in contrast to recent soil (q. v.) and relict soil (q. v.)

Fulvic Acids: (S. ODÉN 1912). Group of very different acid soluble humus substances, extractable from the soil by leaching with dilute alkalines, but in contrast to humic acids (q. e.) not precipitable with mineral acids. In the acid humus sols of the *podsols* and *semi-podsols*, the fulvic acids form the main part. Although the concept fulvic acids embraces an unhomogeneous group of humic substances whose composition is still little clarified, it is already in its present form an essential help for soil diagnostic purposes.

Grain Separation: Characteristic, diagnostically valid peculiarity of strongly erodable, easily silted up soils, which consists in a complete destruction of the original soil fabric by the process of erosion and the subsequent separate sedimentation of the different textural fractions, sorted out by the varying water velocities during transportation. Thus there often arises a series of layers with different colouring (plate VIII) which begins with the deposition of the coarse sand fractions and ends in the uppermost sediment layer with the finest colloidal substances. The grain separation of such soils appears even with moderate rainfalls and the slight differences of relief in the ploughed field surface of a plain.

Humic Acids: (S. ODÉN 1912.) Dark to blackish brown group of nitrogen containing humus substances which extracted from humus (q. v.) by leaching by dilute alkalies can be precipitated with mineral acids. With calcium ions they form compounds (calc humates), difficult to dissolve, of a blackish colour, which are particularly characteristic for the humus of the *rendsinas*. The proportion of humic acids is especially high in true mull formations, where these appear as dyes in the clay substance (also with iron hydroxide and silica), which are difficult to separate (clay humus complexes and other mineral humus complexes).

Humus: In contrast to the organic substance (q. v.) the totality of those organic constituents of a soil, which have proved to be difficult to decompose under the conditions prevailing, and therefore have become accumulated in a characteristic way. In addition to the chemical composition a humus formation in its natural habitat has a particular total biology, a particular macroscopic make-up and microscopic fabric as well as a usually strongly pronounced annual change (see phenology).

Hydrophilic Colloids: Colloidal substances little sensitive to flocculation by electrolytes in dispersions, with strong water attraction, which on thickening form a jelly (in the soil: humic substances, tannic substances, colloidal silicic acid).

Hydrophobic Colloids: Colloids easily flocculated by electrolytes with low water attraction, which do not form a jelly on thickening (in the soil: ferric hydroxide, aluminium hydroxide).

Illuvial Horizon: (WYSSOTSKI 1899) (latin illuere = to wash in). Washed in or enriched horizon. Soil layer in which substances have been deposited, removed from other parts of the profile in the form of solutions or dispersions. The transport takes place either by the percolating waters or by the mobile capillary water. By strong capillary rise illuvial horizons may be formed also in the top soil or in the surface layer. The most frequent forms of illuvial horizons are: lime-enriched horizons (Ca horizons), salt-enriched horizons (Sa horizons), among these, gypsum-enriched horizons (Y horizons, from the Spanish «yeso» = gypsum), raseneisenstein or rasenerde layers in gley soils (Fe horizons), humus orstein or humus orterde layers (B_h horizons), and sesquioxide-enriched layers (B_s horizons) in *podsols*.

Intergranular Spaces: (B. SANDER). Spaces between the mineral granules in sandy soils, which arise due to their irregular form even with the densest arrangement.

Iwatoka Phenomenon: Special form of iron precipitation which permeates gradually the entire soil structure in the form of an initially loose, later more or less connected framework usually of dazzling red, flaky ferric hydroxide gels (Iwatoka precipitates). Ascertained for the first time in *Iwatoka rotlehm* (*Anglo-Egyptian* Sudan) and characteristic of continuously strongly heated and dried *rotlehms*. The Iwatoka precipitations produce a strong loosening and considerable increase in the crumb forming capacitiy of the soil, which leads to an increase in cavities and water permeability and gradually a marked loss of water soluble silicic acids by leaching and a relative enrichment of ferrric hydroxide.

Micro=Skeleton (Fabric Skeleton): The coarse, little weathered mineral particles or little decomposed and humified organic constituents of a soil fabric apparent in thin section preparations or with direct microscopical investigation.

Mining: The hollowing-out of plant remains produced by the feeding of animals, particularly characteristic of the manner of living of certain small animal forms. It stands out particularly in thin sections of humus and is together with the forms of the droppings contained in the feeding channels diagnostically of particular value. It is to be found in the first place in raw humus and raw soil humus (syrosem humus), in which the droppings are always present and usually show low humification.

Morphology: (Greek morphé = form, shape) science of forms. That branch of investigation which is not only concerned with the material nature of the substances but also with their form and arrangement. Soil morphology is divided into *profile morphology* which is concerned with the use of macroscopic methods for the morphological characterization of the horizons and the investigation of the horizon forming processes, and into *micromorphology* which applies microscopic methods (thin section inquiry, direct microscopy with reflected light, micro-chemical and micro-physical methods). The more morphology is a detail inquiry, the more it has to do with the investigation of the simple substances. Its task consists, in contrast to general chemical analysis (on which it is based), in not isolating the substances but in investigating them in situ, particularly with regard to the kind and cause of their shape, their interrelations with other substances and constituents and their rôle in the fabric development of the entire soil.

Natural System: Is in systematics the division and ordering of a multiplicity of objects according to all their characteristics (not on the basis of only one particular or of only a few properties—as in the so-called artificial system) whereby the arrangement of the units is not governed by an arbitrary principle of division, but by their mutual connection and inner relationship, i. e. by which the essential order in Nature itself is represented.

Oligotrophic: (Greek oligos = little, trophós = nourishing.) Designation for soils with low nutrient content and relatively low biological activity, generally formed on base deficient parent rocks.

Organic Substances: In contrast to *humus* (g. v.) and to *humic substances,* the totality of all organic soil constituents including all fresh undecomposed organism remains and all macroscopically inseparable living organisms. Of the above three concepts, only the organic substances and with certain restrictions the humic substances (true humic substances) are directly determinable chemically. The determination of the constituents of the humus is at present only possible microscopically and is of particular importance for the definition and determination of humus forms.

Peptization: The more or less complete dispersion (sol formation) of colloidal particles in liquids (i. e. particles of about 1-100 m. μ diameter). It is the opposite term to flocculation (pectization, coagulation) which means the precipitation of particles into flaky aggregates or coagulates.

Phenology: The characteristic annual change of a soil as a whole i. e. not only in respect to climate (see soil climate), but also to its physical and chemical properties (e. g. pH value, salt content, etc.), its structure, as well as the composition and the activity of its flora and fauna.

Recent Soil: A soil formed under the present environmental conditions.

Relict Soil: In contrast to recent soil (q. v.) and fossil soil (q. v.) one which, in many essential characteristics, nowadays still very prominently indicates a development under the climate and the environmental conditions of a previous period, but which still forms in its present location the living superficial layer of the earth rind. Relict soils are represented primarily by those soils characterized by a high stability (e. g. *roterde, rotlehm*), or which stand higher in their development phase than the present climax formation (q. v.) (e. g. *terra rossa* in a region with *xerorendsina* as climax, brown coloured soils in the region of the *tundra rankers,* bolus-like silicate soils on old land surfaces in the peak region of the Limestone Alps).

Schlick: Silty marine sediment with more or less strong admixtures of fine sand.

Separation (Absonderung): Formation of fragmentary, sharp-edged, angular, platy to prismatic structural bodies in swelling soils and sediments rich in colloidal substances (or in solidified lavas) by the natural breakdown of the entire mass due to volume shrinkage.

Silting-up: Peculiarity of certain soils which tend to complete structural breakdown on moistening and thus to an easy carrying away of the exposed constituents (particularly of the colloidal substances by running water).

Soil: The transformation layer of the solid earth rind, inhabitated by organisms, produced by the influence of life and the special environmental conditions *) of a biological habitat, subject to a particular annual change (see phenology) and a characteristic development (see soil development).

Soil Climate: The average course of changes in the interior of the soil in the form of temperature alterations, variations of composition of the soil air (moisture oxygen content) and the alteration of water relations. The soil climate shows strong differences compared with the air climate (see soil climate of the autochthonous *terra rossa*, the *protorendsina*, the *low moor*), and with the same air climate great differences within the various types or subtypes. It is therefore extraordinarily characteristic of the soil and has a primary influence on its kind of development. The soil climate must not be confused with the climate of the air layer of a particular habitat nearest to the soil (e. g. the climate of the vegetation layer, turf, herb or dwarf shrub cover).

Soil Development: The formation of soil occurring on the bases of a law-abiding process proceeding under a typical change of forms from the most simple to the most complex and higher organized (e. g. raw soil, *ranker, braunerde,* podsolic braunerde, *iron-humus podsol*).

Soil Formation: The process of forming soils in general, which does not entail its being connected with a law-abiding alteration of form or change of type (see soil development).

Spongy Fabric: Biologically favourable soil fabric consisting of aggregates bound to each other in such a way that a system of connected cavities is formed as in a sponge. Also the inner structure of the aggregates is generally porous, not dense. Spongy fabric permits good aeration, optimum water economy, creates living space for the non-digging small soil animals, enables an easy through rooting and offers a protection against soil erosion.

Streaks, doubly refractive: Strikingly prominent, irregular, striped to flame-like fabric parts of higher double refraction produced by arrangement of particles in the clay substance either by movement (fluidal structures) or by deposition of drying ount colloidal masses on walls of cavities, shrinkage cracks, earthworm channels, surface of granules, concretions, etc. (deposition structure).

Structure: (Latin structura, from struere = to layer, to build up). A designation closely related to fabric, but more in the sense of the kind of formation of the structure complexes (crumbs, gravels, small fragments or other aggregates, further also the kind of separation). In earlier practical soil science only two kinds of structure were distinguished, the crumb and the single grain structure. In the literature of some countries, structure is used synonymously with fabric (q. v.).

Texture: The grain size relation, the percentage of the grain fractions of a soil.

---

*) As climate, relief, water conditions, plant cover, animal and human influence.

List of the Pedological Terms
Explaint in the Text

List of Soil Formations grouped according to the Natural System

A. Division of the Sub-aqueous or Underwater Soils

AA. Sub-Aqueous Soils not Forming Peat.

AB. Peat Forming Sub-Aqueous Soils.

Appendix to Peat forming Underwater Soils.

B. Division of the Semi-Terrestrial or Flooding und Groundwater Soils

BA.   Semi-Terrestrial Raw Soils.

BB.   Anmoor-like Soils.

BC.   Semi-Terrestrial Peat Soils.

Appendix to Soil Formations on Old Moor Peats.

BD.   Salt Soils.

BE.   Gley Soils with Land Humus Formation.

BF.   Ungleyed Warp Soils with Land Humus Formations.

C.   Terrestrial or Land Soils

CA.   Terrestrial Raw Soils.

a.   Climax Raw Soils.

CD. Steppe Soils.

CE. Terrae calxis.

CF. Bolus-like Silicate Soils.

(Plastosols.)

307

List of Soil Names

(Including all Synonyms)

310

List of the Illustrated Humus Forms

Profil pictures:

Micromorphology:

List of the Illustrated Soils

Pictures of the profiles:

Micromorphology:

Epilogue

Because of the technical difficulties produced by the numerous coloured plates and the necessity of printing three editions of the book (in English, Spanish and German) 2 1/2 years have elapsed since the time of the delivery of the manuscript for publication. Many publications have come out in the meantime whose results could not be utilized in the present work, particulary the books of my two Austrian friends and colleagues H. FRANZ: *Bodenzoologie als Grundlage der Bodenpflege, Berlin 1950;* and W. KÜHNELT: *Bodenbiologie mit besonderer Berücksichtigung der Tierwelt, Vienna 1950,* both of great importance towards a knowledge of the biology of the soils of Europe, further the new editions of the *Soil Survey Manual* of the U. S. Dept. of Agriculture 1951 and of the *«Dynamique du Sol»* of A. Demolon 1952.

Additional help in the preparation of the English edition has been given in different parts of the book by Mr. B. W. Avery, Rothamsted, Dr. R. Hart, Aberdeen, Dr. A. Osmond, Rothamsted and Miss A. Starkie, Madrid. My sincerest thanks to everyone.

Several new soil concepts which originated in the U. S. A. have found considerable application in Europe in the meantime, in the first place those of the «graybrown podsolic» and the «brown podsolic soil». They have not been treated in this book since their exact definition, and most of all their delimitation against already existant European soil concepts are not yet fully established. To my opinion the introduction of these concepts, as far as new soil formations and not mere synonyms of old concepts are concerned, are very valuable. My investigations of the corresponding soil forms occurring in Europe, and my opinions on the definition and delimitation will be given in one my proximate publications.

There is still much discussion among the pedologists on the genesis of the lime crust soils. In spite of recent explanations which differ greatly from the original interpretation (Blanckenhorn, Ramann), as far as real lime crust soils (not lime crusts in general) are concerned, I would like to keep to the latter. I hope to be able to publish a number of my own observations on the subject in a special paper.

The statement that the terra rossa is characterized by a higher iron content than that of the non-carbonate fraction of the parent rocks is probably in the first place true for the Istrian varieties. According to the mode of soil formation almost every possibility might occur in this respect, from the most extreme iron content caused by intense accumulation of the unsoluble iron precipitations in the Iwatoka-form and simultaneous removal of highly mobile matrix rich in silica, to the almost completely de-ironized varieties of the terra bianca.

W. L. KUBIENA

Madrid, the 11th of November 1952.

Y